LAND AND PEOPLE IN THE PHILIPPINES

LAND AND PEOPLE

GEOGRAPHIC PROBLEMS
IN RURAL ECONOMY

BY

J. E. SPENCER

ISSUED UNDER THE AUSPICES OF THE
INTERNATIONAL SECRETARIAT
OF THE INSTITUTE OF PACIFIC RELATIONS

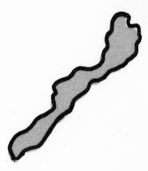

UNIVERSITY OF CALIFORNIA PRESS

IN THE PHILIPPINES

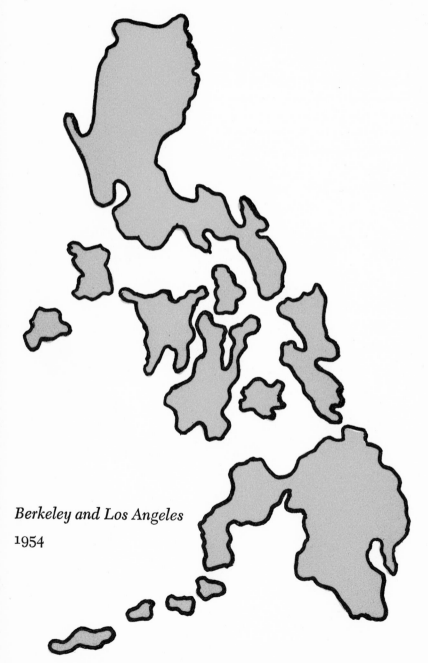

Berkeley and Los Angeles

1954

UNIVERSITY OF CALIFORNIA PRESS
BERKELEY AND LOS ANGELES, CALIFORNIA

CAMBRIDGE UNIVERSITY PRESS
LONDON, ENGLAND

PRINTED IN THE UNITED STATES OF AMERICA
BY THE UNIVERSITY OF CALIFORNIA PRINTING DEPARTMENT
DESIGNED BY WARD RITCHIE

SECOND PRINTING, 1954

The Institute of Pacific Relations

THE INSTITUTE of Pacific Relations is an unofficial and nonpartisan organization, founded in 1925 to facilitate the scientific study of the peoples of the Pacific area. It is composed of autonomous National Councils in the principal countries having important interests in the Pacific area, together with an International Secretariat. It is privately financed by contributions from National Councils, corporations, and foundations. It is governed by a Pacific Council composed of members appointed by each of the National Councils.

Neither the International Secretariat nor the National Councils of the Institute advocate policies or express opinions on national or international affairs. Responsibility for statements of fact or opinion in Institute publications rests solely with the author.

IPR INTERNATIONAL SECRETARIAT
1 East 54 St., New York City 22

v

Foreword

THE CRUCIAL importance of understanding the fundamental rural problems in the countries of noncommunist Asia has become abundantly clear in recent years as is well indicated in the emphasis now being placed on rural reconstruction in the MSA programs of economic aid to Southeast Asia and the Philippines. The most striking recent example of this new awareness of Asia's rural problems is to be seen in the report of the Bell Survey Mission to the Philippines and in the MSA reports on the work of the Joint Commission for Rural Reconstruction in Formosa. Questions of land reform, rural credit, crop improvement, and agricultural extension work have now been recognized by American and United Nations authorities as essential parts of the process of strengthening democratic forces and improving standards of living in the poverty-stricken agricultural societies which characterize most of Southeastern and Southern Asia.

Even with the best will in the world, however, plans for reform will miscarry unless they are based on accurate and up-to-date knowledge of the fundamental geographic and physical conditions which govern so much of the productive capacities of the areas. Professor Spencer's present study, based on extensive recent field work, supplies much of that basic information and should be of real value, not only to Western students of the Philippines, but also to many Filipino officials and teachers.

The present study constitutes one of a series of inquiries sponsored by the Institute of Pacific Relations during the past twenty years into the basic problems of land use and rural social and economic problems of Asian and Pacific countries. Other notable studies in this series have dealt with China, Japan, Korea, Indo-China, Australia, New Zealand, and Indonesia. Other investigations still in progress deal with postwar Japan and India.

The completion and publication of the study were aided by grants from the Rockefeller Foundation and the Institute of Pacific Relations. It should be noted, however, that the author alone is responsible for statements of fact or opinion expressed in the study.

WILLIAM L. HOLLAND
Secretary General

New York
September 26, 1951

Preface

THE REPUBLIC of the Philippines is one of the most distinctive eastern countries, partly because it is less oriental than any other country in the Orient. Americans think that the country should be in excellent condition and that the Filipinos should be very happy with their lot. It has been a shock to many to realize that neither of these assumptions is completely true. The Philippine difficulties arise in part out of a double colonial background. Spain administered the islands indirectly for a long period under a narrow concept of colonial rule. When the United States voluntarily took over the Philippines it had excellent intentions but no experience in colonial administration in the tropics. Now that the Filipinos are independent they face an accumulation of historical problems complicated by a short but destructive period of war and Japanese control. Independence has brought freedom, but it also has crystallized many serious problems, and Filipino inexperience in government, finance, and management is a handicap to the successful operation of the country.

This study deals with selected aspects of the rural background of the Filipinos in an effort to understand more clearly some of their current difficulties. There is little recent literature that examines the basic structure of Philippine economy. The best recent surveys are *Die Philippinen,* by the German geographer Albert Kolb, published in 1942, and *Philippine Economics,* by the Filipino economist

Andrés V. Castillo, published in 1949. Neither volume has wide circulation in the United States, and the former has only scant circulation in the islands.

I have begun, therefore, with a detailed and historical description of rural economy. In such matters as population growth, soils, transportation, and the export trade I have attempted to make clear some of the problems that face the islands, as well as to describe present conditions. The subjects of urbanism and industrialization have intentionally been treated only indirectly, though both pose serious problems for the future. Many of the strictly economic aspects of the Philippine scene are not adequately treated, since I claim no competence as an economist. Beginning with chapter ix I have tried to describe the background of particular problems of island rural economy around which future development must center. The last two chapters attempt to assess the over-all situation of the national economy from the point of view of government and current and future development.

It has not been possible, in one short book, to explore fully every cultural and economic ramification of the rural scene. It is easier to label Spanish, American, and Filipino failures than to blueprint remedial programs that can be kept within the comparatively small purse of the country. By the very nature of its approach this study becomes a critical one, but with admiration for the real progress that has been made, and with the sincere hope that the advantages implicit in the situation will not be wasted.

The University of California deserves thanks for the sabbatical leave which made possible the firsthand study and travel necessary to the volume. The University of California, the Rockefeller Foundation, and the Institute of Pacific Relations all generously provided research grants without which the study could not have been carried out. Ray Hanchett made maps from preliminary sketches. Members of two graduate seminars in geography not only lived through the evolution of ideas around the topic but contributed useful suggestions. My wife, Kathryn, struggled over my grammar, as did Erma Lemberger and Fred Neurath who did the typing. W. L. Holland of the Institute of Pacific Relations has been patient and helpful ever since first suggesting the study. Charles Wolf, Jr. read the manuscript critically but cannot be blamed for my failure to accept all his suggestions. Dominador Rosell and other members of the Philippine Division of Soil Survey and Conservation were of tremendous aid during the period of field work and in later response to my long-distance demands for answers to specific questions.

University of California,
Los Angeles, July, 1951.

                                                          J. E. S.

Contents

Maps and Tables

Maps

Tables

Plates

xvii

Chapter 1

BASIC STRUCTURE OF THE ECONOMY

THE PHILIPPINES today possesses an unstable agricultural economy which is deeply embroiled in international trade. The people are attracted to the Occident, tied by bonds to the Orient, and threatened by the advance of what aspires to be the Soviet World. The islands and their population are chiefly agricultural, chiefly rural, chiefly literate, chiefly Christian, and politically sophisticated, but each term misleads into overgeneralization. An urban resident might wish to add the phrase, chiefly capitalistic; but a rural critic would certainly counter with, precapitalistic. Heterogeneity—the intermixture of diverse elements and trends in the economy and culture of the Philippines—is far more prevalent than are unity and conformity. This involved situation is the result of a double colonial apprenticeship. Two very different patterns of treatment by Spain and the United States, ending in voluntarily given independence, have left deep marks. After severe punishment during World War II and major American postwar aid, the Filipinos began their independence with economic and social handicaps as well as advantages.[1]

Some of these handicaps admittedly arose out of situations over which the Filipinos had no control, whereas many were the results of inexperience in management. By the summer of 1950, after four years of independence, the Filipinos had used large sums of money, supplied chiefly by the United States, without achieving a full measure of reconstruction. They had been on a consumers'-goods buying spree that nearly exhausted their foreign currency reserves and had mismanaged their government finance almost to the point of bankruptcy. Emergency controls over trade resulted, with an impact upon all aspects of island life. Corruption in public affairs had disillusioned many private citizens about independence and representative government.

For example, the Filipinos had failed to provide adequate land reform for a crowded region in which there had been long-standing agrarian unrest. Protest about this problem had assumed such major politico-military importance by 1950 that looting raids were staged even on towns close to the political capital of the country. The very freedom and independence the Filipinos had so long desired was threatened, and normal life for several millions of people was seriously disturbed. The national treasury was drained to support punitive military expeditions, and it was clear that conditions were approaching a crisis.

Early in 1950 this threat of crisis prompted the Philippine president to ask the United States for a survey commission to review the economic situation and to propose remedial measures. The resulting Bell Commission spent the summer of 1950 in the Philippines. It was the latest of several American commissions to study conditions in the islands since the end of the war. Earlier recommendations had been acted upon in part, but many critical needs and basic suggestions had been ignored. The *Bell Report,* to which frequent reference will be made, stated its case more bluntly than had previous commission reports and made proposals for aid conditional upon certain changes in Philippine government procedures.

This study examines rural conditions that led to a state of crisis. This first chapter reviews the basic elements in the structure of Philippine economy, so that later discussion of contemporary aspects can be properly oriented in island economy.

A *Preview of Rural Domestic Living*

The daily menu for three out of four Filipinos includes boiled rice for at least two of the three meals. For others, corn, coarsely ground and cooked like rice, is the basic food, and most families use some breadstuffs. More than half the people eat fish once a day, and the rest eat it as often as possible. Part of the coconut yield is used at home, chiefly as fresh green coconut and coconut milk. Almost everyone eats some beef from cattle and water buffalo, and all but the more devout Moros eat pork. The per capita meat consumption is greater than elsewhere in the Orient but far less than in the United States. Yams and sweet potatoes are the most important of the roots, and green vegetables are eaten by all classes of people. Bananas are the most common fruit. Other home-grown fruits have regional centers and, though bounteous in season, are minor items in the diet. Some American fruits, as oranges and apples, are widely used in small quantities and much liked. Small amounts of many American tinned foods are used throughout the islands, though chiefly in and around urban areas.

To maintain the above dietary patterns, rice, flour, and fish have been regularly imported in the past half century.[2] Sufficient corn is grown locally. American fruit and a wide range of prepared and packaged foods are imported in quantities. Coconut, on the other hand, is almost entirely an export product. Filipinos pay a high price for sugar and never have quite enough of it for home use, since it also is pushed as a commercial export.[3] The great majority of the pineapple canned in the islands goes to the American market.

More tobacco now is imported than exported, since the Filipinos have taken to American cigarettes. Only a small part of the cotton required for clothing is homegrown. Some clothing is made at home, but much is imported. Most textiles other than cotton and abacá come from abroad. Because only a relatively small amount of abacá now is used at home for textiles, the main volume of the crop is exported. Most tools and implements for daily living in the rural environment are homemade, but the more complicated tools and equipment come from abroad. Many articles relating to a higher standard of living come from the United States, are common to city and town dwellers, but are not yet widely distributed through-out the homes of the rural countryside.[4] Wholesale trade and a share of retail trade is controlled by Chinese, with Americans and

Filipinos in secondary position. Wholesale transport both on land and water is handled by Filipinos and Americans, and what may be called retail transport is still primarily old style Filipino.

The cost of living before 1900 was very low; the price of labor also was low, with most work done by hand; and most nonindustrial labor did not work continuously throughout the year. The living cost today is much higher; the price of labor is rising steadily and at present has some government protection; a great deal of the primary work still is done by hand; and most nonindustrial labor still does not work continuously all during the year.[5] In certain parts of the islands, particularly in the Central Plain of Luzon, tenancy conditions are very disturbing, and in general, tenants have satisfactory legal protection in theory but not in practice. The annual income of the rural family dependent upon some kind of basic land use ranges from $75 to about $1,000.[6] This does not include families with members who have jobs away from the land, nor does it include family units of the upper economic levels who have income from tenant-farmed lands or other sources.

The History of Agricultural Land Use

It is improbable that any of the earliest hunting and gathering cultures to occupy the Philippines used fire extensively in their hunting operations, and therefore their impact upon the environment was minor and temporary. The land was largely covered by moist-to-wet forest growth in the day of the simple hunting populations. The Neolithic farmer was the first important agent in a sequence of nearly a hundred generations of users of the Philippine landscape. The Neolithic farmers who first came to the islands were not all of the same culture, so that to some, the inland and more hilly areas appealed, whereas others were attracted by the moist, flat littoral. Gradually different types of agriculture began to evolve in the upland and in the moist littoral, though certain crop plants finally became common to both zones.[7]

Some of the late Neolithic colonists, who came from Indo-China and south China to the northern part of the Philippines, had different concepts of appropriate land use from those who had come

4

earlier from the Indies into the southern islands. These farmer-metal craftsmen from northern Indo-China and south China never bulked large in the population of the islands. They are, however, the source for one agricultural system of which spectacular illustrations have been spread far too widely in the literature of the Philippines. I refer here to the rice terrace culture of the north Luzon pagan peoples—the Igorot, the Ifugao, some of the Kalinga, and a few others. Many books and articles about the Philippines have carried photographs of the terraced landscape of a classic locality in northern Luzon, with the inference that this is the way the Filipino farms. The impression given is that this kind of careful handling is part and parcel of his land-use system.

The builders of these terraces came into the islands more than two thousand years ago. They scattered over northern and western Luzon and seem to have preferred the hilly areas to the flat. They were a crop-cultivating, irrigating, terrace-building people who knew and used bronze and gold; who brought the pig, millet, probably rice, and perhaps some minor crops; who built houses of wood and thatch, and lived in villages; and who had the complex social patterns for group operation in land and water control. For two thousand years they have been building terraced fields, slowly adding to their carefully ordered cultural landscape. The stone walls of those fields are a monument to their labor, but in the intricate patterns of water control lies the real engineering skill of the terracing operation. This terrace system, in the classic photographs, seems a model of efficiency, of exemplary methods of soil conservation, of erosion control, and of long-range planning for a rough landscape. I wish to take no credit from the builders and operators of these terraces, who probably have carried the system further with simple tools and few sources of power than almost any other people. However, it is only right to point out that the spectacular nature of the terraced landscape has completely misled many of the observers who have reported it.

In the 6,000 square miles of rugged hill country of northern Luzon, after two thousand years of building, there are no more than 70,000 acres of well-executed terraces, less than 2 per cent of the landscape. These terraces occur only in small patches or in local valleys, separated by miles of rugged mountain terrain. The population density per square mile of cultivated land is very high, but the standard of living is not high. The possibilities of further extending the agricultural landscape in the same manner are rather slight in the face of rising labor costs. Even with a growing population few extensions are being made to the terraces today. A further truth is that the very people who laboriously cultivate these nicely controlled terraces today also farm steep slope fields in a manner as destructive as their terraces are saving. This is a seldom reported aspect of the cultural practices of these terrace builders, though the practice is fairly common all over the Orient. Stripping the forest goes on far ahead of cultivating the terrace or the slope field, and extraction of minor resources is pushed as far as possible.

The terrace builders today are concentrated in the higher and rougher country of northern Luzon. At one time they apparently occupied more country and land at lower elevations. They now are being infiltrated by groups of lowlanders from different parts of Luzon, coming not as farmers but as retailers, transporters, or government officials. Over the generations their system, excellent in an earlier day, has shrunk somewhat, and their tight hold on social control is slipping. It is my suggestion that this north Luzon system of landscape control is less effective today than are other systems, and that its further extension does not offer the most profitable future development for the island uplands. This is not to say, however, that no further terracing should be done in the Philippine uplands; it will be discussed in later chapters.

Elsewhere than in central to northern Luzon somewhat different patterns of land use were brought in by the first Neolithic farmers. Once introduced, two kinds of agriculture gradually developed throughout the southern occupied parts of the islands. With each system came such additional extractive patterns as could be practiced in the different regional landscapes. A lowland variety of agriculture utilized moist margins, particularly in and above alluvial estuaries. Rice, nipa palm, taro, and related plants are at home here. Associated with the truly aquatic lowlands were the moist lowlands on which similar crops could be grown, and in which jungle-like garden plantings contained coconut, bananas, breadfruit, jackfruit, and similar tropical fruit trees and shrubs. With this pattern of land use an "extractive range stripping" took selected wild forest products out of the jungle lands and swamp fringes between landing and settlement points. Also with this kind of economy there was constant contact with the sea, with fish and shell products, and with trade goods from outside areas. This sea contact gradually became a dominant interest in many coastal settlements, and few lowland Filipinos lacked some direct contact with the sea and its products. The wide range of opportunities in the lowland permitted a variable base for early lowland economy which was unlike the northern highland terrace economy.

Inland and in the hill country outside northern Luzon a more limited type of land use gradually appeared. In earlier periods perhaps no clearly defined boundary between the two types could be distinguished. The lack of direct sea contact and the absence of swamp-margin aquatic culture are obvious. When elevations increase, lowland crops and auxiliary plants drop out one by one, leaving no clear boundaries. Many elevation limits effective in earlier time have been conquered today. In its earlier and simpler phases this variety of agriculture was "shifting agriculture," known by many names in the Orient and termed "caingin cultivation" in the Philippines. This type of agriculture is not unique to the Philippines.[8] It was a common feature of land use on the mainland and islands of southeastern Asia in early periods and is still a widely used system. It meant abandoning old and clearing new fields every one in four years. The rate of rotation depended upon local soil fertility, whether heavy forest and a deep layer of organic matter were present, how long a time had passed since the last clearing, and how quickly grasses and brush came in to take over the clearing. This is an agriculture of sloping surfaces primarily, often of steep surfaces. It ranges from rather low elevations, even coastal plains, to highlands that rise between 6,500 and 7,000 feet. Terracing is not a primary part of this agriculture so any terraces in the Philippines, except in northern Luzon, were built recently and in small areas without laborious effort.

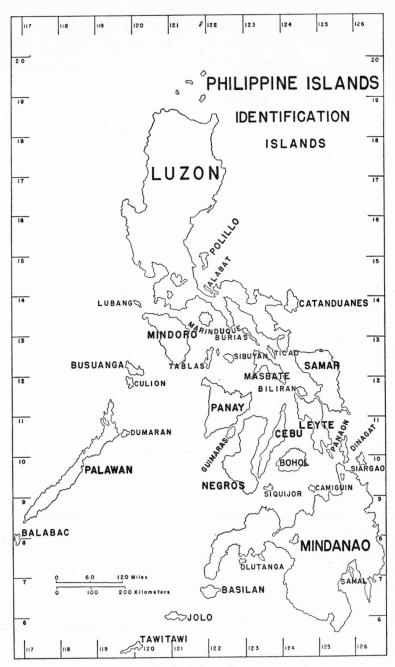

Map 1. Larger islands of the Philippine Archipelago

I interpret this shifting agriculture, the caingin system, to be an early upland system originally applied to all lands away from the aquatic littoral and its moist margins. With the gradual increase in population, caingin cultivators spread farther inland from island coasts and also farther upward into the highlands of many island interiors. During the Spanish period there came many changes, however, both on the lowland and in the upland interiors of islands. The institution of such features as the land tax, forced sedentary residence, forced labor, food and material levies, and the private estates of the Church and of officialdom—all operated to change the nature of the native economy. Most affected were the caingin farmers of the uplands, some of whom became tied to specific plots of ground yet were forced to go on using techniques, tools, and crops quite unsuited to sedentary farming on such land. Those outside the reach of Spanish and American administrations continued to use caingin cultivation. Caingin cultivation, and even hunting and gathering, still is practiced by the tribal, pagan peoples of island interiors. These are diminishing peoples, not well integrated into general island economy even today. It is not with these that I am concerned, but with the average Christian hill-country farmer. Both the tribal peoples and the Christian upland dwellers have supplemented their economy by range gathering.

Three basically separated agricultural systems have been suggested as in use at an early date in the islands. These were the irrigated-terrace culture of the northern uplands, the wet-land culture of the central and southern littoral, and the upland caingin system of the central and southern upland regions. Both of the latter systems have spread widely over the islands. Gradually, with the slow but steady introduction of additional domesticated plants, with the slow growth in populations, with the increase in market-bartering and later in international trade, there came marked changes in crops. Changes resulted also in methods of farming and, to a degree, in the purpose of farming with the growth of local barter and the rising importance of cash, trade, and export crops. These changes altered local systems of agriculture. Expansion by trial and error and the mixing of crops, agricultural systems, and landscapes over the centuries—sometimes by irrational human willfulness—have thoroughly scrambled the original patterns of Philippine agriculture. But these native systems are not all that enter into the agricultural economy of the modern Philippines.

A fourth agricultural system was initiated by the Spanish late in the nineteenth century and greatly expanded during the American period. The plantation system was developed around tobacco, sugar, and coconut by the Spanish, extended during American control, and now produces coconut, sugar, abacá, and pineapple as major items; tobacco, mangoes, ramie, and rubber as minor items. Geographically, the plantation system has inserted itself irregularly into the agricultural landscape from the Central Plain of Luzon southward through Mindanao. Spanish, American, and Filipino owners now use the plantation system in producing crops that, except for mangoes, are destined for the export market. Plantation agriculture has not replaced small-scale production of coconut, abacá, mangoes, and tobacco, but it controls the commercial production of sugar, pineapple, ramie, and rubber. Ramie and rubber, both minor crops at present, are produced only on plantations.

Recently, mechanized farming has been increasing in the islands, both on plantations and on smaller private holdings. There is a lower limit to owner capital and to the size of the landholding upon which mechanization can be applied. Much land has too rough a surface to permit mechanization. Mechanization is being tried on some of the newer colonial lands, as well as on older cultivated lands. Agriculture under mechanization, of course, has labor problems and a commercial aspect quite different than those of older systems of agriculture. In effect, therefore, mechanization sets up yet another though not a widely distributed agricultural system.

Today, therefore, there are five major agricultural systems used throughout the islands: caingin or shifting agriculture, intensive highland irrigated-terrace agriculture, lowland intensive cultivation, plantation, and commercial mechanized agriculture. The first three are of Oriental origin, and the last two are modern Occidental introductions. There is competition between all of them for domestic and foreign markets, and some interest among individual farmers in changing from one system to another. There is also much government concern and activity pointed toward improvement of agricultural production because it is evident that land use in many parts of the islands is out of harmony with its rational and optimum patterns.

In the pre-Spanish Philippines small landholdings were normal, as were communal holdings; at the same time the unrestricted public range was very extensive. Spanish land-grant practice introduced the pattern of large holdings among the wealthy, the privileged, and the Catholic Church. In time Filipinos shared in these large landholdings. Spanish practice also made almost all cultivated or utilized lands into private property. Philippine land laws are framed primarily to maintain small holdings but permit legal incorporation and the claiming of fairly large holdings on the colonial frontier. Most American and other alien landholdings are large. Yet even these are restricted to prevent plantation and mechanized agriculture from expanding adequately in settled areas or accumulating effective holdings on the frontier.

Beyond the agricultural system as such is the matter of cropping systems employed in agriculture. Gradually the Filipino farmer has developed multiple systems of cropping. It is possible to enumerate more than twenty cropping combinations that are now in operation in the islands. Some are chiefly lowland systems, other primarily upland, whereas a number are used in both the lowland and the upland areas. Some cropping combinations are quite new and still experimental, but others already are old and more stable in their patterns. The following table lists these in a fairly arbitrary way. Subsistence and commercial farmers both use most of the cropping combinations. Certain ones are out of place in particular landscapes, but in some regions the entire rural economy would profit by altering patterns of cropping.

Contemporary Cropping Combinations of the Philippines

CHIEFLY LOWLAND COMBINATIONS

1. Mixed lowland crops
2. Small-scale irrigated rice plus minor crops

3. Large-scale irrigated rice
4. Irrigated rice and coconut
5. Coconut and minor crops
6. Plantation ramie and minor crops

CHIEFLY UPLAND COMBINATIONS

7. Caingin upland rice and minor crops
8. Terraced irrigated rice and sweet potatoes
9. Upland rice-coconut-abacá
10. Bananas-vegetables-minor fruits
11. Tobacco and corn
12. Upland rice-coconut-corn
13. Upland rice-cassava-corn
14. Plantation pineapple

COMBINED UPLAND-LOWLAND COMBINATIONS
(found both in upland and lowland)

15. Coconut and corn
16. Corn and minor crops
17. Plantation coconut
18. Plantation abacá
19. Large-scale sugar cane
20. Small-scale sugar cane and rice (irrigated or upland)
21. Vegetable gardens

Nonagricultural Land Use

In older nonagricultural land use the most significant pattern has been that of the exploiting lumber operators. They have run over the more accessible parts of the islands in a screening operation, cutting the valuable woods and leaving scarred forest behind. Agricultural colonists who follow the lumbermen thus have part of their clearing done for them. Commercial forest activities began late in the Spanish period, when special woods were sought and the first commercial sawmills established. Large-scale commercial lumbering is now carried on in perhaps a dozen localities scattered over the islands, chiefly upland regions. Mindoro, northern Negros,

12

northern and western Mindanao, and central southeastern Luzon are the leading lumber-producing regions at the present time, but smaller operations are carried on in many parts of the islands. In the long run the caingin farmer has perhaps destroyed more timber than the lumberman has turned into lumber. Minor forest products include firewood, nipa-palm thatching, rattan, gum and resin, orchids, wild fruit, and nuts. There has been local and regional exploitation of each of these, and the use of the forest ranges has been increasing steadily, both in variety and in volume. In the past these ranges have been so extensive and widespread that exploitation has been easy and relatively cheap. Now, in many parts of the islands the forest ranges have been overexploited and need restoration.

Mineral exploitation on a large scale is new in the islands and so has no long pattern of historic development. Native gold and copper mines were worked on a small scale in the pre-Spanish period and are the oldest types of mineral land use. The Spanish sought out most of the old mines in various parts of the islands, but never enjoyed the success that attended their efforts in the New World. Mining is chiefly an upland activity, a lode mining that does not disfigure much of the landscape. Other varieties of mining—coal, iron, chromite, and manganese—are newer and are not yet stable elements of the economy. Philippine mineral resources are not well known and may be extended by future survey, but at present they are not sufficiently comprehensive to provide a major base for industrial expansion. Mining represents a corporate form of exploitation which may alter local economy greatly through its demands for labor and agricultural produce. Its major impact, however, is largely commercial. As such, mine products contribute significantly to Philippine national income, but at the present state of development they represent a source of income only to a minority of Filipinos.

In the wider aspects of land use, as the term is understood in the United States, little constructive work has been done in the islands. Water and flood-control preserves have not yet been laid out or land use within them prescribed, though a start has been made in both. The first national parks have been located but no development work has begun toward recreational land use. There is one well-developed hill station or summer resort, Baguio, north of Manila, and a few informal spots where local residents have summer homes. A few outstanding natural attractions are developed in a small way. These newer forms of land use will be important in the future, and call for long-range planning of an intelligent sort.

Handicraft and Modern Industry

In comparison with other Oriental countries the Philippines possesses but little handicraft production and that in a minimum range of products.° This has long been characteristic of the islands. It was true before the Spanish came, and the Spanish restricted the development of variety in the handicraft products of the islands. This has resulted in a narrowly based economy. The American period has hurt the traditional handicrafts by the substitution of machine goods, tools, and materials. On the other hand the American period also has stimulated the development of regional specialties that perhaps more than offsets the elimination of particular products. However, there has been inequality in this, since much of the replacement is urban whereas the displacement was rural. There is need for the development of small-scale local industry or commercialized handicrafts of a type that will broaden the base of rural economy and give the rural population a remunerative occupation for periods of the year during which it now is idle. This applies more to rural upland populations than to those of the coastal lowlands where fishing, trade, urban callings, transport, and so on offer seasonal and occasional relief to the coastal farmer. Chronic underemployment is now a significant ailment in Philippine economy.

Modern industrial development began in a small way under the Spanish, who initiated tobacco manufacture in the form of cigars and a little processing of abacá, coconut, and sugar. These primary lines were the first to expand in the American period. However, this expansion was slow and irregular and no effective program was planned for the development of local industry. Today processing agricultural export products is the chief form of manufacturing. Industrial production is now established in such lines as clothing, beer and soft drinks, cement, rubber and leather shoes, rattan and wooden furniture, soaps and cosmetics, candy and confections, embroidery and art goods, truck and bus bodies, paper and its products, ceramic products, glassware, paints and varnishes, and rice and corn milling. Secondary industries such as printing and publishing, food canning, ice production, and automotive repair are growing in the larger cities. These were first developed in Manila, and Manila still is their chief center.

In some products as sugar, coconut, pineapple, soap, cement, and beer, large concerns are now operating, but small companies of low capitalization produce much of the manufactured goods of the islands. Some of this production involves hardly more than home-workshop industry, scattered throughout the cities and small towns in all parts of the islands. Handicraft industry extends also to other commodities such as abacá and cotton textiles, shell products, food manufactures, wooden shoes, wood and iron tools and utensils. Some of the larger companies are American or Spanish in ownership and management, though the Filipino firms are increasing in numbers and in capital resources. Most rice milling is in the hands of the Chinese, who also control a small share of production in other lines.

Smelting and refining of minerals have scarcely developed beyond gold, silver, copper, and lead, though mining of other minerals has become important. The fabrication of metal products and utensils has begun in a number of lines, based upon imported raw materials such as iron bars or steel wire and shapes. Salt production from sea water is an important accessory occupation developed around Manila Bay. Sawmill production has returned to its prewar level, and secondary processing of finished lumber products is beginning.

The majority of manufactured products still must be imported into the islands, since technical skills, capital resources, equipped plants, and management ability are far short of the need. But government blueprints for the growth of domestic industry include pilot plants built and temporarily operated by the government, public power development, restriction of imported goods, the stimulation of Philippine branch factories of alien companies, and educational campaigns to buy home products.

15

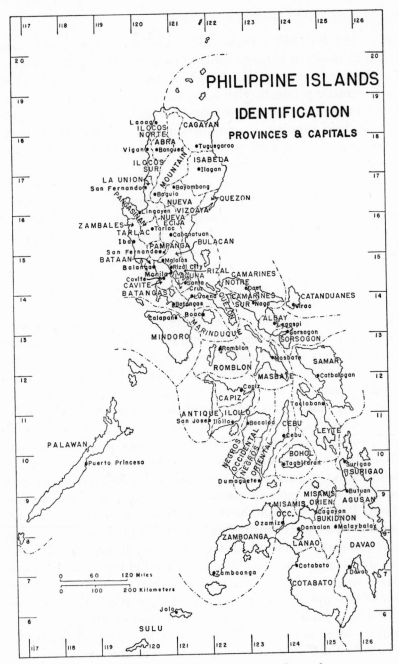

Map 2. Philippine provinces and provincial capitals

Transport and Communications

Roads are comparatively new to the islands, for the Filipinos have been a water-traveling people until recent time. Water travel has meant chiefly sea travel of an island-hopping sort. During late Spanish times a few roadways widened out key routes in the skeleton pattern of trails that had provided for inland travel. In the American period these key roads and many trails were expanded into what seems a fair highway system, until one compares it with similar systems in the United States. Nearly seventeen thousand miles of highways provide skeleton routes that cover most of the larger islands. Almost 95,000 motor vehicles of all kinds use these highways in vain effort to meet the demand for passenger and freight transport.[10] Around the major cities pony carts supplement the taxicabs, and in many rural areas oxcarts or sleds still serve more commonly than do motor trucks.

In a world of many small islands rail transport is handicapped, particularly when motor highways parallel the rail lines. Only two islands now have rail systems, but only on Luzon is the railroad relatively successful as an agent of economic transport. Both air traffic and water shipping serve the islands far more effectively than do railways. A widespread network of usable air fields and dozens of small ports have permitted the postwar expansion of airlines and interisland shipping. However, along the coasts and between main coasts and offshore islands, native outrigger sailing craft still furnish much of the transport, as do dugout canoes on rivers and streams of many island interiors.

Telephone and telegraph systems serve less well in an island world than does radio. Many cities and even some small towns have telephone systems, but only Luzon has anything resembling a telegraph or telephone network. However, communications and broadcast systems have effectively tied the islands together. And today Manila-published newspapers, shipped by air in a few hours to all parts of the islands, add a further link to unite the various parts of the archipelago.

Government, the Church, and the Big Families

In large part the organized social, religious, and political patterns
of the islands are a heritage from the Spaniards. Only among the
pagan or Moslem peoples are there many residual features of law,
government, or religious custom. The Spaniards substituted the
barrio or local district, the municipio or municipality, and the
province for tribal patterns and territories. With these came new
officials and administrative procedures, new types of settlement
and of social cohesion. And with major temporal change came the
adoption of Catholic Christianity as replacement for tribal ani-
mism. But these Spanish influences never pushed into the central
interiors of the larger islands, thus leaving a core of territory populated by pagan peoples with older culture. The Islamic faith had
been brought into Palawan, the Sulu Archipelago, and Mindanao
by Indonesians before the arrival of the Spaniards. The history of
the contact of Christians and Moslems in the islands is as militant
as was the earlier contact between the two religions in the western
Mediterranean. The Spaniards never dominated the peoples of
Islamic faith in the islands and, therefore, did not succeed in replacing local government or the social and religious patterns among
them.

As befitted civilizing conquerors, Spanish officials of both government and Church acquired large landholdings and privileged
positions in the trade of the islands with the Spanish New World.
Such persons accumulated great wealth by island standards. Slowly
and gradually a few Filipino families acquired similar status, sometimes through intermarriage with Spanish families.

The transfer of the islands to the United States introduced
changes in over-all policy and, therefore, in the detailed patterns
of island culture. The Americans kept the basic machinery of Spanish government but made it elective and gradually added new
features. Many of the bureaus and services that were part of government in the United States in the early twentieth century were
set up in island administration. Church and State were separated,
and the long quarrel between the Christian and Moslem Filipinos

slowly quieted. Protestant missionaries came and made some headway, particularly in education, though the Philippines has remained Catholic. Some expansion of island culture occurred, with changes becoming cumulative over the years. Colonial settlement on the smaller Visayan Islands, formerly most exposed to Moro raids, took place, and the settlement of Mindanao was expanded.

The freedom that came with United States administration provided many Filipinos with economic opportunity that had not existed under Spanish rule. General expansion of the economy and improvement in the standard of living resulted for a large share of the population. The opportunity to acquire large landholdings and to accumulate great wealth from the rapid growth of the import-export trade permitted families who had prospered under the Spaniards to build up fortunes unusually large compared to the Filipino general average. Today a small number of families hold a large share of the wealth of the islands and have a part in almost every important type of economic endeavor. Although this has not reached the danger point of monopoly, it is a factor in the wide range in standards of wealth and economic well-being among both rural and urban populations. The existence of wealth in the hands of a restricted group has made possible a start in domestic industrialization, whereas the widespread lack of even small capital funds among the majority of Filipinos renders them incapable of action and suggests precapitalism.[11] This fundamental cleavage and the generally inadequate capital resources of the islands have led to specific government aims and programs for future industrialization.

The separation of Church and State under American control of the islands limited the economic and social position of the Church. No longer does the Church occupy the central, powerful position it did under Spanish rule. The resulting freedom of the population may be advantageous on the one hand, but the very lack of social restraint and of economic responsibility on the other, constitutes a present handicap, both in urban and rural society.

Squatters and the Chinese

One of the traditional features of life in the Indonesian world has been the carefree mobility of much of the population. Shifting agriculture, movable home sites, and a love for the sea are some of the chief elements in this mobility. In island interiors during Spanish times the shifting cultivator who eluded Spanish control became what is known today as a squatter, an occupant without title. In the contact of Indonesian and Occidental cultures and the interweaving of new culture patterns, the conflict of ideas over land, cultivation rights, ownership, personal mobility, and fixity of residence has not yet been fully resolved. The lawful occupant-user of tribal times became the unlawful squatter of Spanish times and continued as such during the American period. The land-survey agencies of organized government never have been able to keep pace with the spread into the interior or onto the newer colonial lands by the individual Filipino. This is largely because of the unconcern of the settler with legal rights, and the failure of Spain or the United States to make adequate provision for survey in a land not previously well mapped. A large floating population is still characteristic of the islands.

Something of these traditional patterns has been perpetuated. Among the rural populace of the newer settled lands the caingin farmer, the migrant laborer, the colonial, and the mobile pagan tribesman represent older tendencies. Subsistence economies, changing land use, deforestation, the appearance of tropical grasslands, primitive farming practices, low productivity, low annual income, and low standards of living are the results of such patterns, patterns out of step with newer ones produced by other changes in Philippine culture. No accurate tabulation can be made as to how many Filipinos are included in some phase of this development, but these are basic elements in Philippine precapitalistic rural life. Although newer patterns of culture are widespread it is unfortunate that, so far, there has been only a gradual evolution of a small middle class in modern Philippine society.

At the other extreme—commercial urban life—progressive

change has come through participation of the Chinese in Philippine economic life. Again, the Spanish and the Americans were instrumental in elaborating the process, though neither was responsible for the advent of the Chinese. A few Chinese traders worked throughout the archipelago in pre-Spanish times. Used by the Spaniards to bring to Manila the varied products of the East for transshipment to the New World and to Spain, the Chinese have steadily increased their economic stake in the islands. Opposition to them has been periodic but only temporary. During the American period, with its emphasis upon import-export trade and with its premium upon merchandizing skill and management ability, the experience and natural aptitude of the Chinese gave them an advantage over the unpracticed Filipinos. This advantage has continued, until at present the Chinese all but dominate the domestic trade and have a fairly large share in foreign trade.

In the Philippines restrictions upon land ownership by the Chinese never have been effective. Neither has recurrent opposition to their commercial activity been effective, though there are local regions without Chinese merchants. Occasional efforts are made to further restrict them, and national legislation definitely has subordinated the Chinese to a position below that of Filipinos and Americans. However, the Chinese today have a double vested interest—heavy financial investment in the commerce of the islands and intermarriage with all levels of Filipinos. Full-blooded Chinese in the islands number in excess of the official census tabulation, and Chinese blood is present in more than a million Filipinos.

The War and Independence

What was to have been a specific ten-year period of preparing the Philippines for independence was interrupted by World War II with its tremendous destruction of agriculture, industry, transport, housing, and personal well-being. After the war the Filipinos, eager for the promised independence, were launched upon their own, only to face tremendous problems of social and economic rehabilitation. The interruption in preparing the country for its freedom left many important things undone, matters which now seriously affect the operation of independent Philippine government, economy, and society.

The most obvious of these lies in the realm of government. A mixture of native psychology, Spanish framework, and American mechanics, the new government leaves much to be desired, a judgment reached as often by Filipinos as by alien critics. This is not a criticism of a political party or of any administrative personnel, but is a commentary on the operation of the administrative tools of a society. With continued practice and good will the government should steadily improve, if social and economic maladjustments do not erupt into violent conflict imperiling, in their militant expression, the very operation of peaceful government. The present, therefore, is a period of change in which new processes are struggling amid numerous handicaps.

The economy of Philippine society is on treacherous ground. The islands, as a colony, became too closely tied to the factories and markets of the United States. Political liberty does not carry economic independence, as many Filipinos now realize. With an unusually liquid volume of financial resources from American postwar aid and the high prices of Philippine exports in the markets of the world, a tremendous boom in purchases abroad set in immediately after the war. These purchases were composed of reconstruction materials on the one hand, but of costly consumers' goods on the other. The free-buying cycle was short-lived; import controls became effective in 1949. A declining preferential position within the American framework will continue for some years. Developing industries in the islands can provide more manufactured products at a cheaper over-all cost than by buying American goods.[12] Counteracting this will be the increased competition from producers of similar export commodities, and a living standard that has been pushing upward toward more expensive levels. Regional and local inequalities in both sets of factors are significant. Between rural and urban populations, and between economically developed and undeveloped segments of society, there is deep cleavage. Serious rural tenancy problems in central Luzon have grown into a postwar quasi-political movement that continues to disturb the entire

Philippines. Repeated mediation in urban wage and labor problems has prevented any damaging urban situation. No one description fits all parts of the islands and rapid change is more characteristic of Philippine economy than is any one static pattern.

Reconstruction has not yet restored the physical volume of production to its prewar status. The combined index of physical production for September, 1950, stood at 98.2 per cent of a 1937 base of 100.[13] Manufacturing has progressed most rapidly, its September, 1950, index standing at 103.1. Agricultural production at the same date stood at 97.6, whereas mining was lagging with a figure of 58.6. Until this physical volume of production moves upward there can be little real improvement in the standard of life for the islands as a whole.

The social climate of the Philippines also has been changing steadily. Filipinos pride themselves on having the only Christian country in the Orient and often claim it is the third largest English-speaking country.[14] In spots, very old patterns of social culture remain relatively unchanged. There are local regions with a strong Spanish hue, and something of Spanish culture persists throughout the islands. In recent decades the rate of Americanization has increased markedly. Wartime contact with the Japanese left little that was prized, but the liberation contact with the American army started anew the process of Americanization. In spite of independence, the close alignment with American trends in education, music, literature, cinema, radio, clothing, house furnishing, and so on is noticeable. In good part this alignment is still an urban matter, but it is reaching into the smaller towns, the barrios, and the rural homesteads at a significant rate.

Chapter 2

BASIC REGIONALISMS

THE PHILIPPINE ISLANDS today present conditions which can be expressed in regional terms. These patterns, termed regionalisms, are made up of many separate elements. Regionalism is derived from the physical landscape itself, from climate, vegetation, drainage, and soils. Regionalism is contributed by the variable patterns of land use—agriculture, forestry, fishing, mining, or industry. And regionalism also is contributed by the group psychologies and the culture patterns that descend in part from historical events and from the racial and religious differences of the various peoples who make up the Philippine archipelago.

Environmental Differences

The Philippine landscape is made up of very different elements, but the range of differences is less than might be expected. The essential fact is, of course, the physical separation of the archipelago into islands. The relative isolation of many smaller islands creates a number of rural problems and also sets up regional divisions. Except for a few sizable pieces the islands themselves are divided into small patches of many landform types. The mountains of northern Luzon and the Central Plain of Luzon are the only large units on the biggest Philippine island. Similarly the Bukidnon-Lanao Plateau country and the lowland basins of the Agusan River and of the Rio Grande de Cotabato are Mindanao's only large units.

24

Elsewhere, for the most part, upland and lowland, mountain peak and swamp fringe occur side by side throughout the islands. This is important in the island story because many kinds of land use occur even in small areas and a given population may be using several types of land simultaneously. Therefore, remedial measures must be varied and applied in many places, and no sweeping regional measures may be taken in blanket fashion. Most of the formerly vacant lowlands now are becoming occupied and some of the heretofore empty upland regions are becoming settled. The lowlands naturally are the first to be settled, for they are easier to use and normally more productive. Although sections of the uplands, of course, have long been occupied, for the most part they will remain as reserve regions for marginal development.

It may be well to inquire into the meaning of the terms lowland and upland as used here. The chief variation in the Philippine landscape is change in elevation, the shift from the coastal lowland to the mountainous island interior. There are no simple height divisions into which the various levels of the islands can be separated. Definition of upland and lowland, therefore, is an arbitrary matter. In this study the term lowland will refer to the lands of the seacoast fringe, the estuary mouths, alluvial plains, and the basins of subdued-to-negligible relief located close to sea level. High ground-water tables, incomplete drainage, seasonal flooding, and fresh-to-brackish waters make irrigation unnecessary for much of the agriculture in this zone.

Above these lowlands are other kinds of landscapes. There are rough hill lands, small mesas, large table lands, plateaus, piedmonts, mountain valleys, and the mountains themselves. Disregarding, for the moment, natural precipitation and its variations, all such lands are, to the farmer, dry lands. Land use must incorporate techniques and practices not required on the wet lowlands. This distinction is found to be effective as soon as the relief and elevation provide efficient drainage—drainage that during dry seasons really dries out the surface soils and introduces a seasonal aspect to plant growth. This can occur throughout the Philippines, except only in the most humid parts of the islands, and at an elevation of as little as seventy-five to one hundred feet above sea level.

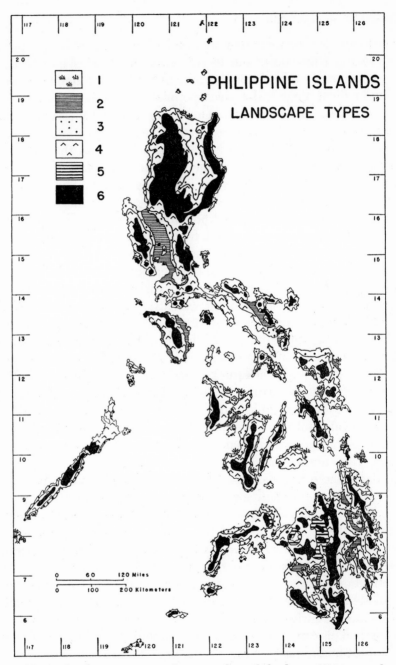

Map 3. Landscape types. 1 = Swamp and marsh lands. 2 = Moist, smooth lowland plains. 3 = Dry, open lowlands and slopes. 4 = Rough and hilly uplands. 5 = Open plateaus and smoother uplands. 6 = Rough mountain lands

The term upland, in strict reference therefore, would apply to everything above the moist lowland fringe, meaning that uplands and dry lands are synonymous. In practice the distinction here made restricts the lowland regions of the islands too severely. There can be no definite division between lowland and upland, but only a transition zone somewhat vaguely recognizable. The smoother, easily cultivated landscapes lying at lower to moderate elevations, with alluvial piedmonts and intermontane basins, form the transition zone, which often is broad enough to take in most of the area. An accompanying map (map 3) shows this physical relationship.

Considered practically, perhaps some 75,000 square miles, or 65 per cent of the total area of the islands, can accurately be called uplands. Of this upland total, roughly 42,000 square miles are covered with forest today, and 11,000 square miles are already in cultivated lands or farms. The balance of the area is in grassland or parkland, where the grass has appeared largely because of the farming methods employed by the Filipinos. These uplands consist in part of high plains, tablelands, and plateaus—surfaces of relatively smooth local relief and of very real usability. But rougher lands also are included in this upland total. A scattering of rolling to strongly dissected and rough hills occupies a part of every major island and comprises the whole of many small islands. Above the hills and plateaus rise a variety of mountainous highlands, for the most part too rugged for cultivation. Many of these mountains are volcanic craters set in an otherwise usable landscape. Some mountains and mountain ranges are cultivated and used quite to their summits. None of the mountian ranges reaches above the limits of plant growth, but many of the highest elevations possess landforms too severe to be cultivated.

Climatically we are dealing with what is essentially a humid tropical region, without very great range in specific characteristics. The primary climatic variation involves elevation and the shift from the coastal lowland to the mountainous island interior. Everywhere the lowlands are almost fully tropical. As one goes into the higher uplands the temperature regimes lower steadily, but never to the point of stopping all plant growth during any time of the year. The altitudinal zoning does set upper limits of elevation upon many wild plants and also upon a good many crop plants. Whether present limits of crop plants in all cases are those set by nature or by man is not at all clear. The mountainous country of north Luzon, a few isolated peaks or bits of highland on other small islands, and the plateau country of northern Mindanao are the only areas with temperature regimes that offer extensive relief from the heat of the coastal lowlands. These regional climatic differences were not particularly significant in earlier occupation of the archipelago and today are only beginning to be exploited.

More significant to land use are the marked differences in regimes of precipitation found in several parts of the islands. It has been customary to map the islands in terms of four primary precipitation regimes. Lines of separation between regions of these regimes run north-south through the islands. They are related to the chief seasonal meteorologic phenomena, the Asiatic summer and winter monsoons, and the Pacific Ocean northeast trades. These wind movements cross the archipelago at variable angles and bring moisture seasonally from different directions. The multiple island landscape, with frequent mountainous island cores trending chiefly north-south, causes many localities to be in windward, rainy position during one season, in lee, sheltered position during the other. Although only four major rainfall regimes are recognized for the islands, it is the writer's impression that this is a matter of severe overgeneralization. There must be a great many local precipitation regimes, now loosely grouped together. The recent reorganization of the Philippine Weather Bureau should facilitate forming a better picture than the present one, and the Weather Bureau now should be able to assist in the more intelligent framing of a number of land-use programs for different localities of the islands.

One climatic feature that does set an east-west line across the islands, distinguishing them regionally, is the typhoon—the hurricane of the Caribbean Sea and Gulf of Mexico. Storm paths are well plotted; the seasonal and annual damage, precipitation, and other aspects are well known. The frequency and severity of typhoons is disastrous for certain crops, particularly coconut trees, abacá, and banana plants. A serious typhoon season causes an interruption in abacá cropping. Abacá is not grown north of central Luzon for this very reason, but southern Luzon has been one of its centers in the last century. One could well ask whether losses from interruption are not sufficient to warrant a major southward shift in crop patterns. A substitution of other crops less subject to typhoon damage might, in the end, produce a higher economic return from land use. The accompanying map (map 4) shows precipitation regimes and zones of typhoon occurrence.

The soils of the Philippines present a bewildering complexity, though soil surveys are yet far from complete. When the final map of soil types is completed it will be a mosaic of patches and small areas of soils of widely different types. Probably there are close resemblances of soil types in regions of like characteristics on different islands. A good part of this variety occurs in the uplands, where soils change within short distances. It is the natural evolution of soil variations on upland surfaces undergoing denudation, soil formation, and, in some localities, volcanism within geologically recent time. But in addition to these natural developments, man has wrought important changes in soils within the period of agricultural land use. Much of the upland area not now in mature forests has been worked over repeatedly by generations of farmers following one system or another. For the most part man and his farming systems have been hard on soil resources. Most uplands not now in old forests have rather poor soils that also have suffered severely from erosion. Locally deep soils of volcanic origin have not been impoverished, but these are exceptions. In northern Luzon the terrace lands have largely escaped soil erosion except in localities where decimation of local populations or abandonment of farms occurred during World War II. However, as pointed out earlier, not all farmland in this mountain region is terraced, and soil erosion on slope fields has been severe, since many of them are extremely steep.

Soil survey and conservation work in the islands has not yet proceeded far. Reconnaissance surveys of soil types are being made as rapidly as inadequate funds and interest permit, and a small start has been made in a conservation program. Surveys and con-

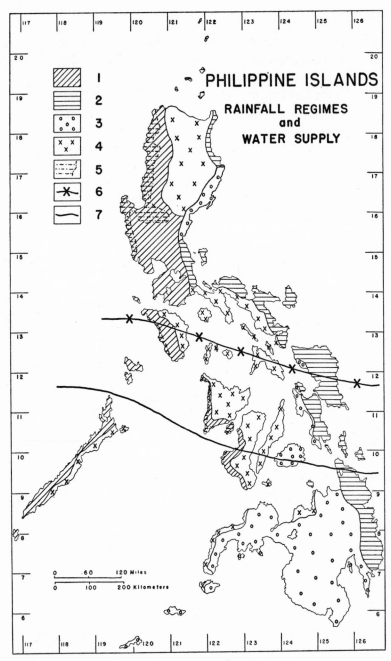

Map 4. Rainfall regimes and water supply. 1 = Marked dry season in winter and early spring. 2 = No dry season but maximum of rainfall in winter. 3 = No strong seasonal variation in rainfall. 4 = Short spring dry season. 5 = Regions of inadequate water supply. 6 = North of this line typhoon damage is serious. 7 = South of this line typhoon damage is very slight.

servation programs are inadequate, largely because public and legislative opinion is not aware of the need. It will be long before detailed soil and conservation studies can attack the many urgent problems of the damaged regions of the uplands. Man can do a great deal to prevent destruction and to repair the wounds of the recent past. Nature, herself, will repair the damage under certain conditions within reasonable periods. Where man's use of the land is but temporary, jungle growth will reclaim the area and forest finally will reappear. A forest cover usually gives protection from further rapid erosion, and gives soil-forming processes a chance to build up a new surface soil.

There are conditions under which natural restoration of soils does not occur. When once-farmed areas are abandoned and grasses get a start, jungle and forest growth have a very hard time gaining control of a region. If let alone, nature will do this job in time, but when man and his fires come into the picture the natural trend is so badly disturbed that whole territories may go permanently into tropical grass. This has taken place in many parts of the islands in irregular patches and localities, but in Mindanao a large share of the Bukidnon-Lanao Plateau area in the north is one great expanse of grass, and much of the southern Cotabato country is also in grass. Large areas in Luzon, Masbate, and Panay are now grass covered also. The total area of such lands is extensive, though no accurate figures are available. Estimates of the present grass cover run between 15 and 20 per cent of the total area of the islands. Many areas are burned over every year to renew the grass growth for pasture, even though these tropical grasses are poor animal browse for more than a few weeks early in the growing season. These tropical grasses form a very heavy turf, spread through root growth as well as seed dispersal, and are not killed by the annual fires. Although they do prevent heavy erosion, the periodic burning and the very nature of the grasses themselves are not helpful in rebuilding soil. Hence many of the grass-covered uplands today possess soils that are seriously impoverished and which nature is not aiding man to rebuild. A simplified map of plant cover is presented in map 5.

31

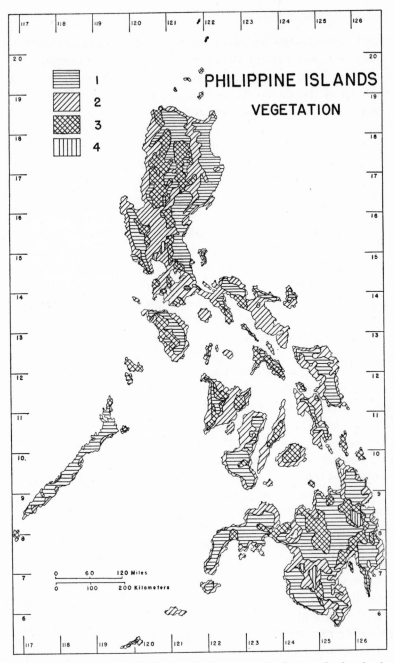

Map 5. Vegetation. 1 = Predominantly forest. 2 = Predominantly farmland.
3 = Mixed form, grass and parkland. 4 = Major marsh and swamp lands.

Distinctive regional features are the tracts of marsh and swamp scattered around many an island coast and in a few of the lowland river basins. There are many more small patches of salt water or brackish marshlands at the heads of small bays or estuaries, or along flat coastal fringes than appear on the accompanying map, which indicates the larger areas only. And in a few of the larger drainage basins are areas of brackish marshlands at some distance from the sea. The three inland marshlands shown are the southern part of the Central Plain of Luzon, the upper Agusan River Valley of northern Mindanao, and the central and lower parts of the Rio Grande de Cotabato in southern Mindanao.

Historic and Economic Regionalisms

Western Negros Island is identified in the minds of most Filipinos with sugar-cane plantations, sugar-milling centrals, and the production of sugar and its by-products. Similarly Mindoro Island is first of all a lumbering center, and the Cagayan Valley of northeastern Luzon is known as the best tobacco-producing region of the islands. The volcanic plateau surrounding Lake Lanao in northwestern Mindanao is associated in most Filipino minds with Mohammedan Moros and their militant fierceness, but also with excellent brassware and a cool climate. The great valley plain inland from Cotabato in southern Mindanao is best known as a colonial agricultural zone, though its alligator-infested Liguasan Marsh was once its most famous feature. The Central Plain of Luzon is the most productive rice basket of the islands, whereas the near-by Zambales hill country is one of the poorest landscapes in the islands. The Legaspi Peninsula of southeastern Luzon is noted for its abacá but even more for the perfect contours of ever-smoking Mayon volcano. These features are regional distinctions based on occupational economy or upon some other outstanding characteristic.

Less easily accountable, but as noteworthy, are the differences in the people of the several islands. There is the expansive generosity and love of good living of the inhabitants of Iloilo Province of southern Panay as contrasted with the canny thrift of the natives

33

of Bohol Island a bit farther east in the Visayas. The Ilocano from the northwest-coast provinces of Luzon willingly goes as a poor but thrifty colonist to many parts of the islands to obtain a better standard of living than he had in the overcrowded Ilocano territory. But the Tagalog from near and south of Manila willingly goes outside his home region only as a government official or merchant's representative.

Historically there have been three arbitrary divisions of the Philippines, namely Luzon and near-by islands in the north, the Visayan group of smaller islands in the center, and Mindanao, once the empty land of the south. Such a grouping omitted the Sulu Archipelago and Palawan in the extreme south and southwest. Also, this grouping neglected regional separations within each of the three units that sometimes were greater than those between units.

Other divisions include that of corn-eating and rice-eating parts of the archipelago. An irregular and discontinuous kind of division results from such a criterion. Regional divisions based on language are far too complex, with eighty or more languages spoken by groups ranging from several millions to a few hundreds only. The threefold religious pattern of Christians, Moslems, and pagans produces distinctive but also irregular divisions of very real significance in the affairs of the islands. That the tuba (a drink made by tapping the blossom stalk of the coconut tree) of western Panay is dyed by mangrove bark to a mild yellow-brown hue, and that of eastern Leyte is dyed a deep brownish red may be of less significance, but it is one of the regional distinctions of which the number is legion.

No attempt has been made in this study to present maps of these regionalisms. The geographer often summarizes them into what he terms the geographic regions, but my own knowledge of the Philippines is not sufficient to attempt a summary map of local regions. It should be recognized, however, that many problems facing the Filipinos are related to these regionalisms, and that many of the characteristics of people and economy are likewise produced by them. The problems facing the population of Siquijor Island of

34

the southern Visayas are related to such varied regional facts as the thin and dry coral soils, the severe infestation of the island by several species of the lantana plant, the reliance on corn as the dominant crop and staple food, the overpopulation of the island, the reluctance of the people to emigrate, the subdivision of the island into too many political districts and municipalities, and the physical separation from its parent province, Negros Oriental. Likewise, those facing the Ilocanos of northwest Luzon pertain to the long and severe dry season from November through May, the narrow coastal strip of lowland with its inadequate water resources, the sandy and relatively smooth coastline without good seaports, the long-standing insistence upon rice as the chief crop and food staple, and the problem of severe and long-continued overpopulation. The thrifty nature of the Ilocanos, their adventuresomeness as colonists, the variety of their handicraft and home industry, the strong imprint of the Spanish period, their distinctive housing and the relative lack of floral and decorative planting—all are features related to the historic patterns of culture or produced by the problems of the region.

Some pattern of regionalism, of course, is found in all parts of the earth. The mountainous, multiple world of the Philippines seems superficially homogeneous and, indeed, many similarities can be noticed in different sections. But in the varied historic patterns of populating, cultivating, and developing the resources of the islands a large number of differences have arisen. Although there are similar problems from the far north to the far south, their effective solution depends upon the recognition of local problems in the regional units and of solutions geared to those regions. In a politically young country such as the Philippines, with a rapidly changing culture, the awareness of regional differences and of the need for selective administration and long-range planning is not as clearly recognized as it should be.

Chapter 3

POPULATION GROWTH AND STANDARDS OF LIVING

PART AND PARCEL of the whole rural situation are questions about changing standards of living, population growth, and its limits in a specific environment. The visitor in the Philippines becomes aware that many Filipinos feel there is ample space for the present population and also plenty of room for future expansion. There are those who refer to overcrowding, and to the need for developing some kind of planned population control against the time when their home territory becomes saturated. One is aware of children everywhere and feels that the population is a young one, with a large growth potential. Just over half the total population is less than twenty years of age, approaching its most productive period as far as the birth rate is concerned.[15] The high standards of living in certain districts are impressive, but there may be seen also evidence of very low standards among certain classes and in particular regions of the islands.

Population Comparisons

The October, 1948, Philippine census recorded a population of 19,324,182 people in a territory of 115,600 square miles. Map 6 presents a map interpolated from the preliminary census releases. This is not a dense population if compared with some parts of the Orient. Java with approximately 51,000,000 people on about 51,000 square miles represents a far denser distribution with ominous future problems. Formosa, with about 6,000,000 people on its 13,890 square miles, roughly triples the density of the Philippines. Nor do the Philippines represent the more lightly populated parts of the Orient, for Thailand has only about 17,000,000 people in its roughly 200,000 square miles. Two comparisons in the United States are interesting. The states of New York, New Jersey, Pennsylvania, Delaware, and Maryland are almost exactly equivalent to the Philippines in area, and had a 1950 population of almost 33,000,000. This greatly exceeds the Philippine total and indicates a higher density for the American region. However, this region is the most highly industrialized and strongly urbanized section of the United States, with an economy in marked contrast to that of any part of the Philippines.

A closer comparison in many respects is with the two states of Florida and Georgia, which are slightly larger in area than the Philippines, and had a 1950 population of approximately 6,200,000, slightly less than one-third that of the Philippines. This American region has about the same total urban population as that found in the Philippines, and has a roughly comparable volume of industrialization. The tourist is more numerous in this American region than in the islands, an economic factor of real importance. Florida and Georgia have better road and rail transport, but the Philippines has much better water transport facilities. The American region has about 10,750,000 acres of cultivated land, with a possible maximum of some 30,000,000 acres. The comparable figures for the Philippine Islands are perhaps 11,000,000 and 30,000,000 acres. Although the two landscapes are not similar in surface contour, the comparable total farmland and maximum cultivability indicate a not unreasonable comparison between the two regions. The contrast in population, however, is startling to the American, particularly when one realizes that the Philippines is growing at a much more rapid rate than are the two American states.

During the early Spanish period the annual rate of Philippine population growth was not high, and by 1800 the total barely exceeded 1,500,000. In the last and milder century of Spanish rule the average rate of growth increased, and was particularly impres-

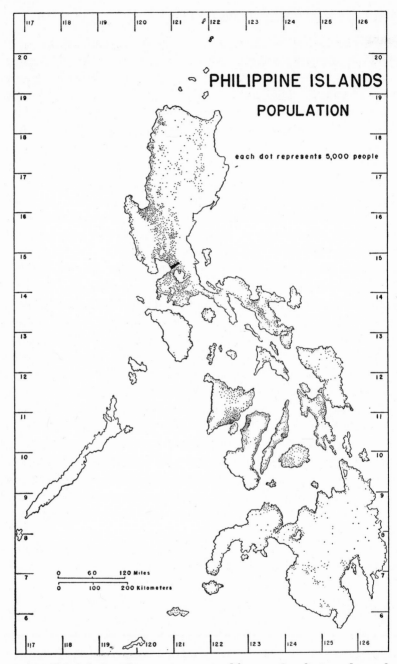

Map 6. Population. This map was prepared from 1948 preliminary data and is subject to correction when detailed 1948 census data become available. No attempt was made to demonstrate graphically the population of Manila metropolitan area.

sive in certain parts of the islands—northwestern and central Luzon, Cebu, and southern Panay. In 1903 the total for the archipelago stood at 7,635,000. The American period has seen annual increases comparable to those of the Spanish period after 1800, annual rates that range between 2.0 and 2.7 per cent. This represents an average net increase of more than 250,000 people per year, but in the last decade the annual increase has exceeded 300,000, in spite of the war.[16] This indicates an advancing birth rate and a declining death rate, as improvements in public health make themselves felt.

If similar rates of growth continue in the future, the population could be almost 40,000,000 by the close of the century. It is difficult to estimate what share of the total may be engaged in agriculture. The urban population is now slightly more than 10 per cent, but growing more rapidly than is the total. By the end of the century, it could stand between six and nine millions. At present about 47 per cent of the adult working population is occupied in agriculture and fishing, a figure that is decreasing slowly as urbanization and nonagricultural pursuits develop. It is reasonable to expect that this total may drop to less than 40 per cent by the end of the century. Projecting the present into the future—with about 1,700,000 farms or 17,000,000 acres in farmland with 12,000,000 acres in crop including double cropping, 9,000,000 people farming of whom 40 per cent are tenants—one estimates for the year 2000 about 3,200,000 farms or 30,000,000 acres with some 26,000,000 acres in crop each year, 16,000,000 people working in agriculture, and possibly more than half of them tenants. Such an expansion would require the availability of an adequate amount of land that can be put into cultivation.

These speculative increases would involve accumulating something over a third of the annual population increase in urban settlements, with the balance in the rural countryside. This would require adding more than 30,000 farms or almost 300,000 acres per year to the existing total.[17] This must be a highly selective process to be at all successful, because in some provinces the total acreage in farms already exceeds the maximum limit of land that can be farmed

Table 1

AREA AND POPULATION OF THE LARGER ISLANDS[a]

Island	Rank by area	Area in sq. mi.	Population totals			Rank by population
			1903	1918	1948	
Luzon	1	40,420	3,798,507	5,000,000	9,020,000	1
Mindanao	2	36,527	499,634	870,000	2,450,000	2
Panay	6	4,445	743,646	915,000	1,445,000	3
Negros	4	4,904	460,776	540,000	1,430,000	4
Cebu	9	1,702	592,247	770,000	1,040,000	5
Leyte	8	2,785	357,641	536,000	915,000	6
Samar	3	5,049	222,690	320,000	660,000	7
Bohol	10	1,492	243,148	320,000	523,000	8
Mindoro	7	3,757	28,361	50,000	166,000	9
Masbate	11	1,262	29,451	48,000	164,000	10
Catanduanes	12	620	39,288	62,000	112,000	11
Jolo	17	323	44,718	6,000	111,000	12
Basilan	13	488	27,017	2,200	108,000	13
Marinduque	15	367	50,601	56,000	86,000	14
Palawan	5	4,549	10,918	9,000	65,000	15
Tablas	19	278	24,648	32,000	64,000	16
Camiguin, South	32	90	30,754	37,000	60,000	17
Biliran	22	207	19,147	32,000	55,000	18
Siquijor	27	130	46,023	56,000	48,000	19
Guimaras	21	227	21,306	27,000	40,000	20
Ticao	29	123	10,183	16,000	37,000	21
Siargao	24	180	9,556	12,000	33,000	22
Dinagat	16	326	5,243	8,000	31,000	23
Panaon	36	70	8,610	19,000	30,000	24
Bantayan	42	40	18,325	24,000	25,000	25
Sibuyan	23	183	10,716	14,000	22,000	26
Total of 26 islands		110,544	7,354,154	9,774,000	18,740,000	
Total for Philippines		115,600	7,635,426	10,314,310	19,234,182	

a There are 31 islands with areas of more than 100 square miles each. Those not given in the above list each have populations less than 20,000. They are in rank by size: Busuanga, 14th; Polillo, 18th; Tawitawi, 20th; Burias, 25th; Culion, 26th; Dumaran, 28th; Balabac, 30th; Samal, 31st. A number of provinces include populations of small coastal islands excluded in the above totals.

SOURCES: *Philippine Census*, 1903, 1918, and preliminary data for 1948.

safely. In this development Mindanao must figure prominently, as will be discussed in later chapters.

A farm area of 30,000,000 acres would include almost half of the total area of the Philippines which, for a country of irregular surface patterns, is a large proportion to be cultivated. Such a total certainly will require a large area of uplands in permanent farmland. Also, such a total will approach the maximum area of land that can safely be devoted to permanent agriculture. If that farming is done more efficiently, with better yields resulting, the crop return to the farmer and the standard of living will be higher than today's. If rates of growth and general progress of the islands are greater than those postulated above, then the urgency of the problem increases. Lower rates of growth will lessen, but not remove, the problem, since it already faces the farmer and the agricultural arm of the government today.

Population and Living Standard

Population increase must be viewed relatively. Tables 1, 2, and 3 set forth the increase and density from different points of view. Almost half the total population resides on Luzon, but not all the problems of overpopulation are restricted to Luzon. In this main island, however, the provinces that are part of metropolitan Manila—Bulacan and Rizal primarily, but also Cavite and Laguna— must be considered separately from all others. Simple square-mile density figures are of little value in regional comparisons. The physiologic density figure, expressing the ratio of population to cultivated land, is more useful for interregional comparison, though one must be careful when comparing an Oriental and an Occidental country in this respect. It is necessary, however, also to consider the availability of reserve farm land to interpret properly the several density figures. Reserve cultivable area is shown in table 8. All data indicate that northwest Luzon, Panay, Cebu, Negros, Bohol, and Leyte are reaching their saturation points. They indicate that certain sectors of Mindanao and Palawan are filling up also, in spite of the enormous reserve areas still available there. It is also evident that recent colonization has settled areas in much the same manner as were

41

Table 2
COMPARATIVE CENSUS DATA BY PROVINCES

Province	1903 Population	1918 Population	1918 Density per sq. mi.	1948 preliminary data Population	1948 preliminary data Density per sq. mi.	
	a					1
1 Batanes		8,214	109	10,705	141	1
2 Abra	51,860	72,731	49	86,600	59	2
3 Cagayan	156,239	191,320	54	311,088	89	3
4 Ilocos Norte	178,995	219,129	169	251,455	192	4
5 Ilocos Sur	187,411	247,458	228	276,278	266	5
6 Isabela	76,431	112,960	28	264,495	65	6
7 La Union	137,839	178,386	237	237,340	447	7
8 Mountain	99,995	194,324	36	278,120	51	8
9 Nueva Viscaya	62,541	35,838	13	82,718	31	9
10 Bataan	46,787	58,340	114	92,901	180	10
11 Batangas	257,715	340,199	285	510,224	397	11
12 Bulacan	223,742	249,292	244	411,382	402	12
13 Cavite	134,779	157,355	316	262,550	527	13
14 Laguna	148,606	195,546	420	321,247	457	14
15 Manila City [b]	219,928	285,306		983,906		15
16 Nueva Ecija	134,147	226,721	106	467,769	221	16
17 Pampanga	223,754	257,620	311	416,583	503	17
18 Pangasinan	397,902	565,922	280	920,491	455	18
19 Quezon	153,065	212,017	46	416,719	90	19
20 Rizal	150,923	230,356	290	673,060	749	20
21 Tarlac	135,107	172,251	148	327,018	278	21
22 Zambales	104,549	83,750	59	138,536	98	22
23 Albay	240,326	323,234	210	394,694	254	23
24 Camarines Nor	°	52,081	62	103,702	125	24
25 Camarines Sur	239,405	218,733	106	553,691	266	25

No.	Province						No.
30	Iloilo	410,313	302,320		1,0__,___		
31	Negros Occ.	308,272	396,636	132	1,038,758	341	31
32	Negros Or.	201,494	272,524	132	443,461	215	32
33	Bohol	269,223	358,387	228	553,407	351	33
34	Cebu	653,727	855,065	456	1,123,107	596	34
35	Leyte	388,922	597,950	195	1,006,891	326	35
36	Marinduque	51,674	56,868	161	85,828	241	36
37	Masbate	43,675	67,513	34	211,113	134	37
38	Mindoro	39,582	71,931	18	167,705	43	38
39	Palawan	35,696	69,053	13	106,269	18	39
40	Romblon	52,848	64,610	127	108,817	212	40
41	Samar	266,237	379,575	72	757,212	143	41
42	Agusan	e	44,740	10	126,448	30	42
43	Bukidnon	f	39,684	13	63,470	20	43
44	Cotabato	125,875	171,978	18	439,669	49	44
45	Davao	65,496	107,385	15	364,854	48	45
46	Lanao	g	91,459	36	343,918	127	46
47	Misamis Occ.	175,683	81,015	101	207,575	259	47
48	Misamis Or.	115,112	126,788	83	369,671	244	48
49	Surigao	98,068	123,001	38	264,952	85	49
50	Zamboanga		147,333	23	521,941	80	50
51	Sulu	90,589	172,776	158	240,826	222	51
	Totals	7,635,426	10,314,310	91	19,234,182	166	

a Then a part of Cagayan province.
b The political area only. The metropolitan region overflows into Rizal and Bulacan provinces, contributing urban elements to their high average densities.
c Both Camarines included under one total.
d Then included as part of Albay province.
e Then included as part of Surigao province.
f Then divided between Misamis and Cotabato provinces.
g Then included as part of the single Misamis province.

Table 3

PHYSIOLOGIC DENSITY OF POPULATION BY PROVINCES

	Province	1948 population[a]	Estimated cultivated area in sq. mi.[b]	Physiologic density per sq. mi.[c]	
1	Batanes	10,705	5.5	2,000	1
2	Abra	86,600	46	1,910	2
3	Cagayan	311,088	310	1,005	3
4	Ilocos Norte	251,455	141	1,786	4
5	Ilocos Sur	276,278	133	2,120	5
6	Isabela	264,495	330	805	6
7	La Union	237,340	131	1,818	7
8	Mountain	278,120	132	2,118	8
9	Nueva Viscaya	82,718	77	1,100	9
10	Bataan	92,901	65	1,450	10
11	Batangas	510,224	420	1,214	11
12	Bulacan	411,382	286	1,441	12
13	Cavite	262,550	208	1,262	13
14	Laguna	321,247	332	968	14
15	Manila	983,906	. . .	. . . .	15
16	Nueva Ecija	467,769	880	530	16
17	Pampanga	416,583	352	1,126	17
18	Pangasinan	920,491	446	2,066	18
19	Quezon	416,719	740	561	19
20	Rizal	673,060	96	7,005	20
21	Tarlac	327,018	342	956	21
22	Zambales	138,536	82	1,716	22
23	Albay	394,694	410	963	23
24	Camarines Norte	103,702	155	688	24
25	Camarines Sur	553,691	522	1,062	25
26	Catanduanes	112,121	120	942	26
27	Sorsogon	291,138	435	669	27
28	Antique	233,506	152	1,540	28
29	Capiz	441,871	352	1,256	29
30	Iloilo	816,382	641	1,328	30
31	Negros Occ.	1,038,758	782	1,328	31
32	Negros Or.	443,461	300	1,378	32
33	Bohol	553,407	380	1,462	33
34	Cebu	1,123,107	548	2,051	34
35	Leyte	1,006,891	792	1,271	35
36	Marinduque	85,828	126	685	36
37	Masbate	211,113	242	876	37
38	Mindoro	167,705	230	737	38
39	Palawan	106,269	82	1,306	39
40	Romblon	108,817	144	760	40
41	Samar	757,212	625	1,230	41
42	Agusan	126,448	170	743	42
43	Bukidnon	63,470	100	634	43
44	Cotabato	439,669	350	1,279	44
45	Davao	364,854	500	729	45
46	Lanao	343,918	314	1,095	46
47	Misamis Occ.	207,575	230	917	47
48	Misamis Or.	369,671	266	1,388	48
49	Surigao	264,952	360	736	49
50	Zamboanga	521,941	480	1,087	50
51	Sulu	240,826	190	1,272	51
	Totals	19,234,182	16,209	1,186	

[a] Census figures from the 1948 Philippine Census.
[b] Estimated area of cultivated land has been interpolated from several sources, but has not been statistically finalized. The provincial totals fall slightly short of the total.
[c] Since the cultivated area is not precisely determined, the density figures can only be considered as approximate estimates.

older areas, *id est,* in relatively dense patterns of small-sized farms. This is the only way that Cotabato, for example, can have such a high physiologic density and at the same time have a huge reserve of cultivable land. This dense, small-farm pattern is natural to a population lacking transport and mechanical farming equipment.

These tables cannot make clear the relative potential capacity of different parts of the islands. If it were possible to compute mathematically the maximum potential of each provincial landscape on its present economy and then to place these figures against the present densities per square mile, the relative approach to maximum capacity would be indicated for parts of the islands. The geographer would prefer to make such comparisons on the basis of regional landscapes or geographic regions rather than on the basis of provincial political boundaries. Future alterations in the economy of different areas would, of course, alter the potential of each. Such shifts are continuous matters in reality, though often major components are blocked out into historical periods. Alterations in the economy and in the potential have been occurring continuously in the past, during pre-Spanish, Spanish, and American periods.

The inhabitants of northwest Luzon, Panay, Siquijor, Cebu, Bohol, and Leyte have long considered their home regions to be overpopulated. They have thought of these landscapes as limited in resources and lacking in expandable potential for their own continued use. They have regularly migrated to other parts of the islands where the local population pressures have been lighter and the local land resources greater.

There are tremendous differences between the agricultural potentials of many of the separate Philippine provinces. This is more than a simple matter of mountainous land or flat land. It is a complex of the conditions of the physical landscape as a whole. Integral parts of this complex are the length and severity of dry seasons and other climatic factors, the volume and accessibility of water supplies, soils—their fertility and degree of erosion already suffered—plant and mineral and other auxiliary resources of value to a rural population, the accessibility of the various local districts, transportation and communications, and numerous other physical factors.

45

It is this physical environment made to produce in a given manner by the skillful or unpracticed hands of a population that essentially supports a population at a given standard of living. Ilocos Norte and Siquijor, in terms of their populations and economies today, are lands of limited futures, nearing their maximum population densities unless standards of living are to decline as the population rises further.

In the final analysis regional differences involve more than just the physical environmental complex. Populations themselves become part of an environment, and the regional psychology of a people enters into the whole complex. Some of the peoples of the archipelago put different values on the several elements in a standard of living. Certainly this must be true of a population which ranges from urbane and sophisticated city folk to educated and modernized Catholic Christian rural inhabitants on the one hand and to shy, tribal, pagan peoples of simple culture on the other. And it is equally true where some of the obvious regional differences show up among Christian Filipinos, as between the Ilocano of northwest Luzon and the Tagalog whose home lies just south of Manila. To some of these peoples a landscape's final potential cannot be measured in its sheer productivity alone and, therefore, final assessment of the true potential of a region of the earth can probably never be produced as a formula or a statistic by an electronic mathematical brain.

This current internal shift of population has been moving in a southerly direction, toward Mindanao and other southern islands still lightly populated. It is important to understand the directional currents of migration in the islands. Those most common in the earlier, pre-Spanish past involved northward movements, from Borneo through the Sulu island group and along Palawan. These were the currents in motion when the Spanish came into the islands. The effect of Spanish military and civil control was to cut off the northward drift of peoples, who were at that time largely Moslem in religion. The present patterns of population movement began during the middle Spanish period, once regional stimulation of the birth rate had occurred and once the earlier countermovements had ceased. Continued and periodic Moslem raids northward made trouble after the start of Spanish rule, and inhibited colonial re-settlement of certain islands and local territories for a time. This internal migration began on a small scale and on a purely voluntary basis, as a personal means of improving the chances of life. It finally became a part of government policy, with somewhat the same ends. It affects the rural population of the islands rather than that of the towns and cities, for whom other programs are being developed.

In the last century the standard of living for the urban parts of the islands and for much of the rural landscape has been moving upward. Increased Filipino participation in trade, manufacture, and an expanding agriculture marked the last half century of Spanish rule. It certainly has marked the half century of American rule, though Americans, Chinese, and Spaniards have continued active in island affairs. The relaxation of Spanish rule, the real interest of the American, and the increasing ability of the Filipino—all have merged into improving life in the islands. A higher standard of living may be an intangible thing impossible to define, but it means an increasing volume and quality of food, clothing, housing, health and sanitation, education, and recreation. For a rural population these must be judged differently than for an urban group. And what may constitute improvement for a tribal group may mean little to an advanced rural community.

I believe it true that the general standard of living has been moving upward in the Philippines.[18] There are frontier regions in which there is a serious lag in this upward spiral, where internal migration has outrun the services of government. And there are rural areas of older occupation that have not participated fully in cultural improvements. In rural areas increasing standards of living come only with increased productivity of the landscape, unless they are subsidized from without. And as yet the industrial strength of the Philippines cannot subsidize improvement throughout all the rural sectors. Productivity must increase more rapidly than the population, to keep the living standard spiraling upward. With significant areas of the islands close to their maximum population potentials at present, problems in stimulating the economy become major and pressing.

Accepting the obvious differences in potentials of regional landscapes of the islands, one may ask whether some of the best regions may be able to carry some of the less productive, in a continuing upward spiral. It is implicit that in every country something of this sort goes on. Already some of the bountifully productive regions of the Philippines are carrying some of the poorer regions, just as in the United States. But in the unplanned and unchecked patterns in the Orient the historic tendency has been to crowd the bountiful areas to their limits, with neglect of the less fertile regions.

One may ask whether the genuine public concern of all groups will combine, under independent self-government, to carry forward programs that will produce the upward spirals in the standard of living that came, somewhat unplanned, during the last century; not only whether these can be developed and executed, but whether they can be paid for; or must such programs continue to be a donation to island economy by the United States. Or, again, will nationwide gains cease in the face of difficulties that may be made an excuse for the lack of improvement?

Chapter 4

SOILS, TECHNIQUES, AND THE PRESSURES OF MEN UPON THE LAND

ALTHOUGH the Filipinos do not yet overcrowd their homeland, the pressures upon their land are severe and damaging. Soil depletion and soil erosion are two of the most serious problems. They are responsible for much of the agrarian problem and the critical position of competitive agriculture. Seventy-five per cent of the land in farms in the Philippines now shows serious soil erosion. Soil depletion is causing crop yields in older areas of cultivation to decrease steadily, and yields in new areas often decline by 50 per cent within the first decade of occupation. This is a cumulative result of misuse of the soil, without concern for the future. Relatively few Filipinos even now are aware of what their agricultural systems have done to their lands. It is a natural result in a region of simple economy and small population trying to compete with other regions of more advanced economies and larger populations. The basic systems of agriculture have not changed adequately to accommodate greater populations and more exacting land use. The correction of this whole pattern in the Philippines constitutes one of the major problems facing a newly independent population.

The land problem is not only to correct past and current errors in the use of the landscape. The demand for land is a continuing one which may become greater in coming decades. With a net increase in population of more than 300,000 people per year, the need for more land, for new farms, and for farms better adapted to modern agricultural practice is a continuing one. The pressures upon the land of the Philippines are diversely expressed. At present they are centered in the areas of rural overpopulation and in the cities, and in the national economy—in a direct need for more land by the rural farmer, in increased food requirements by the cities, and in increased commercial products for home use and export sale by the national economy now struggling to stabilize itself.

Soil Erosion

A key factor in the problem of soils and their depletion and erosion is shifting agriculture, or caingin cultivation, described in the opening chapter. Shifting agriculture, when properly used, is a long-range system of land rotation. A small population with a large resource range could use shifting agriculture almost endlessly without encountering real restriction in their crop returns or in the auxiliary return from their resource range. Soil erosion would follow them from old garden patch to new clearing, and soil depletion would result from the interruption of the normal vegetative cycle and the sudden withdrawal of soil minerals by their crop harvests. But in the long-range rotation patterns they would practice, nature would have restored the balance before they would clear the same garden patch a second time. When a population increases in a given resource range, so that it must too soon depend again upon a previously used piece of land before nature's restorative processes can operate, then the consequences of soil depletion are reaped in decreased yields of poorer quality.

Shifting agriculture mines the soil of its resources in a short-term exploitation; then lets nature restore the soil in a centuries-long program. It requires few tools, little cultivation, the simplest planting and harvesting techniques, and nothing in the way of restorative techniques, because all these lie with nature. It is widespread in southeastern Asia, old in use, applied to all kinds of landscapes, and is the only kind of agricultural system known to many peoples. It has been suggested that when populations have built up to high levels by practicing shifting agriculture, the excessive drain upon the fertility of the landscape has been one of the factors bringing about the downfall of their culture. Even in less dire circumstances, such a land-use pattern has been retained long after it should have been transformed into a more complex system in which man performs some of the work of nature. This is the situation in the Philippines. Shifting agriculture is even now too widely practiced, still ruining lands that must come into regular use in the next generation with the current expansion in population. Too much land now being taken up by permanent settlers has had no time to recover from the last quick mining given it by shifting farmers of the past generation.

Shifting agriculture is not the most commonly used system in the islands today, as indicated in the opening chapter. However, the practice of mining the soil for basic crops is still the plan of other agricultural systems and was the policy of the Spanish at a time when they had no realization of the needs of the tropical landscape they controlled. American control of the islands brought little help for the problems of tropical agriculture, problems not even well understood today. Current American advances in soil conservation were not applied to the Philippines until late in the American period, and have made only a small start even now. Philippine concern with these matters is responsible for the laying out of a real program, but its development had to await the dramatic forcing by major problems endangering the whole Philippine economy.

A preliminary canvass by Philippine soil students suggests that, of the total land now in some kind of farm use, about 22,000,000 acres are "subject to all stages of erosion."[19] This is more land than is annually put into regular crops. Much of it is the permanently farmed slope fields in all parts of the islands that resulted from making sedentary farmers out of shifting agriculturists. Some is land recently put into steep slope agriculture by farmers who turned to the only land left to them, regardless of the fact that most of these lands should be left in protective forest. Some of it is lowland subjected to floods made destructive by stripping upland watersheds, or lowlands upon which no proper controls were provided for sheet wash during rainstorms.

Although soil erosion is not restricted to any one region of the Philippines, the uplands naturally have suffered the most. This means the interiors of most of the large islands, and the whole of many of the smaller islands. Primarily this is a landscape disease affecting the rural landscapes of the islands with first repercussions upon the rural population. Some areas nearer to cities and centers of agricultural information and experimental control work show arrested stages. But it is precisely hinterland areas that comprise the land reserves of the future in which this whole destructive phase of land exploitation is most serious. Yet it is not too late to take hold of the situation and by education, survey, and conservation programs stay the further ruinous effects of soil erosion. The active coöperation of all branches of the Philippine government will be needed to inform the public of measures that can reverse the present trends in island agriculture.

Soil Depletion

Even more serious than the active erosion of soils is the matter of general soil depletion. Generations of Filipino farmers had no program for restoring to the soils the chemical elements removed with the crops. The shifting agriculturist depended upon nature's processes to provide him with soils of a quality that could stand short-term farming. His slash-and-burn techniques by chance fertilized the lands he used. In the lowlands the earlier emphasis on gardening the aquatic and moist fringes of estuaries, stream deltas, and flood plains also reaped the renewal processes of nature. Farmers spreading over the lower hinterlands and into the rolling-to-rough uplands gave no thought to depletion as such because virgin land was always available. Long-continued use of the same fields, when that became necessary, has brought about serious depletion, and the lack of any restorative program has accented it. Where terrace culture has been practiced there are "cultural soils," in that weathered rock and soil material were gathered and placed behind the rock walls that held the fields together. The continuous processes needed to keep fields in shape for farming have automatically but not deliberately renewed soil quality and fertility.

Traditionally the Filipino farmer never has used much fertilizer.[20] On permanently farmed lands there has been no program equivalent to the burning of forest or jungle slash and brush. Roots and short stubble are left on the land, to be burned or plowed under, but this alone is not enough. Nothing corresponding to the elaborate programs in China, Japan, and a few other parts of the Orient—the use of animal manures, canal and pond mud, farmstead plant wastes or night soil—is found anywhere in the Philippines. The efforts of the agricultural agents only now are beginning to make a little headway. Two exceptions are the sugar-cane planters and the big pineapple plantation. Cane planters are almost entirely Filipino, but work in close conjunction with millers and exporters, and they have benefited from the extensive international research in cane-sugar production. The pineapple holdings are American in administration and management, closely integrated with the pineapple production in Hawaii. Elsewhere, in other crops and in less well-organized surroundings, the Filipino farmer has not accepted much of the growing body of material on soil control.

Soil Survey

Although the Philippines, in many ways, is a tropical region, one cannot dismiss the soils of the islands with the random term "tropical soils." The archipelago is a young one, geologically, with landscapes of many types. Few of its surfaces have been stable land area long enough for uniform soil patterns to have developed. There appears to be no true laterite in the islands, the crusted hard surface material that inhibits productive agriculture in many parts of southeastern Asia. There is a great deal of volcanic material strewn over the surface of the islands, though sedimentary rock strata are numerous and widespread. Soil survey work still is in a reconnaissance stage. A number of provinces had been studied and mapped, and reports published, when the war came in 1941.[21] Copies of those reports have almost vanished and, though they may be of value to the members of the Division of Soil Survey and Conservation and to a few scholars outside the Philippines, they can hardly assist any farmers directly who live within their areas. Postwar work is progressing steadily, but too many limitations still stand in the way of the whole program of soils studies.

In the current program of reconnaissance surveys, soils are divided into three broad categories, each of which contains a number of subdivisions. These three primary groups are: (1) swamps, marshes, estuaries, and coastal fringes; (2) lowland plains and rolling lowlands; (3) hills and mountains. The first group refers to those areas I have elsewhere termed the moist and aquatic fringe. Group two spreads across the moist lowlands of my earlier reference into the dry lands which to the individual farmer may be uplands. Group three obviously refers to the roughest parts of the area—termed uplands in earlier pages.

Although the first group of soils is fairly uniform in surficial features it is composed of fresh-water, brackish, and salt-water patterns, lakeshore, strand line, swamp, and marsh. Its uses are somewhat restricted. It presents no major problems of control, but could stand detailed use studies. The second group ranges all the way from alluvial river sands and silts through old lakeland clays to heavy lowland soils, with a wide variety of types and problems for the farmer. These are the most important soils of the islands. Preliminary studies indicate serious depletion of soil quality and some erosion. Detailed studies of remedial programs are in progress in a number of localities, but as yet no conclusions are available to point up changes in land use or farming practice that could quickly increase productivity. That fertilizers are needed is obvious but that is only a starting point in such a remedial program. It is upon this group of soils that most further effort must be expended. The third group of soils, that of the hill and mountain country, is of necessity being summarily dealt with in mapping and land-use study. But here lies the most serious need for conservation programs aimed at erosion control, at restriction of caingin cultivation and exploitive slope agriculture, and at the restoration of protective forestry. Some of the broad uplands and plateaus of Mindanao— reserve areas in the further development of the agricultural economy of the Philippines—might be said to compose a fourth group of soils, but these have not yet been studied.

Pressures upon the Land

Traveling over the islands and listening to stories of the struggles of the farming population, one is impressed that in certain regions the pressure of men upon the land has become extremely heavy. Some of the most dramatic illustrations of this pressure come from the island of Cebu, but this island is not alone in its land troubles. Cebu is a hilly-to-mountainous island with but little flat land. Only in a very few places does the Cebuano today seriously try to preserve his land for the future. Around the island fringes, on stony coral soils, coconut and corn are the main crops, with smaller yields than needed by the farmer. In the interior man has scaled the steep hillside like a mountain goat, scraping off the native vegetation and growing small crops of corn, cassava, sweet potatoes, and other vegetables on slopes so steep they never can be effectively terraced—slopes so steep they never should have been cleared. Soil erosion and depletion both have taken their toll. Soon the rugged interior will show itself a rocky and barren landscape, and the rural economy of Cebu will deteriorate.

The interior of the island of Panay shows the heavy hand of man upon the land in other ways. There are many sections in which the rough-to-rocky landscapes have been partly cleared of forest but have now gone largely to cogon grasses. These lands are often farmed by squatter or tenant farmers who till scattered patches and eke out a bare subsistence by traditional methods that defy the efforts of the agricultural agents. Here soil erosion, soil depletion, inefficient farming—a losing struggle against nature's attempt to recover the landscape—show a downhill trend unless man can redevelop the region. This landscape presents a contradiction to the theory of an expanding economy with a steadily lifting standard of living.

Northern upland Luzon, the heart of the terrace culture, shows few new terraces today though there is ample mountain land. Labor costs and the whole pattern of the economy are pitched too high to permit the extension of this effective but demanding system of land control. Around the terrace blocks lie expanding patterns of

55

Table 4

ESTIMATED AREAS SUFFERING SOIL EROSION, 1946

Province	Acres subject to erosion	Per cent of total area
Batangas	632,000	83.1
Cebu	916,000	76.3
Ilocos Sur	489,000	73.8
La Union	238,000	70.3
Batanes	33,000	67.9
Masbate	667,000	66.1
Bohol	664,000	66.0
Abra	610,000	65.1
Iloilo	832,000	63.5
Cavite	192,000	60.6
Rizal	300,000	58.4
Capiz	600,000	55.2
Marinduque	114,000	51.7
Negros Occ.	840,000	49.7
Tarlac	363,000	48.4
Ilocos Norte	390,000	46.7
Pangasinan	595,000	46.2
Mindoro	1,138,000	45.7
Antique	300,000	45.6
Bukidnon	825,000	42.7
Pampanga	225,000	42.6
Mountain	1,482,000	42.5
Sulu	286,000	41.5
Leyte	808,000	41.0
Albay	256,000	40.5
Catanduanes	141,000	39.9
Negros Or.	464,000	35.5
Camarines Sur	450,000	34.3
Zambales	303,000	33.7
Isabela	956,000	32.9
Nueva Ecija	422,000	31.1
Romblon	101,000	30.9
Bulacan	173,000	26.6
Sorsogon	124,000	24.7
Misamis Or.	238,000	24.6
Nueva Viscaya	375,000	22.4
Laguna	67,000	21.8
Cagayan	471,000	21.4
Misamis Occ.	107,000	21.3
Quezon	583,000	19.8
Bataan	67,000	19.4
Cotabato	984,000	15.6
Lanao	243,000	14.7
Camarines Nor	74,000	14.3
Zamboanga	500,000	12.0
Davao	506,000	10.5
Samar	357,000	10.5
Palawan	281,000	7.8
Surigao	110,000	5.7
Agusan	115,000	4.5
Total	21,972,000	29.9

SOURCE: J. P. Mamisao, "Soil Conservation Problems in the Philippines," *Journal of the Soil Science Society of the Philippines*, I (1949), 15.

steep slope fields, often stripped of soil and weathered debris which has piled up on fields below to ruin them in turn. Far too many spots throughout the archipelago show the blighted landscapes that go with caingin cultivation, followed by abandonment. Valuable forests are slashed and burned, scarred stumps stand against the skyline, gullies and bare rock surfaces are being covered over with grasses, vines, and shrubs. These scars also represent the severe pressure of man upon the land.

Pressures of men upon the land have come in various ways: from the shifting cultivator who uses and passes on, constantly seeking new land; from the sedentary farmer who has learned no new techniques with the land but now is tied to one farm; from the man who can acquire no new land to support his start in life and, knowing only simple farming, goes into the hills where he can practice his farming regardless of the toll; and from the new settler on the frontier who thinks in terms of inexhaustible wealth and who draws from his land but does not pay back. The pressures *for* land today are heaviest in older and more thickly populated parts of the islands where already too much land has been put under farm. The pressures *on* land today are widely scattered throughout the Philippines. Table 4 indicates a preliminary measure of one phase of the problem.

One has but to ask from what areas have come the new settlers in Mindanao to see where the pressures for additional land are the most severe. "From where do the settlers around here come?" is sufficient to produce a list of areas in which there now is all too little land for the coming generations. Northwest Luzon, southern Panay, Cebu, Bohol, Leyte, Siquijor, Masbate, and Marinduque are the home areas of the voluntarily migrating colonists. From the land statistics one could expect migrants also from the whole southern half of Luzon. "Are there no people from Laguna or Batangas?" I sometimes asked and sometimes received the slightly scornful answer "Tagalogs only come here as government officials!" And though the data indicate that some of the southernmost Luzon provinces such as Sorsogon and Albay, including the now separate island province of Catanduanes, and a few areas in the Central

Plain of Luzon such as Pangasinan and Pampanga are becoming overpopulated, these areas have filled but lately and the populations have not yet developed the habit of turning to Mindanao, Mindoro, or Palawan for relief. It is true that a good many Batangas people have gone to Mindoro recently, but it also is true that the Tagalog seldom has been a rural colonist in new areas. Tagalogs seem to gravitate more readily to the cities, to trade, to industry, and to bureaucracy than to the colonial settlement fringe.

In some areas the attempted solution has been to push farther back into the hill country, to round out the vacant spaces in the existing area rather than to break out of the home region and migrate to a new and distant home. Less and less can this serve in the future. More and more carefully will the canvass have to be made to find remaining near-by spots that can be drawn into the cultivated landscape. And more careful efforts will be needed to proscribe those areas which should not, in the interests of the country, be put under crop.

Chapter 5

The Balance in Domestic Food Supplies

SEVERAL MAJOR questions about the self-sufficiency of the Philippines today may be asked. What are the basic food items demanded? Are adequate quantities of each available within the country? What are the regional inequalities of supply and demand in the important commodities? Are there regional preferences for specific items or important differences in the dietary patterns between the cities and the rural countryside?

The Basic Dietary

A list of the foods basic to the domestic economy of the Philippines would include rice, fish, vinegar, meat, fruit, sugar, and sweet potatoes. Few urban Filipinos would wish to live permanently on just this list, even with a variety of fish from day to day, but it undoubtedly represents the goal of most rural people of the islands. If the list is doubled to include corn, wheat, milk, cassava, taro, a sauce, and a beverage, it would fill the needs in all parts of the islands. Ten of the items are traditional in domestic economy, but at least eight are now in inadequate supply in domestic production. Not all items on this list are used equally, nor are they available everywhere. There are recent developments which have altered the traditional dietary on a regional basis. Sugar and coconut are the only basic foods related to export agriculture, the latter used in several different places in the above list—vinegar, fruit, and beverage. Regional production of rice, corn, sugar, and sweet potatoes is shown in maps 7 and 8, and tables 6 and 7 present data on the acreage allotted to various crops, on the livestock count, and on the production of fish.

Table 5

REGIONAL DEFICIENCY OF FOOD SUPPLIES, 1939

Region	Estimated surplus or deficit in short tons of rice	
	Deficit	Surplus
Batanes	54	
Northern Luzon		88,200
Central Luzon		125,423
Southern Luzon	151,800	
Mindoro	2,426	
Marinduque	6,085	
Romblon	8,538	
Masbate	11,134	
Samar	24,419	
Leyte	17,714	
Bohol	24,583	
Cebu	80,262	
Negros	55,677	
Panay	27,623	
Palawan	7,416	
Mindanao		4,977
Sulu		21,443
Totals	417,731	240,043
	240,043	
Net deficit	177,688	

SOURCE: R. G. Hainsworth and R. T. Moyer, *Agricultural Geography of the Philippine Islands*, Washington, D. C., 1945, p. 65.

Rice and fish are unquestionably the chief support of the population. For at least a half century the domestic production of each has been inadequate, with constant recourse to importation. It is somewhat anomalous that the two most distinctive cultural practices of the islands should be insufficiently productive. Current programs in both fields aim at making the country self-sufficient.

Both can be successful, but only with major effort. Only because both rice and fish have been losing their complete dominance as basic foods, the shortages have not been more serious in the last two decades.

Vinegar may seem an unusual item to list in the basic dietary of the islands, but it plays a most important role in food preparation, flavoring, and preserving. Most vinegar is made from coconut, is widely produced over the country, and should be in adequate domestic production. Although its cost is not great, and it has not been a major item, there is some annual import of the commodity into the islands.

Meat products are chiefly water buffalo, beef, and pork from domestic sources, with chicken and duck the primary fowls. The Filipino eats a comparatively small amount of meat per capita per year. He would eat much more were it available. The Japanese reduced the numbers of livestock and fowl to a seriously low level during the war, so that currently there is much less meat and fowl available for public consumption than is desired. Even if one makes allowances for this temporary shortage, the demand for meat products has increased more rapidly than have domestic supplies, and one finds all kinds of meat products in the import lists. Were they not so high in price as imported foods, the totals would be even larger.

The islands today show a wide variety of fruits. There are, perhaps, a dozen common fruits that are traditional in island economy, and perhaps a like number that were brought in by the Spanish or the Americans. Of the older items, bananas, jack fruit, coconut, mango, santol, pomelo, calamondin, and lanzones are the most important. Of the newer kinds perhaps the pineapple, guava, sapote, sugar apple, and papaya are most important, all coming from Middle America with the Spanish. The newest are the avocado and the orange—both Valencia and tangerine. They are now grown in the islands—the avocado still being restricted in area and in variety, and the orange slow to spread as an orchard fruit in spite of its widespread popularity. Other fruits that are not suitable for production in the islands have become standard import items from

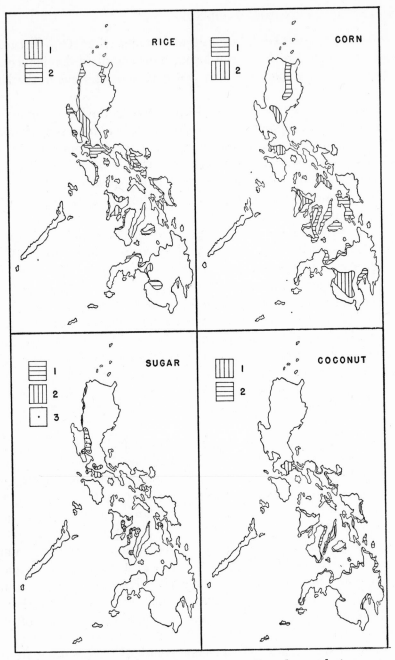

Map 7. Crop map. 1 = Major producing areas. 2 = Secondary producing areas.
3 = Sugar milling centrals.

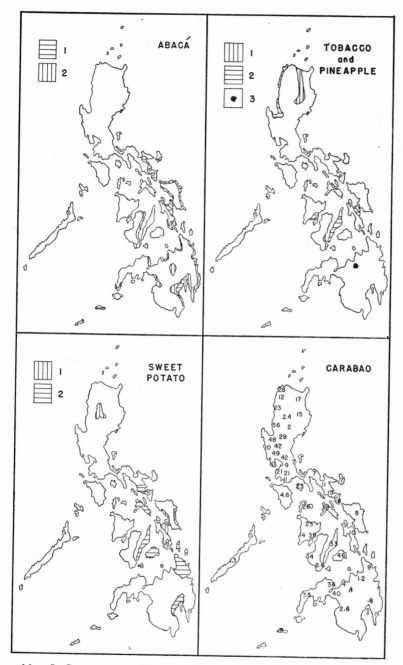

Map 8. Crop map. 1 = Major producing areas. 2 = Secondary producing areas. 3 = Plantation pineapple producing area. Carabao per square mile, December, 1945.

the United States, chiefly grapes and apples. Both of these are popular in the islands today despite their high prices. Many American tinned fruits are imported in large volume and have wide distribution throughout the islands.

Filipinos pay a high price for sugar and never have quite enough of it because it is pushed as a commercial export. It is a heavily borne cross that the home population pays more for its sugar than do American consumers to whom the bulk of the crop is sent. And for some years the domestic tonnage allowance of sugar has been less than the population has desired. There are many uses for it, from cooking to a wide assortment of native, Chinese, and American types of confections and candies.

The sweet potato-yam crops are almost indistinguishable in the markets or in the fields to anyone but an expert. The group as a whole is widely raised and is used to some degree by almost everyone, and special uses have been developed for particular species. Domestic production has, of course, been adequate to the demand though the acreage has risen slowly.

Vegetables and spice-sauces are important adjuncts to the dietary patterns of the Filipinos. Some of the Chinese green vegetables, introduced long ago by traders, are widely cultivated in small patches throughout the islands and used by many. Others, like the white potato and onion, are new introductions by the Americans and still are imported from the United States. The cucumber, the tomato, various of the beans, eggplant, and gabe (the taro group) form a series of new and old vegetables grown in small plots that seldom are accurately tabulated in agricultural statistics. Chinese sauces are widely used, since the Chinese are scattered among the Filipino townsmen. Many Indonesian spices are part of the daily menu. And occasionally a new item is amusing. Tomato sauce or American ketchup has become one of the most popular sauces in the islands and can be found in almost every grocery in the archipelago. Of many of these foods the islands produce a sufficiency, but also there are significant imports. Onions, potatoes, tomato sauces, tinned vegetables, and spices added together, bulk fairly large in the import trade.

Dairy products are another new item in the trade returns, growing larger as the appetite for them increases, and knowledge of them and their availability spreads over the islands. None of the native cattle, carabao, or imported water buffalo are good milk animals, and the Filipinos are not yet skilled in the production of dairy products. Hence the annual import volume is large, including butter, cheese, and milk in evaporated, condensed, and powdered form.

A beverage is a normal part of the domestic economy of most peoples. Where coconut trees grow well and are common in the islands, the traditional drink is tuba, collected from the fruiting shoots at the top of the tree.[22] It may be drunk fresh or fermented. Coconut trees tapped for tuba are not customarily used in producing coconuts. Statistically, coconut trees are found in every Philippine province, but the frequency of typhoons in the northern half of the archipelago restricts the number and the commercial significance of the crop. Trees tapped for tuba are similarly limited so, in effect, tuba is the common rural and market-town drink of the southern Philippines. In the earlier period the northern half of the country seems to have had no one common everyday beverage. Beer and soft drinks such as Coca Cola and orange and fruit juices, supplemented by cocoa and coffee, have taken over, particularly in the cities and towns. Bottling of the various beverages is now done in almost adequate volume in the islands, but most of the raw materials come into the country as imports, including much of the cocoa and coffee.

Cassava, from the root of the manioc plant, is one of the less important starch plants, widely grown in small plots as a minor crop in the southern two-thirds of the islands. It is chiefly a rural crop, eaten mainly during hard times when other crops fail, or if other crop plantings have not been possible in adequate volume. It is often one of the first crops grown by the pioneer settler, but also is a crop for poor lands that have suffered soil erosion and depletion.

Corn is one of the chief crops of the Philippines today, a basic food for many people, both rural and urban, and a subsidiary food for the majority of the islanders. Brought to the islands and popu-

Table 6

COMPARATIVE AGRICULTURAL DATA

(Area given in acres, production in metric tons; ooo omitted from all figures)

Crop	1940		1949	
	Acres	Tons	Acres	Tons
Rice (Palay)	5,038	2,364	5,345	2,491
Corn	2,255	572	2,140	534
Fruit and nuts	496	256	501	269
Root crops	438	615	425	528
Beans and vegetables	121	42	121	59
Miscell. food groups	52	?	79	70
Subsistence total	8,500	3,900	8,611	3,951
Coconut	2,596		2,384	
Copra		738		698
Dessic. coconut		40		59
Domestic oil		3		3
Sugar cane	568		319	
Sugar		997		693
Molasses				142
Abacá	721	172	700	75
Tobacco	132	32	96	22
Commercial total	4,017	1,982	3,488	1,692
Totals	12,517		12,099	

Livestock numbers	Jan. 1, 1940	Jan. 1, 1950[a]
Carabao	3,051	2,152
Cattle	1,396	735
Horses	343	222
Hogs	4,447	4,678
Goats	420	336
Sheep	40	29
Poultry	27,775	28,386

[a] Estimated only.
SOURCES: *Bell Report; Central Bank Statistical Bulletin*, Vol. 2, No. 3 (1950).

larized by the Spanish, it has steadily become more important. With it as a major crop, many areas have become able to support dense populations where rice would never have served so well. The varieties grown are not very good and the production per acre is far below the American average, entirely apart from the worn-out condition of many of the lands devoted to corn. Only a small amount of corn products is imported into the islands today, and corn is the only major basic food in which the islands are practically self-sufficient.

The role of wheat and its products in the islands is interesting. Gradually the use of breads, cakes, pastries, and other bakery goods has increased to major proportions. "Do you eat rice or bread for breakfast?" is not a rhetorical question, and it may be asked again for the other meals of the day. Because wheat is not grown in the Philippines, what has become a major food commodity must be entirely imported.[23] With population increase and the greater popularity of bread products the import volume of wheat has grown steadily over the decades. My own reaction has been that the Filipino would eat quantities of baked-wheat products whenever and wherever he could get them, but that the art of baking has not yet spread all over the islands. Table 14 gives figures on grain and dairy products imports.[24]

There are many other minor food crops not here discussed. They, of course, add to the food volume domestically produced. Few of them are represented in the import list. However, food imports also show a number of minor items not mentioned here, and these may balance each other in importance.

In summary, then, it appears that the Philippines does not really feed itself in terms of the basic list of everyday commodities used by almost everyone. If one were to canvass the luxury foods, beverages, and the menu items of such special national groups as the Chinese, British, Spanish and American residents this would be even more true. These non-Filipino national groups are mostly urban residents of the larger towns and cities. Many individuals within these groups do draw upon island supplies of rice, fish, meats, vegetables, and fruits, but also they account for a significant share of the processed special foods, beverages, and condiments imported into the Philippines.

The Regional Balances

Beyond the shortages already indicated are matters of regional unbalance and special preferences in basic foods. The basic list given above was essentially an urban list made by putting together lists from separate major regions of the islands. Some of the differences are important in a psychological complex attached to geographic regions but are more distinctive than significant in domestic economy. Such is the Moslem avoidance of the pig and the resultant scarcity of the animal in the Moslem provinces. In truth this avoidance is less rigidly observed in private than it is in public. Another difference is the varying color of tuba, which ranges from dark in Leyte to light in western Panay. The far-southern liking for durian, a foul-smelling but excellent-tasting tropical fruit, is much talked of but is only a detail in the regional variation of the use of fruits, promoted by the fact that the durian is strictly a tropical tree seldom found north of Mindanao.

Of another sort is the regional concentration on corn as a primary food. Corn is a currently characteristic Visayan Islands food staple. Although much rice is grown in the area from Negros to Samar, local consumption of rice is rather low. It is chiefly a cash crop sold by the rural farmers into the cities and market towns, whence much of it moves to the chief deficit areas of the Philippines. What colloquially is known as "corn rice" is used as the basic food of much of the rural population in this region, and similarly serves the poorer townspeople. Also some of the upper and urban classes of the Visayas stick to the food they may have eaten as children. "Corn rice" is made by coarse-grinding mature, dried kernels of corn, which is then boiled and eaten like rice. This food followed the earlier Visayan settler to the north coast of Mindanao, and more recently into interior Mindanao. Just how old this regional specialization may be is not known, but corn is post-Spanish, and the custom of eating corn is only a few generations old, a habit formed on farms and in villages during the nineteenth century.

68

The Cagayan Valley of northeastern Luzon is the only other region in which corn assumes the importance it holds in the Visayan Islands. Here it is the principal food crop for the local population, with tobacco the chief cash crop. Elsewhere corn is normally eaten as a green vegetable, grown in repeated plantings during the year in fairly small garden plots. This regional specialization on corn originally was planned as an agricultural improvement. Where corn now is a major crop with a fair yield, rice would be a poor producer, owing to the types and aridity of the soils. Most land now devoted to corn cannot be used for rice and would not have been brought into the cultivated landscape with rice as the chief crop. This specialization on corn has not been a long-run improvement, however, because no special cultivation practices and soil conservation techniques were devised to accommodate a new type of crop grown in a manner different from the broadcast planting used with rice. Self-sufficiency in corn supplies was achieved largely because of the constantly increasing acreage devoted to the crop. With a steadily increasing population in the corn-eating belt, local self-sufficiency may not continue, but Philippine self-sufficiency may remain by virtue of the steadily increasing settlement of parts of Mindanao better suited to corn than to rice.

From pre-Spanish stimulation came the growth of duck culture as a special regional pattern. Early Chinese traders ranged through the islands, but most of their early shore settlements seem to have been along the west coast of central Luzon. And here they taught the Filipinos duck culture as practiced in China. Large flocks of ducks are today kept in the region of Laguna, Rizal, Bulacan, and Pampanga provinces. Other provinces have partly copied but are not equal in duck culture. The Filipinos added a twist of their own to standard Chinese use of duck eggs. Duck eggs, almost fully incubated, and duck form a significant part of the diet of these provinces, including the metropolitan region of Manila.

Fish culture is less regionally concentrated than is duck culture, but it is a distinct part of Filipino land use. Swampy coastal lagoons, bays, and inlets are stripped of their vegetation and turned into diked ponds with water control, spawn planting, and fish harvesting on a formalized and continuing basis.[25] This source of fish is steadily growing in importance in island economy. Most of the yield goes to Manila markets, but as an economic resource fish culture is widely important. It gives the largest return, by value, of fish produced in the islands today. Fishponds are most numerous along the north coast of Panay Island, and in the Cavite and Pampanga sections of Manila Bay. Inshore fishing by small boats and shore-line traps brings the second largest share, by value, of fish

Table 7

COMPARATIVE DATA ON FISHERIES

Categories	1938	1949[a]
Boats over 3 tons	283	826
Fish ponds	8,445	10,000
Fish pond area in acres	150,000	173,000
Persons employed in all types of fishing	264,608	500,000
Fish pond yield (bangos) in short tons	16,109	27,500
Commercial fishing yield in short tons	21,500[b]	60,000
Total fish caught in short tons	89,578[c]	261,800[c]
Fish products imported, in short tons	18,000[b]	47,300

[a] Data represent estimates.
[b] Data for the year 1939.
[c] These figures represent minimum data which do not include all direct sustenance fishing.
SOURCES: *Yearbook of Philippine Statistics*, 1940 and 1946; *First Annual Report, 1949*, Central Bank of the Philippines; *Manila Times Mid-Week Review*, 27 Sept., 1950; *Bell Report*, 1950.

produced in the islands. Their production is not regionally concentrated but is found everywhere around island shores. Fishing as a whole is a distinctly rural phase of Philippine economy, participated in by a large number of people who are primarily farmers, but who fish as a sideline.

A number of fruits are regionally restricted to producing areas, though restriction in use has not remained complete with the development of modern transport. The durian, the mangosteen, and a number of similarly tropical native fruits are confined to the southern one-third of the archipelago. The mango tree today has spread widely over the islands but fruits only in those areas with a dry season corresponding to its blossom period. Restrictions are matters of elevation also.

BALANCE IN DOMESTIC FOOD SUPPLIES

Bananas seldom do well above 3,500 feet in the northern half of the islands, though the elevation can be somewhat higher in the south. Many other fruits will not succeed at even these elevations. This rules out a large number of fruits in the northern half of Luzon, in some areas in Mindanao, and in mountainous patches on many smaller islands. Sugar cane for chewing is more widely grown than is cane for commercial sugar making, but still is not found everywhere in the islands. Coconut and its products are rare in much of interior Mindanao, in a number of upland localities above about 2,000 feet, and in the whole northern half of Luzon.

In general it seems obvious that the food economy of the upland population, based on local sources, is more limited than that of the lowlander. But less mature rural landscapes are everywhere more limited in their local food resources than are older areas. One is struck by the simplicity of the array of foods in the markets of many of the newer villages and towns in parts of Mindanao, as compared to the variety available in some of the older localities of the central or northern islands. For the purely rural population, without easy access to village and town markets, this is even more true. And one is impressed with the short season in which some commodities are available in rural areas, for it is not true that in this nearly tropical region all things can be had all of the time.

One finds that the variety increases in the urban communities. In a few large centers, such as Manila, Cebu, Iloilo, and possibly Davao, served with the best in island transport, one can find the products of all parts of the islands during the producing seasons and for some time afterward, as storage and warehousing facilities provide better and better equipment. Manila, of course, is the most highly developed center of all, with the best facilities for gathering and handling all kinds of island produce. Manila also has the widest clientele, since the native population of the metropolitan region is drawn from all parts of the islands and represents the widest range of economic levels of Philippine society.

In imported goods and their role in regional food economy, one finds in the markets of Manila products from all over the world. Today one can buy almost any standard food product of American,

Australian, Canadian, Spanish, or Chinese origin, with a liberal variety from several European countries. In the two regional centers, Cebu and Iloilo, one can repeat the experience, though not quite so completely. Below these three urban centers, the provincial capitals and larger towns the country over provide surprisingly wide variety of imported packaged goods. Fish, meats, dairy produce, vegetables, wheat products, sauces, candies, and fruits—all are to be found. In the smaller and more out-of-the-way places, the selection narrows, the volume decreases, and consumption falls off. In the rural uplands of island interiors one finds the processed, imported foods limited to a few basic items—fish, wheat noodles, a sauce or two, a little tinned fruit, and a bit of candy. Even here, of course, the list has increased in recent years, but it has many gaps in terms of the desired standard, even of the rural uplander.

In summary one may pick out certain parts of the country that more than feed themselves.[26] Other regions do not feed themselves but concentrate on export products that bring in, in return, domestic foods from near-by regions or islands and from outside the country. The urban centers neither feed themselves nor produce commercial export products, but form continuous deficit areas that draw both on island and outside sources of food. The Manila metropolitan region is the most pronounced area of food deficiency in the islands, and the other urban centers are localized deficit areas drawing upon local regions. The main sugar-producing area of Negros Island and the whole island of Cebu are the chief deficit regions, with marked food shortages. Minor deficits, under average conditions, exist in parts of northern Luzon, most of southern Luzon, Marinduque, Romblon and associated islands, much of Samar, most of Leyte, Bohol, Siquijor, coastal strips on northern and southeastern Mindanao, Basilan, Jolo, and Tawi Tawi islands. Palawan and many smaller islands not shown in map 10 also possess food deficits, because of the rather peculiar regional economy operative in these restricted regions.

This internal geographical unbalance in food supplies is perfectly normal to many large regions of the earth. It is harmless in a country whose transport system functions with sufficient smoothness to spread economically regional surpluses around, and whose regional balances in labor serve to keep the economy operating productively. Neither of these qualifications is true of the Philippines. Unbalance in import of foodstuffs from abroad has sufficient precedent to be called almost normal. However, there should be effective compensations if the unbalance is to remain and the standards of living are to continue rising. These compensations, in the case of the Philippines, have been tied up with the peculiar economic position of the islands within the American tariff framework. In the highly competitive world of the future the complex of unbalances may well bring economic privation to some if not to all parts of the islands, directly or indirectly.

Chapter 6

TRANSPORTATION
IN THE HINTERLANDS

TRANSPORT in the early Philippines was simple. Outrigger sailboats around the coasts and on the larger lakes and dugout canoes on the island rivers served the basic needs of most of the pre-Spanish Philippines. On land a system of simple trails threaded the interior and the upland country. In the smoother lowlands water buffalo pulled simple sleds or served as pack animals. In an island world of water and boats this shortage of land transport and road system was not abnormal. Island culture has developed far from these traditional patterns, but transport has not kept pace with other phases of Philippine culture.

Evolving Road Systems

The Spaniards intentionally tried to turn the Filipinos into a sedentary and land-occupying people, though their success was by no means complete even with those over whom they established political control. Restrictions upon trade and travel were many and were maintained well into the nineteenth century. The development of a land economy should have called for a transport system—a good road and trail pattern. Something of this sort did evolve slowly, but because restriction of movement was part of the Spanish program the transport system did not develop and did not greatly facilitate land trade or passenger movement. Apparently on the islands of Cebu, Panay, and Leyte there gradually emerged a simple

74

system of roads and trails. Southernmost Luzon had a small network of roads and trails centered on Legaspi and connecting the regional lowlands of southeastern Luzon. From Batangas northward through the Manila hinterland, the Central Plain, and along the northwest coast of Luzon ran a connected system of land routes that formed the best transport network developed during Spanish times. Although handicapped by the tropical landscape, the Spanish did fairly well in starting a road system in this section of Luzon.

In 1896, there were already some 2,600 bridges and culverts in use in the entire country, and a road and trail system of three to four thousand miles in length. No accurate statistics on roads were available until after 1907. Horses and cattle were added to the animal population, the former for transport, the latter chiefly for food. Two-wheeled carts for cargo, pulled by water buffalo or cattle, were introduced, and also light two-wheeled, single-horse, covered carts for passenger transport. The former were used wherever there were good enough roads, but the horsecarts for passenger use seem to have become an urban feature. At least this was true by late Spanish times.

The Americans began their period in the islands with enthusiasm for developing the archipelago. The first interest in roads stemmed from the efforts of the American army to complete the transition from Spanish to American control after the war with Spain. Some road work was done in those early years, but the maintenance provisions were completely inadequate in a climate extremely hard on the types of roads then being built.[27] Maintenance under Spanish control had been largely by *corvée* labor; no local government in the early American period voluntarily provided either finances or labor to maintain the old Spanish or the new American roads. Gradually there developed a system for building and maintaining roads which only partly resembled domestic American methods. The continuance of this system is perhaps one of the reasons why the roads of the islands are unequal in quality and not better than they are today.

Road construction and maintenance are centered in provincial Bureaus of Public Works, which also have many other duties. There

75

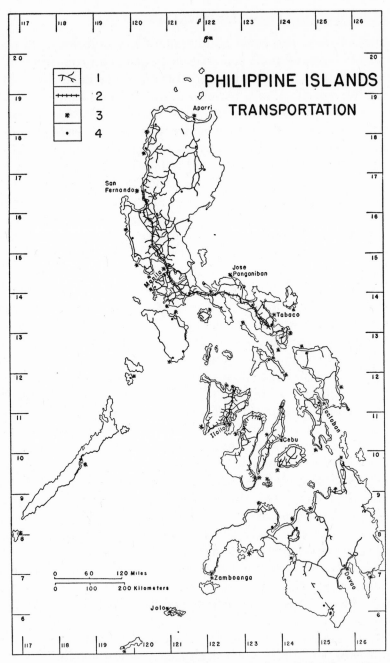

Map 9. Transportation. 1 = Primary highway network. 2 = Railroads. 3 = National ports. 4 = Air fields. Ports open to foreign shipping are named.

are offices at the provincial capitals and a few other places in each province, but road construction and maintenance receive only part of the attention and budget of the bureaus. A great deal depends upon the district engineer. The *caminero* system still is used for maintenance, by which one workman has permanent charge of a small section of highway. Weed cutting, ditch and culvert cleaning, surface patching, and other duties—all are done by the individual caminero after the main construction and surfacing of the road have been completed. The surfacing especially suffers from caminero care because of inadequate tools and improper methods. As part of the postwar rehabilitation program of the Bureau of Public Works, with the financial and engineering assistance of the United States Public Roads Administration, there is being developed a system of sectional maintenance by united working crews which will have equipment for real maintenance work. For construction, maintenance, and record purposes, roads are divided statistically into national, provincial, city, and barrio (local district) roads and, except for barrio roads, are further subdivided into three classes. However, in practical operation the third-class provincial road of one province may well be better than the first-class national highway in another province.

In a humid landscape as irregular as that of the Philippines, the bridge problem of the highway system is a major one. Typhoons and dry seasons cause enormous variation in the flow of rivers. In certain areas premature building of too small bridges, long continued building of purely temporary bridges, and some bad engineering have kept the road builders at work on particular bridges far too long. And in some districts rivers in flood still cause the same trouble today. At the end of 1949 there were more than 10,000 bridges and culverts in the island highway system.[28] There had been more than 1,700 permanent bridges in 1941, of which more than one-third were damaged during the war, and at the end of 1949 permanent bridges numbered 1,774. Nearly half the 6,500 wooden and other temporary bridges were damaged or destroyed during the war, a total since increased to more than 7,500.

There are sections of the islands that now have good highway networks which adequately serve all parts of the local district. On the accompanying transportation map (map 9) only major highways are shown for the Central Plain of Luzon. Similarly, a few local secondary roads are omitted in the northwest coast provinces of Luzon, in southeastern Panay Island, and on the island of Jolo. Elsewhere every public road is entered, as of the data for the end of 1949. In a number of places in Mindanao and elsewhere, cart and motor traffic has been operating for years over routes not shown on the map, because they are cross-country traverse zones that are not formal roads in any true sense. Most barrio roads and field trails are not shown on the map either, though there are many of these in some of the lowland regions of the islands. They are unpaved dirt tracks that become impossible for traffic other than water buffalo in the rainy seasons of every year. The map clearly indicates that most parts of the islands—the Central Plain of Luzon and southeastern Panay perhaps excepted—do not yet possess an effective highway network. Economic development is so closely related to effective transport that the development of a transport system becomes a key point in any program of rural improvement.

Roads and Transport Today

The formal road system of the Philippines as of December, 1949, totaled 27,170 kilometers, equivalent to 16,883 miles of all classes of roads. This means that the rehabilitation program, if not yet complete on certain projects, has gone beyond mere rebuilding of war-damaged highways. The national Bureau of Public Works has a number of new projects in the planning stage, and there is no question that the road system will expand year by year and become steadily better as heavier surfacing is applied, and as realignment of certain sections increases the potential traffic capacity. Hard surfacing of roads in the Philippines began only in the 1920's to replace the water-bound macadam formerly used. Total motor vehicle volume at the end of 1949 stood at 94,000, with an estimated one and a half billion miles of travel annually. No detailed breakdown on cars, trucks, or busses is available for this total, but my own estimate suggests about 42,000 passenger vehicles, 38,000 trucks, 13,000 busses, and about 1,000 motorcycles.[29] Metropolitan Manila's share of this total was about 16,000 passenger cars, 8,500 trucks and 5,500 busses, barely a third the national total. Against this number of motor vehicles stand approximately 21,000 calesas and other types of horse-drawn passenger carts, of which about 3,500 belong to metropolitan Manila.[30] No current estimate for oxcarts or sleds has been found, nor can even an estimate be given of how many horses, cattle, or water buffalo serve as pack or riding animals in local transport and travel.

Even though the above figures are expanding from year to year, it is clear that inadequate transport is one of the major problems of the islands.[31] One cannot travel anywhere on land in the Philippines without becoming aware of the need for better facilities. When the totals for the country are broken down into provincial or regional figures their inadequacy becomes more significant. Data for late 1949 for the island province of Mindoro give total road mileage of 217, over which operated 121 passenger cars and jeeps, 346 cargo trucks, 36 busses, 4 motorcycles, and about 375 horse-drawn passenger vehicles. On the main island of Mindoro itself there are fifteen municipalities or political districts in 3,922 square miles and a population of about 150,000 people. The population lives close to the coastline; the island interior is rough and forested; the road system is divided into three sections, with most of the mileage along the east coast. There are three airports, two national seaports, and a variety of boats ranging from outrigger canoes to motorized landing barges acquired from American military materiel. It is obvious that increased transport facilities on land would not only improve the standards of life, but would permit the expansion of island economy. Mindoro is still an undeveloped colonial frontier, and its need for increased transport exceeds that of some of the older regions. Mindoro is no worse off, however, than other regions where lack of transport facilities is one of the chief obstacles to economic development.

By contrast, Connecticut, the American state nearest Mindoro in size shows these figures: area, 5,009 square miles; 1950 population, 2,000,000; 1943 rural road mileage, 11,206; 1944 automobile registrations, 499,452. There can be no direct comparison of automobiles and population in the two areas because of economic disparity, but it is true that Connecticut has a road system which serves the people of the state, whereas Mindoro does not. The figures for Mindanao show this lack to an even greater degree than do those of Mindoro. Mindanao has a total area of 36,906 square miles, a population of some 2,700,000 people, but only some 2,500 miles of roads, perhaps almost 3,000 motor vehicles, of which a good two-thirds are trucks, and something more than 400 horse-drawn passenger carts.

Public bus transport is one of the most interesting and significant aspects of land transportation in the islands. With the few private automobiles, for the use of only a very small share of the population, the bus has become far more important than in many countries. Generally speaking, Philippine bus-transport economy compares with that of almost any place in the world. Likewise it compares in service to its customers. Except for a few of the long-run "limited" schedules, a bus will stop anywhere to pick up or discharge passengers. Most lines will carry any small cargo on the ticket, often include freight in small consignments on their regular runs, and operate fairly fast schedules. Most busses are regular truck-rolling stock, with Philippine-built bodies adapted to people of smaller girth and stature than most Americans.

A typical set of operating details for one of the larger companies, competing with several others in southeastern Luzon, reveals these figures for the first six months of 1948: 45 routes totaling 553 miles in length, with 167 busses carrying 4,821,000 passengers and 158,000 freight consignments for a total mileage of 2,518,000, at a tariff rate of approximately one and one-fifth cents per mile, and a 50 per cent discount on round-trip fares. This company operated over 400 busses before 1941, starting as a one-truck line in 1914. It was one of the first transportation companies given a franchise for island operation.[32]

Not all companies can show this good a record, and few of the smaller concerns which have not specialized on one type of truck, do not maintain good repair shops, and do not run on definite time schedules, can long compete with firms which follow these basic rules. However, there are more would-be passengers than transport services in most parts of the islands today. Currently busses operate almost everywhere. Busses may go only where there are roads, however, and to get better transport services the road systems must be extended more rapidly than in the past. There are too many large and well-populated sectors of country without road services at all, and too many regions soon to be settled that cannot be developed without transport. The public bus company gives the best transport service so far available to most of the Philippine population.

One may speculate endlessly upon the volume of road transport currently needed by an area like the Philippines. Certainly if Mindanao, Samar, Palawan, and Mindoro had more roads, settlers would push along them to find new homes, towns would spring up, and economic production would result. Mindanao today needs at least double her 2,500 miles of highway for even basic contact, probably four times that to facilitate the agricultural development of reserve crop land, and perhaps six times the current figure in the foreseeable future. Perhaps the suggestion that the road-building program of the islands should seek to double the present mileage in the near future would not be amiss. A corresponding increase in vehicular equipment is needed, with the increase distributed over the countryside of many islands rather than concentrated around Manila and other urban areas.

The Place of the Railroad

Technically the beginning of railroad transport belongs to the Spanish period. Starting with a concession to a British firm in 1887, a 122-mile line of 3'6" gauge was built from Manila northward through the Central Plain to Dagupan on Lingayen Gulf, with construction completed in 1892. The road was not an outstanding operating success, and further railway development belongs in the American period. During several decades after 1900 the line gradually was extended southward to Legaspi, northward to San Fernando, and a number of side branches were started, some of which were never completed.[33] Maximum mileage before 1941 was 708, with 159 locomotives, about 2,000 freight cars, and some 375 passenger cars. The railway seldom made money after 1910, and destruction during the recent war placed a heavy debt burden upon it. Currently only the main line is operating, between San Fernando and Legaspi, a distance of approximately 550 miles. As early as 1910 the fate of the railway was indicated, when a highway paralleled the route through the Central Plain. It never has given the service that should be expected of a primary public carrier.[34] The line became government property in 1917. Since the early 1920's the railroad has run a number of bus lines over the highways of central Luzon, sometimes in competition with its own rail-passenger service.

Two other islands had railroads before 1941. On Panay a line was built from Capiz to Iloilo, north to south coasts, a distance of 72 miles, and on the east coast of Cebu a line 66 miles long was built north and south of the city of Cebu. Both lines were built by an American company in 1906–1911. Both were losing money before 1941, and the Cebu line was abandoned late in 1948.[35] The Panay line continues to operate with a small amount of rolling stock.

The history of railway building and operation in the islands indicates clearly that railways are uneconomical in a multiple island landscape of small elongated areas where coastal water traffic and highways parallel the rail lines. The railway era has passed for the Philippines, and further development of transport, save under exceptional circumstances, should employ other forms that can be more conveniently fitted to the peculiar landscape and its needs.

However, reconstruction of all war-destroyed branch lines should be completed. On Luzon the Cagayan Valley should have a rail connection with the present system.[36] Probably best would be a loop, with a southern connection into the Central Plain and a northern connection rounding the north coast and skirting the edge of the mountain country to San Fernando, La Union. On Mindanao it is possible that a few key rail lines could be planned in connection with highways and industrial programs so that they would be profitable and productive, but no major rail network is justified at present.[37] The Manila Railroad Company system could undoubtedly be made more efficient and economical, but a critical survey would be required to disclose the needs.[88]

A different issue are the light rail systems used by the lumbermen, the cane planters and millers, and some of the abacá plantation operators. Movable track systems, light rolling stock, and small economical diesel engines make feasible the use of light rail systems in a number of localities. Such rail systems as these could undoubtedly be extended for specific economic developments but not as public carriers with all the obligations and vested interests which that implies.

Interisland Water Transport

Originally water transport was predominant among the 7,083 islands and rocks that make up the Philippine archipelago. Changes in water transport have been taking place steadily. In the earlier days of small coastal outriggers and even the larger deep-sea craft, every estuary, inlet, bay, and beach was potentially a port of call. For centuries a number of spots in the archipelago have been much used by seafarers because of their sheltered waters. Several places in the Sulu group, and such protected spots as Zamboanga, Iloilo, Cebu, Legaspi, and a number of localities around Manila Bay have long been key meeting points in land and sea contacts. The ships of foreign traders from all over the Orient anchored in shallow waters, and cargo was handled to shore in small lots by lighters. Early Spanish trade used similar methods. Discouragement by the Spanish of outside contacts, except for the periodic renewal of trade with the Chinese, minimized the use of the sea and boats in that part of the islands controlled by the Spanish. But in Sulu, Palawan, and much of Mindanao, the Moros used the sea in many peaceful ways and also to approach the Christian lands in the looting raids that characterized much of the seventeenth and eighteenth centuries. In all the southern zone, therefore, the sea and the boat remained more a part of life and culture than in the northern part of the islands.

There are not many interior water bodies in the archipelago of value to transport. The Laguna de Bay and Taal in central Luzon,

Naujan in eastern Mindoro, Mainit, Lanao, and Buluan in northern, central, and southern Mindanao respectively, are the only sizable lakes, though there are many small lakes and ponds. The Cagayan River in northern Luzon is the longest in the islands, some 275 miles, and the Rio Grande de Cotabato in southern Mindanao and the Agusan in northern Mindanao are each more than 200 miles in length. Each of the three today is traveled by power launches, but both the Agusan and Rio Grande basins have swamps that hinder river navigation. Other large streams are either rapid-filled or so shallow and shifting in bed as to be of no value in transport. Many small streams are navigable for a few miles inland from their mouths, but none open up a large territory.

As modern international trade developed, only a few spots in the islands could be used as ports. The Spanish had just begun to develop Manila, Cebu, and Iloilo when their period of control ended. Since then, under American stimulation, some two hundred and fifty sites have been provided with port facilities. At most of these, of course, facilities consist only of short piers, wharves, land-loading grounds, and a road leading inland. There is a minimum of warehousing, and few ports have mechanical equipment. Most of these ports are designed for coastal traffic only. Approximately forty-five are designated as national ports, whereas about one hundred and fifteen others are only municipal ports with the simplest facilities. There are other points having simple facilities—restricted, private, or for special uses. Eleven ports, scattered over the archipelago, have been declared open ports at which foreign ships may call without special permit. Their distinguishing feature is a customhouse with regular staff to process foreign ships. These open ports are starred and named on the transportation map, the national ports are starred only, and municipal ports are not shown. Some of the national and municipal ports are on islands too small to show on the transportation map.

About 1,100 of the 7,083 islands and rocks of the Philippine archipelago are permanently inhabited. Only a small number of these are provided with port facilities of the kind suggested above. Obviously many of the smaller islands do not need large-ship facilities. Many municipal ports on the larger islands are without roads leading into the hinterlands. What the Philippines need, for effective development and integration, is a well-developed system of interisland transport. This cannot be created merely by establishing ports or by encouraging shipping companies to lay out regular routes. The recent history of island shipping indicates that American government action, through the Bureau of Navigation, did much to stimulate interisland shipping after a period of relative quiet in which the Spanish had done what they could to discourage it.[39] The recent war was enormously destructive to interisland facilities, some of which will not be restored for years. Postwar availability of American ships has permitted the reëstablishment of many Philippine shipping companies with good fleets.[40] But coastal water transport does not yet serve the islands as effectively as it should, since many good areas lie completely out of touch. A well-planned program for coastal shipping, tied in closely with road development inland from ports, could keep abreast the rural development of the islands rather than lagging far behind it.

The Air Transport Pattern

Air transport in the Philippines already is a tremendously useful addition to the transport picture. It can be even more useful in the future if more and better air terminals are available for use. The transportation map indicates almost sixty airfields open to commercial traffic at the end of 1949. No airport in the islands is more than a daylight flight's distance from Manila, the hub of the air route pattern. This means fast mail delivery, newspapers distributed widely, rapid and relatively cheap travel, and freight shipments that can go anywhere on the major islands quickly. But air transport is of primary use to the government, organized business, the urban, trading, industrial elements of society, and not to the rural folk whose lives and needs are far removed from the air strip and plane travel.[41]

Chapter 7

THE BALANCE IN INTERREGIONAL TRADE

MANILA IS the magnetic center which alters and acts upon the patterns of contemporary Philippine domestic trade. There are several smaller centers such as Vigan, Dagupan, Legaspi, Tacloban, Cebu, Bacolod, Iloilo, Cagayan, and Davao, each affecting a regional zone in a lesser way. The multiple island environment, with its extensive coastal fringes and rough island interiors, is responsible for two distinct kinds of interregional trade. First is the sea trade between islands and between regions. Second is the trade between coastal fringe and island interior, a repetitive pattern occurring in island after island. Manila, chiefly, and each smaller center to a less extent, plays a role in both phases of internal trade.

The Background Conditions

Manila has not always been the center of Philippine internal trade but became so during Spanish times. The west coast of central Luzon has long been one of the key regions of the islands, but the most important trade region, until mid-Spanish times, was the Sulu archipelago. In the early barter economy, differences in environment produced a commodity trade unlike that of today— fish, shells, rock for tools and weapons, salt, jungle products, gold, and possibly textile fibers. In the pre-Spanish period of trade carried on by the Indians, Arabs, Chinese, and Indonesians, the chief commodities were iron, gold, silver, jewel stones, copper and copper wares, tin, porcelains, slaves, abacá, coconuts, rare woods, and similar items. The Philippine contacts with this trade centered in the Sulu region. Other districts of the islands fed native products to that area and absorbed some of the imported products. The Sulu region was relatively more populous than many other parts of the islands, and supplied pearls, shells, and coral to the trade. Rice came from the Central Plain of Luzon and from Panay, gold from several parts of Luzon and eastern Mindanao, copper from northern Luzon, abacá from southern Luzon and the Visayan Islands, coconuts from all over the southern Philippines, and jungle products such as rare woods, gums, and oils from a wide range of local areas.

The first important effect of Spanish control in the islands was a lessening of international trade as such and a decreasing of the Filipino role in it. Second was the curtailment of the extensive internal sea trade that had developed between various regions and islands. Third was a separating of Spanish-controlled parts of the islands from the Moslem fringe of the south. A period of looting raids replaced the earlier peaceful trade between the littoral and the interior.

The Spanish altered the regional balance in the islands. After Manila became the Spanish capital, economic emphasis inevitably shifted toward it. The centralizing of affairs around the capital was new in island history. Where the Central Plain and Manila Bay environs had been unimportant political regions but the sources of one of the important trade products—rice—they now gradually became the center of political influence and an economic center toward which products moved. Population increased and the Manila Bay hinterland gradually replaced the Sulu area as the chief economic region of the islands. The Spaniards encouraged the Chinese to bring to Manila the products of the East which Spaniards could ship to the Spanish New World and to Spain. Despite setbacks the Chinese trade prospered and brought a steadily larger Chinese population. The Chinese also began to extend their trade into domestic fields, dealing with and serving the Filipino population. By the beginning of the American period there was no question of the supremacy of the Manila Bay region in political and economic matters, both in international and domestic matters.

The restrictive bonds of Spanish control began to relax early in the nineteenth century, and by the last quarter of the century other occidental merchants could find opportunity in the islands. Trial shipments on the international market were made with a number of domestic products. In turn, manufactured goods began to come into the islands. Manila, with its excellent harbor, its political control, its labor, warehousing, and interregional connections was the logical center for this new trade. Chinese immigration was increasing, and Chinese merchants had gone into some of the smaller cities of the islands as wholesalers, and in a few places like Iloilo they held a dominant position in trade over both the Spanish and Filipinos. Although at first they may have engaged in what might properly be termed distributive and collective ends of international trade, it was not long before they spread their influence definitely into the field of domestic and interregional trade within the islands. With slowly increasing land and sea transportation, domestic trade patterns revived. Overpopulation had, by 1900, markedly changed the older regional patterns of production and consumption. Pioneer settlements in Mindanao, Mindoro, and other vacant spots throughout the islands set up new production regions that contributed their own volumes of produce to both international and domestic trade.

The American period has seen the greatest development of trade in the economic history of the islands. Most of this growth has been pointed toward foreign trade, either export or import, but much of it comes into the field of domestic trade because of the patterns of handling it inside the country. Foreign trade now is greater, both in volume and in per capita participation, than it ever has been in the past. Domestic trade, too, has risen to levels never reached during the Spanish period. This total trade is predominantly in the hands of Filipinos, Chinese, and Americans, with small participation by British, Spanish, Swiss, Indians, and in prewar times, Japanese. These natonalities represent firms operating within the islands and not just those shipping goods to, or buying in the Philippines, as would be indicated in a tabulation of foreign trade by origin or destination.

There are no effective means for measuring domestic trade such as are readily available for international trade. In the section on Domestic Trade and Commerce, the Bureau of Census and Statistics, in its several Yearbooks of Philippine Statistics, presents such statistical data as can be summarized, and the new Central Bank is gathering similar data.[42] Arrivals in Manila by rail of such items as rice, sugar, firewood, lumber, and tobacco are for domestic use but also are partly planned for export. Commodities carried by rail on Panay and Cebu (as long as the rail line operated on the latter island) are another measure of both domestic and international produce movement. Such data cannot be given for other regions of the islands. Issues of rice in the provinces by NARIC (National Rice and Corn Corporation, a governmental agency) indicate one important aspect of domestic trade. Data on commercial firms, arranged in a number of ways, form another indication of current domestic trade. All these tabulations are useful but fail to point out many important domestic trade features. Under the categories of Finance and Banking the Yearbooks present other trade statistics but neither do these correctly indicate internal trade flow.

The primary conditions for extensive internal trade are, first of all, marked regional inequalities of produce and goods and an effective internal transportation network. They include also the absence of restraint by any branch of government; the availability of adequate local capital; a satisfactory condition in property ownership; the adequacy of labor resources in local regions; an effective system of rural and urban education; and a continuing program of research and development in agriculture, transportation, and domestic industry. In the modern world this depends partly upon the adequate functioning of government, because the complex interplay of world-wide economic forces is too great to be mastered by purely private agencies. In a few parts of the world such social organizations as a church or a farmer association such as the American grange perform much of the task and, in cities, chambers of commerce also carry some of the load, but these are special situations.

The Patterns of Trade Movement

The domestic trade of the Philippines involves three elements: the exchange of domestic products among local populations, the gathering for export of island products at the various ports of shipment, and the island distribution of imported commodities. The total of this trade, of course, is far larger than the foreign trade of the country. Much of it consists of local movements of goods from rural farm to village or town market for sale, or of the similar sale of an urban product. Some of it involves long-distance shipment, as the movement of mangosteens from the southern Sulu region to the Manila fruit markets, or the shipment to Palawan of Manila-made margarine or rubber shoes. No complete picture of internal trade can be had in a country like the Philippines, but some indications of it are possible.

Perhaps the most important single product in internal trade is rice. Map 10 shows the chief deficiency regions for food supplies, and table 5 summarizes the most recent available data of this sort from the 1939 Census. In large part these food deficiencies are a deficiency of rice, but in the Visayan Islands they refer chiefly to corn. Other food products add to the trade volume, of course, since they are surplus in some local regions and deficit in others. The chief producing region with a surplus of rice is the Central Plain of Luzon, and the chief deficit area is the metropolitan region of Manila. This is a zone of good transport facilities, with rail, truck, and bus haulage moving the available volume fairly easily. Some rice moves from the Central Plain into Mountain Province of northern Luzon by truck, bus, and pack animal, or by rail and coastal water shipment into southern Luzon. The Central Plain rice surplus does not fully take care of Manila metropolitan needs, which are balanced by imports from abroad, as are those of much of southern Luzon and the Visayan Islands.

The second important zone of surplus rice production is the Cotabato Valley and the north coast of Zamboanga Peninsula, both of which move surpluses into other local regions of Mindanao and the Visayan Islands area. Here local transport conditions are much less satisfactory. This is reflected in land transport costs to coastal ports, rice from interior Cotabato sometimes selling at a higher price on the Manila or Cebu markets than does imported rice. The rural Mindanao rice farmer often is hard put to make more than his subsistence because of the regional handicaps facing him, in spite of the national scarcity of a basic food commodity.

The Cotabato Valley is the chief southern producer of surplus corn, most of which moves via water to the Visayan Islands, Leyte, Cebu, Masbate, Siquijor, and Bohol. The Cagayan Valley of northern Luzon sends a small share of its surplus corn to the Visayan area, but isolation and the lack of effective transport again prove a bar to profitable disposal.

Today perhaps the second most important commodity in internal trade is lumber. It formerly was possible to secure building materials in all regions of the islands, but deforestation has been too destructive in the most populous areas, and today more distant sources must be used. Also it formerly was the custom in building houses, furniture, or other products, for the carpenter to start with a raw log, from which he cut what was needed as his job progressed. Commercial lumbering has been carried on in almost every part of the islands at some time in the last half century, and small operations still proceed in many rural areas and near small towns. The cities and the older and more heavily populated rural regions are today the market areas for commercial lumber from a limited number of island areas. Northern Negros, Mindoro, northern Mindanao, and the northern part of the Cotabato Valley in central Mindanao are today the largest producers of commercial lumber. Northern Camarines in southern Luzon and the mountain region of north Luzon still provide some lumber but have passed their peak. Water transport is of course the chief means of moving logs and lumber, but limited local transport in cutting regions handicaps operations. Manila, Cebu, Iloilo, and the Ilocos coastal ports are the chief domestic market areas.

Lumber is only one of the construction materials that participates in island trade. Cement, bamboo, and nipa palm thatch are other important items. Nipa palm thatch, the most frequent wall and roof material in island housing, is a product of the coastal salt-water swamps and marshes. Bulky, fragile, and cheap in price, nipa does not go far inland except in areas of good transport. Also it seldom moves long distances in interisland traffic. Today it probably penetrates farther inland than ever before, but there still are many island interiors in which nipa thatch becomes too expensive for use. Bamboo is an almost ubiquitous product and rarely moves more than short distances. Cement moves from the one producing plant on the east coast of Cebu all over the islands, where it is primarily an article of urban use. The Manila metropolitan area is the chief consuming region of the islands.

The normal fuel in most Filipino homes is firewood, though rice hulls also are frequently used in rice-producing areas. Most rural areas have no fuel problem, but the towns and cities of the long settled areas are major deficit regions for fuel supplies. Coal is not used as a domestic fuel in the islands, and electricity is still a minor urban domestic source of heat and power. Firewood, therefore, is an important local trade commodity. The Manila metropolitan region is again the chief deficit area, drawing upon all Manila Bay shores and upon coastal areas of southern Luzon lying along the railway. Such older and larger cities as Cebu, Iloilo, Legaspi, and Davao must also draw from a wide hinterland and coastal fringe. Coastal mangrove swamps are regularly cut over for firewood, and inland wood lots also provide perennial supplies. One of the commonest freight cargoes carried by bus and truck in urban hinterlands is firewood moving toward a city. Firewood is a cheap commodity when cut and sold by the rural producer, but it is a not inconsiderable item of expense to the lower- or middle-class urban population which must depend upon it.

Domestic manufacturers of consumer goods amount to a large volume and occupy a prominent position in domestic trade. Manila, of course, is the chief producer for almost the whole range of products, and her sales area includes the entire archipelago. Most of this involves water transport to the outer zone, but rail, bus, and truck transport carries much of it in central Luzon. Processed food and beverage products probably rank highest in volume. Vegetable margarines and cooking fats, a wide range of candies and confections, beer, Coca Cola, and other soft drinks flow outward from Manila to wholesale distributors throughout the islands. Such clothing products as rubber and leather shoes, cotton yardage, and finished garments of cotton and rayon are growing in volume. Fabricated metal articles such as nails, aluminum utensils, and hardware products are increasing. A variety of paints and varnishes, matches, and chemical products also are represented. A large part of the soaps, cleansers, and cosmetics is of domestic manufacture, produced in and around Manila. Practically all the books, magazines, and newspapers of domestic origin come out of Manila, though a few other towns publish local newspapers. Metropolitan regional industries produce other goods too, but much of the balance is chiefly designed for export purposes.

Cebu and Iloilo are the only other centers of manufacture for domestic purposes with a significant list of products, but their role as regional distributors is greater than as producers. Other smaller centers are beginning to develop special products. Lipa, in Batangas, is becoming an important center of clothing manufacture, with its products scattering over most of the Philippines. The Ilocos towns of northwest Luzon long have produced handicraft cotton textiles which find consumers outside their home region. A little of their cotton is homegrown, but most of it is imported. Lesser commodities of wide distribution have regional centers. Wooden sandals are produced in small volume almost everywhere in the islands, but the largest share comes from the small towns around the southern half of the Laguna de Bay in Laguna Province. Brass and copper wares, widely used by the Moros in the southern part of the islands, originate in and around Cotabato.

A significant aspect of domestic trade is the gathering at the processing centers and export ports of agricultural export commodities. Abacá is grown everywhere from southeastern Luzon southward in the archipelago. As a domestic textile it formerly was widely manufactured and distributed over the islands, but today abacá textiles, sinamay, and similar products are steadily losing ground in favor of cottons and rayons. This has seriously hit the rural, village, and small-town producers. Abacá today is largely an export product, except for its use in string, ropes, fishing nets, and similar cordage. As an export product it must be graded, inspected, and baled. Facilities for this have become centralized in a few open-port cities. Recent exports have moved through the five open ports of Davao, Cebu, Manila, Tabaco, and Tacloban. The 1949 exports, however, moved through four ports only; in order of rank these were Davao, Cebu, Tabaco, and Manila.[48] Cebu and Manila are not close to present important producing regions. Domestic trade gathers this widespread volume and funnels it to these few open ports, thus increasing domestic trade. This procedure, however, removes the rural producer further and further from the export point, increasing handling charges and reducing his financial return. Also an important volume of abacá flows through domestic trade channels to Manila where it is manufactured into rope, hawsers, and cordage for export.

Coconut products are varied but are chiefly produced for export. Tuba, as a beverage, is the most important item of domestic use and is locally manufactured. Fresh green coconuts are used throughout the coconut-growing area as food. Ripe coconuts form a domestic trade commodity, moving by land and sea routes into northern Luzon where local production is small and less than demand. The use of coconut oil in the manufacture of margarines and cooking fats is drawing off a steadily increasing volume for domestic consumption. Coconut products for export include copra, coconut oil, dessicated coconut, and copra meal. These manufactured commodities enter trade chiefly from the Manila areas. The largest volume of export is through the seven open ports that are in the coconut-producing zone of the islands. Hence, the regional gathering of coconut products involves some domestic trade activity. However, special permits for loading copra at many of the national ports are continually granted, so that there is less centralizing of coconut products than of abacá.

Tobacco also goes through a centralizing process before entering the export trade. Small-farm, home-use tobacco enters only into local trade, whereas much of the commercial crop, whether for export or for domestic sale, comes into the Manila metropolitan area for final processing.

Other export products such as timber and lumber, sugar, iron ore, chrome ore, pineapple, and embroideries enter domestic trade in smaller degree. Much of the volume of each of these moves from its major producing zone through local ports on special export permits. Pineapple for export moves directly from the cannery wharf, and only the small amount diverted to domestic consumption enters internal trade. Export embroideries are chiefly a product of the Manila metropolitan region, and only those sold locally to island inhabitants or tourists figure in domestic trade.

Straw and palm leaf products, such as hats, mattings, fans, and bags are among the cheaper products that have regional centers of production for particular types and qualities. However, items of this sort are so typically Filipino that one finds them produced in most parts of the country. The exceptions are the frontier zones where labor shortages do not permit this manufacture. Production is rural and village rather than urban, but the articles find their markets at all levels in domestic economy. A large volume of these goods enters export, as well as domestic, trade.

Commodities like salt also are regional products. Most salt used in the islands is from solar evaporation of sea water and is produced around island fringes wherever flat shorelands are available. Salt beds compete with fish ponds for space in several areas. But the narrow coastal fringes of most islands do not provide adequate salt for today's needs. About half the producers are located along the northwest coast of Luzon from upper Zambales northward, and another fourth are scattered around the southern fringe of Manila Bay. The western coast of Panay Island is the only other significant salt producer." All these locations reflect the long winter dry season, favorable to commercial production of salt. Traditionally salt was a commodity traded from coastal fringes into island interiors. Today a few areas are the big producers, and domestic trade distributes the commodity among the islands and into the interiors.

Imported manufactured goods come into the country primarily through the port of Manila.[45] Cebu is a very poor second and Iloilo a weak third in the import cargo handled. Of the open ports, Aparri, San Fernando, Jose Panganiban, Tabaco, and Jolo seldom record sizable imports in the customs returns. Most ships in foreign trade call at Manila before stopping at any port for outgoing cargo, and incoming freight normally is discharged at Manila. This means that a large share of the domestic trade is occupied with dispersing the import volume from Manila out over the islands. Regional territories assigned to wholesalers or distributors are common. Luzon frequently is divided into three or four territories. The Visayan Islands often are lumped into one distributorship, based on Cebu, but frequently the region is broken down into the six major island territories. Mindanao usually is divided into three parts. Sulu and Palawan, Siargao and Dinagat, Catanduanes and other smaller islands often are omitted from ports of call, and domestic trade machinery does not take them into account. This means fewer consumer goods for such areas, but it also means that the population of such marginal areas is not included in the flow patterns of domestic economy. It means that the local export of regional goods also is inhibited, whether these are destined for the foreign export market or merely for domestic markets elsewhere in the islands.

Much has been said about the variable role of the Chinese, Filipinos, and Americans in the domestic and foreign trade of the Philippines. The Chinese often are blamed for many of the patterns of island trade and the ills of island economy. Although no census count is available I estimate that about 95,000 business enterprises of all sorts are engaged in productive activity other than agriculture.[46] Nearly 18,000 are grain dealers, including both wholesale and retail dealers. The share of Chinese among grain dealers is not known, but it is large, and many of the larger wholesalers are Chinese. Some 72,000 of these enterprises are retail commercial establishments. Of this total about 15,000 are owned by Chinese; less than 200 by Americans. Most retail stores are general stores with very low capitalization and very low annual sales. The largest share of Filipino-owned stores falls into this category.

There is no question that the Chinese are active in all three aspects of trade in the islands, or that they are owners of the larger and more active enterprises in almost every town and city. They engage in almost every form of commercial operation. They are the best distributors of manufactured goods in the islands. They are more active in import than export trade, a fact sometimes held against them. But since the largest share of island exports go to the United States, the American firms naturally are in a favored position. The Chinese population in the islands is increasing steadily, an urban population that promotes business activity and serves the Filipino population, but not one that accounts for much of the primary production of wealth. Nevertheless, not all the ills and troubles in Philippine economy, either rural or urban, can be laid at the door of the Chinese.

Most of the comments about regional movement indicate traffic between major islands by sea transport, or between sections of Luzon by land transport. Traffic movements between regions do not exactly balance each other. For example, more still comes from Mindanao than goes in. Some of it goes to support Bohol, Cebu, Siquijor, Leyte, the Ilocos provinces of northwest Luzon, or to heighten the urban economy of Manila. Unquestionably Manila, at the focal point of trade movement, profits by this position. And without doubt Palawan, Tawitawi, or Dinagat do not secure great profit from the domestic or foreign trade of the archipelago.

The multiple division of the Philippines into more than a thousand inhabited but separated units places a distinct handicap on the inhabitants of the smaller, marginal units. Water contact between the units was relatively less expensive, and per capita more common, in the days when outriggers were the standard seagoing craft than today when seagoing powered ships, with large overhead costs, are the chief means of trade movement. The lack of an effective transport system currently restricts Philippine economy, both in island interiors and along coastal margins. Earlier, when those island margins and interiors were not needed, the problem was less urgent. Today the need for these margins has increased at a far greater rate than has their possible effective incorporation into the trade economy of the islands.

Chapter 8

FUTURE COMPETITION IN AGRICULTURAL AND MINERAL EXPORTS

The Trading Background

THE MODERN history of Philippine foreign trade has been a happy one, but there are many uncertainties in the future. Trade history can be summarized as one of an increase in the variety of trade commodities, of expansion in regional trade, and of an increasing volume of international trade, both per capita and in total. There have been a number of departures from the upward trend, and one serious setback in the Japanese occupation. During most of the period for which information is available, the islands have enjoyed a favorable balance of trade. The present brief period of an unfavorable balance comes at a particularly critical time. In the pre-Spanish era, Chinese, Arabic, Indian, and Indonesian traders came into the islands with a variety of commodities to trade for local products. The Filipinos themselves did little long-distance voyaging as merchant traders. During the period of Spanish control of the islands, the Filipinos found themselves greatly restricted. They had but little share in trade until the last decades of the nineteenth century. Trade was chiefly between Chinese and Spaniards, centered around Manila, or between local Spaniards and those of the New World. It distributed products for which the Orient was famous, gathered from many sources throughout the Far East by the Chinese.

In the late Spanish period something of free trade gradually was permitted and buyers for Philippine products again appeared in the islands. Filipinos began to share in this expanding trade pattern, and the basis was laid for much of the present export business. Throughout the American period even greater freedom of trade was permitted, but American traders almost monopolized the market, taking most of the exports of the islands and shipping in by far the greatest volume of foreign products. Trade with other nations did not die out, but it failed to grow at the same rate as American trade. Spain is an exception to this general increase, since her trade with the islands declined markedly in relative percentage. The 1947 trade returns show that thirty-seven countries each had a total trade volume with the Philippines of more than $1,000,000." The 1949 trade returns show only twenty-six countries with such a trade volume, perhaps owing to the lower value of the Philippine export total.

American trade has exceeded the total trade of all other countries with the islands since 1916. Free trade with the United States was on a legal basis by 1909 but a few years passed before American-Filipino commercial relations developed. The American near-monopoly of Philippine trade was, of course, greatly aided by the favored position of the islands inside the American tariff wall. Independence makes probable the reorientation of Philippine trade away from an American near-monopoly toward a more widely diversified pattern. This will be stimulated by the tariff wall that rises between Philippine products and the American market, unless present legislation is altered. Filipino trade diplomacy also will work for this. It is clearly to the interest of the islands to expand their trade pattern with other countries to be less dependent upon the American market. This cultivation of other markets naturally involves an adjustment of the Philippine import program, a difficult matter since Filipino consumers are now accustomed to American-made goods.

Major Commodity Patterns

Basically, Philippine economic structure rests upon two separate foundations. First is the subsistence agriculture-trade-handicraft pattern based upon rice, corn, sweet potatoes, bananas, fish, abacá and cotton textiles, and handicrafts. This support is somewhat insecure in that domestic production of rice, fish, and cotton has been inadequate. The second base is the international trade pattern of agriculture-handicraft-mining-industry founded upon processed coconut, sugar, gold, abacá, and tobacco. A few newer items such as pineapple, embroideries, some of the ferro-alloys, rattans, and special woods have so far gone almost entirely to the United States. Iron ore and ramie, exceptions to the list, are sent chiefly to Japan and Europe, respectively. Although the second support to island economic structure has been a profitable one inside the American tax wall, there have been problems at all times. Since most Philippine products first came into the American market about 1890, their competitive relation to similar American commodities is significant.

Expansion of coconut shipments to the United States for edible and industrial oil needs has been confronted with the competitive interests of American dairymen and the producers of oils from cottonseed, soybeans, corn, and peanuts. In this connection the islands have been subject to the conflict between the popular farm-bloc plea for a high tariff on all imported products and the administrative tendency to consider the islands within the American tariff zone. Elsewhere in world markets, coconut products from other southeastern Asian countries, and palm oil, peanut oil, and such oil seeds as sesame have been direct competitors. Quality considerations, preferential colonial economic agreements, and other factors have combined to operate against the expansion of Philippine world markets.

For decades sugar has held a competitive position against the American beet-sugar industry and Hawaiian, Cuban, and Puerto Rican cane sugars. It has prospered on the American market, but stands in constant jeopardy of losing ground through changing American legislation or through government-sponsored international contractual agreements. Much of the island sugar industry is American or Spanish owned, but enough is Filipino to make its prosperity a vital economic factor. Wartime destruction of refineries and complete dislocation of the cane-planting program has seriously hindered return to the prewar position of the islands in the American supply picture. By the 1952–1953 crop year, production should again be high enough to fill the American import quota.

The high world price of gold and the price level maintained by the United States government have benefited the islands but only indirectly, since the chief mining concerns are American or Spanish owned. Gold is one of the oldest Philippine trade commodities, but subsidiary silver, copper, and related minerals are newcomers in the large-scale production pattern of the mining industry. Competitive marketing of precious metals is admittedly a less serious matter than is the disposal of agricultural products.

Tobacco production in the islands has been waging a losing fight for many years. This is related to the changing smoking habits of different parts of the world. Philippine tobacco production during Spanish times was chiefly directed toward cigar manufacture. The increasing popularity of cigarettes, the trend toward mild tobaccos, and the mechanization of the American tobacco industry with its tremendous productive capacity—all have combined against the continued success of the island industry. Postwar invasion by American cigarettes, for the first time in really large quantities, has kept local manufacture in the doldrums.[48] Spanish ownership or control of most of the commercial production results in lessened benefit to the domestic economy of the islands. Once a chief trade item, tobacco has both decreased in actual quantity as an export and slipped successively farther down the commodity list. The competitive future is not a happy one, and in this industry success is not connected with the American tariff wall.

Abacá has been a traditional Philippine monopoly, a product not grown elsewhere because the plant, a close relative of the banana in earlier centuries, did not prosper when transplanted away from its home region. Abacá fiber is one of the oldest Philippine trade commodities—one of the chief items sought by Chinese and other traders far back in the pre-Spanish era. Abacá has been sent abroad in both raw and processed forms. Its products have ranged from cordage to fine cloth. Some domestic consumption takes a share of the annual crop, but today it is produced primarily for export.

Modern export volumes include the raw fiber in baled form, varieties of cordage, and decorative mattings and art goods. Much of the abacá is exported through American hands, but its market destinations are worldwide because it is a superior fiber for ropes and marine hawsers. Though not in a strongly competitive market the product occasionally has faced the problem of oversupply, chiefly in depression years of shrunken purchase patterns. In more recent years of war and postwar readjustment, major hazards have appeared in the abacá industry. The wartime threat of domination of the Philippines by the Japanese and the resulting alien control of a monopoly product led to successful Middle America experiments with abacá. The Dutch also succeeded just before the war in experimental plantings in Borneo and Sumatra. Postwar confiscation of Japanese plantations on Mindanao and the allocation of those lands to native settlers unskilled in abacá culture led to a steadily lessened island production. Earlier plantation production in the islands had somewhat undermined small-farmer production. Only herculean efforts can restore production in the Philippines before world demand forces large-volume production elsewhere, production that would end Philippine monopoly of one of the world's best fibers. Such a result can only further increase the competitive risks in the Philippine export program by introducing a comparative price element into the abacá industry.

New Commodity Patterns

Consideration of the newer items in the list of exports reveals a close American consumer relation for many of them. Plantation pineapple production in northern Mindanao is considered by Filipinos an admirable means of further economic development. American and Filipino ownership, on a half-and-half basis, plus a sympathetic corporation concern for domestic economy, is a vital aspect of the program of pineapple growing and canning. Consumption of tinned pineapple, however, is almost entirely American and at present other markets are lacking. So far there has been no serious competitive situation in marketing both Hawaiian and Philippine pineapple in the United States.

Embroideries and various kinds of textile handicrafts are today important exports of the islands, now going almost entirely to the United States. Spanish influence restrained local handicrafts and regional specialties, whereas American interest in such things has stimulated their production. The volume and variety have been steadily increasing. Working in native cotton, abacá, pineapple fiber (known as piña), or imported linen, rayon, or silk, the native craftsmen use both traditional and modern designs. Largely Filipino owned and operated are the small shops and establishments turning out most of these products. There is international competition in such luxury goods as these; however, the distinctive Filipino patterns are not yet well known, and possess an appealing novelty.

Chromium and manganese are the chief ferro-alloys now being prospected and mined throughout the islands. Both are new items in Philippine mineral production. Neither has any significant demand in present island economy. Both are capable of expansion and are in general world demand in iron and steel production. Although neither is particularly high priced, the total yield should add to the export trade of the islands. Scattered ownership control of both minerals gives island interests a share in the economic yield.

Lumbering is an old occupation in the Philippines but until late Spanish times it was restricted to the search for special kinds of woods. The modern lumber industry has grown slowly with the gradual realization that even though the Philippines constitute a tropical forest region, economic cutting of different kinds of timber in large volume now is possible with modern equipment. Today the domestic market can be fully supplied while providing a large surplus for foreign markets. The islands are beginning to be an important source of fine woods of distinctive types, and good markets should result from trade promotion measures. Forest reserves are large and the annual growth cycle in a humid and hot climate is so rapid that cultural forestry on well-chosen sites certainly can provide a permanent forest income.

Related to lumbering is rattan, produced almost throughout the islands. Formerly rattan was exported only in the form of cut lengths of cane, whereas today there is an increasing export of

103

rattan manufactured into furniture, art products, and decorative objects. This is an industry with a good domestic market and also a slowly growing American market. In other markets throughout the world there is some competition from other tropical lands which also export rattan products.

Iron ore, the last of the important new commodity exports, is in a different position than the others. The islands have a large amount of good iron ore easily mined and shipped. Lack of an iron and steel industry in the country precludes any large domestic market for ore. Furthermore, cheap ore prices and the distance of the Philippines from the major industrial nations almost prohibit shipping any great volume of ore. Japan is the only country close enough to provide a real market for Philippine iron ore. Just before the last war Japan had begun taking large quantities. In the postwar restriction of Japan to her main island area, the Korean and Manchurian ore sources, though nearer than the Philippines, lie outside her economic and political control. This should promote a limited development of iron mining based upon the Japanese market. Perhaps selective ores may also be ballast shipped to the United States west coast ports near new iron and steel developments, for blending with domestic ores.

Minor Commodities

There are a number of minor products that have figured in small amounts in past export trade patterns. Some of these may again reach significant proportions. Derris, from the root of a small native Philippine plant, is a new and valuable ingredient of insecticides. Just before the war it was becoming a significant minor export, as plant breeding efforts made it economically productive. It may again expand its pattern in the islands, though now it must compete with derris from Malaya and India.

Maguey, a fiber-producing plant introduced from Mexico by the Spanish, has had a checkered career as an island crop. It was widely planted on the drier lands of the islands at an early date. Maguey and sisal fibers have been steady but minor export commodities, with scattered destinations. The maguey plant is not particularly popular as a crop plant in the islands today, and there are a number of competing countries in better position to produce maguey or sisal fiber than are the islands.

Ramie, the product of a tall, weedy east Asian plant, now enjoys a mild boom in the islands. Ramie fiber has valuable qualities, but difficulties of degumming it and the entrenched position of other fibers have so far prevented the large-scale development of ramie production anywhere in the world. It has been grown on a small scale in the islands for some years for export. If the problems of processing the fiber and overcoming market resistance can be met, the islands have much land that can be devoted to ramie production without disrupting any existing agricultural pattern.

Rubber production in the islands never has grown as it has in Malaya and the Indies. This is a matter of government land policy and the fact that government agricultural policy did not foster the planting of rubber trees as did the Dutch in the Indies. What volume is produced moves from an American holding to the United States. Extensive competition from several tropical lands, coupled with pressure from synthetic rubber producers, makes any real expansion unlikely in the Philippines at this time.

The mango, one of the world's best fruits, currently has a small export volume, going mainly to Hong Kong and the China coast. Both distance and competition from India, Burma, Malaya, and the Indies probably are sufficient to head off any significant expansion in the present small trade volume.

Raw shell products, largely destined for pearl buttons, have formed one of the smaller Philippine export commodities for many years. The United States takes practically all the island supply. A fairly stable trade position suggests that it will continue but will not promise any marked expansion in volume.

Hides and skins from cattle and native carabao, or water buffalo, also form a stable minor item of the export trade directed almost entirely to the United States.

American Trade Quotas

In the early period of American control of the Philippines, when new trade patterns were being worked out, there were many varied reactions from, and also many different programs proposed by, both mainland and island interests. The Treaty of Paris, December, 1898, settling matters between Spain and the United States, called for a ten-year period of no trade discrimination against Spain. Only slowly, then, did the Congress of the United States set up trade provisions which replaced Spanish practices. The first arrangements, in the 1909 legislation, establishing a so-called free trade pattern at the termination of the ten-year period, provided for unlimited free entry into the islands of American products, but set maximum quantity limits for certain Philippine products entering the United States. In 1913 the legislation was changed by provisions that amounted to complete free trade in both directions, providing the Philippine exports to the United States contained purely native or American raw materials. In later years trade regulations were changed in some detail at almost every session of the United States Congress. Philippine products were never given complete and unrestricted right of entry into the United States whereas American products always had unrestricted entry into the islands. The relaxation of bans against island products, or limits upon them, came only when it was proved to American satisfaction that no serious harm would be done to any domestic American interest. More than one Filipino has felt and expressed himself in terms similar to these: "Protection of American manufactures has been the keynote of Philippine tariff legislation."[49]

Legislation of 1934, providing for eventual Philippine independence, introduced an annually graduated tax provision on both American and Philippine products entering the other country, and retained both absolute quotas and maximum reduced tax quotas on Philippine products entering the United States. The whole program was to start in 1940. Before these provisions did go into effect, however, the American Congress again began altering the pattern of legislation almost annually, in practically every case without consultation with Philippine interests. Concerted island protest led in 1939 to some long-term commitments to taxation, quotas, and trade agreements. The war upset these arrangements, of course.

Postindependence legislation, passed as the Philippine Trade Act of 1945 and known as the Bell Act after its congressional sponsor, took points, quantities, and items from various pieces of earlier legislation as the start for its primary rulings. Absolute quotas were set on volumes of cordage, sugar, and rice that can be shipped into the United States in any one year. The persistent retention of a limit upon rice exports to the United States is a concession to American southern feelings, since the Philippines normally is a rice importer. Graduated maximum quotas under preferential tariff rates were set for cigars, leaf, scrap, and filler tobacco, coconut oil, embroideries, and pearl-shell buttons. A graduated tax schedule was set up to begin in 1954, increasing steadily at 5 per cent a year until tariffs on products moving in both directions reach the parity levels of other countries, and at which time reduced tax quotas will have been lowered to nominal amounts. The Bell Act may not be the final piece of trade legislation before the Philippines become finally and totally independent.[50]

American opinion holds that our Philippine economic policy was a very liberal one, whereas Philippine opinion inclines to the view that the policy, though liberal from several points of view, was implemented by legislation which was restrictive in effect. This position holds that it turned the islands into a supplier of raw materials to American economy, hindered industrial growth of island economy by limiting entry of processed Philippine commodities to the United States, and gave no really constructive assistance to economic programs enabling the Philippines to compete internationally when political independence was finally attained. Reviewing the history of this legislation, it seems true that just as soon as so-called free-trade patterns were set up, American merchandise, American purchases, and American commercial firms began to dominate trade patterns in the Philippines. In a very few years the islands were more tightly tied to the United States economy, through liberal legislation, than they ever had been tied to Spain through restrictive legislation. There is no question that the new trade policy tremendously stimulated Philippine agriculture, and that this was good, as long as special political relations continued to give the islands a protected market. But in the midst of this economic policy and legislation, declared political policy was pointed toward preparation for independence. There can be no question that this nonconformity in implementation of American policy created a situation that now begins to show as a real disadvantage. The competitive position of the islands is not good when compared with other tropical lands, producers of the same commodities that flow out of the Philippines.

Trends and Prospects

A first reaction to the export situation of the Philippines in a world still short of many staple food commodities is that there will be continued demand for island products and that the shift in political relations should raise no particular problem. In the immediate postwar period, prices of the basic commodities—abacá, sugar, coconut, gold, and even tobacco—were higher than they had been for many years. The Philippines have been able to sell at a favorable price almost every ton of produce that could be brought to a port. Even some minor commodities without assured markets have done well in terms of their normal production price and sale patterns of the past. Perhaps there is no need to worry over the fact that the Philippines, ranking near the top in quantity production of copra, rank almost at the bottom in quality standards. Perhaps in the politically independent future, the islands may still enjoy preferences in the American market and face no serious competition in the disposition of their export commodities.

A second reaction, however, points in another direction. With enormous agricultural surpluses possible in the United States in commodities competitive with those of the Philippines, will the islands definitely be able to count on this export market? In a Europe needing cheap imports, but large exports with which to buy imports, can the Philippines hope to sell large volumes of goods without purchasing similar volumes of goods in return? Filipino consumer appetites have strong American tastes and may not adjust to European styles and patterns very quickly. Can the islands build up quality patterns, and develop sufficiently widespread mutual trade relations to escape being too tightly tied to the economy of the United States? The very soundness of the economy of the United States seems related to the fact that she is not closely dependent upon any one region or upon the economy of any other country. It follows that the economy of the Philippines should not be too dependent upon even so large and sound an economy as that of the United States.

Current trends seem to be toward international price controls or regional allocation of some of the basic plant and mineral products. Rice, sugar, gold, tobacco, edible fats and oils at least are among the Philippine products so affected. As long as this type of control operates, it may help to stabilize regional economies rather than serve as an additional source of trouble.

An important issue is whether the islands shall focus upon re-developing former export items damaged by the war, or upon new products for world sale. Should the islands now invest capital in trying to regain a dominant position in the world abacá market? Or should they recognize that the monopoly is gone, and that the best thing for the future would be expansion in some other line while maintaining existing abacá plantings as long as profitable? Similar questions arise in sugar production. Wartime destruction of mills made the islands unable to fill the export quota to the United States in any year since the war. Perhaps in 1952–1953 the quota can just be met by holding down domestic consumption. By 1954 a tax will begin on all sugar shipped to the United States. As this tariff builds higher year by year, will there be any profit to the islands in meeting the prices set by United States government agreements among the producers who normally supply the United States? Can a certain quota of sugar be sold in any other market for more money, to compensate for the lower net return from American sales? Should sugar land be put into other crops now rather than wait for an unprofitable era? As the tariff increases, which element in the islands will it affect most seriously: the companies operating the sugar centrals—mostly family-owned corporations; the large-scale contract planters of cane; the seasonal and somewhat migrant labor groups that work the cane plantations; or the Filipino consumer of sugar who now pays more for his sugar than do American purchasers? Similar questions pertain to coconut and tobacco as agricultural crops affecting the livelihood of large numbers of Filipinos.

No definite answers to these questions can be given by one group alone. At one large sugar central, in 1948, the stated conclusion was that only such investments would be made in plant and lands as would clearly pay a good return within the next decade. After that, long-range investments in plant and lands might be considered, depending upon the state of the sugar trade. The small farmer, the laborer, or the regional interests of that part of Luzon did not enter the calculations of the mill operators. The same viewpoint was shown in Mindanao by the decision of a relatively small rice farmer to exploit his land in as short a time as possible with successive rice crops but not with practices good for the land in the long run. Since he was occupying public land by squatter's rights, and since he could move to another plot in a few crop seasons, considerations of regional well-being, of Philippine economy, or depletion of the soil meant less to him than profitable short-range exploitation. Balancing the trade accounts for the whole archipelago, with no backlog of capital resources, is an important issue. The islands have been living beyond their means in the short postwar period. But the proper conclusion about the export trade and what should be the national resources program can no more be decided by the Philippine treasury alone than by any one operator in the rural hinterland.

In actual practice efforts are being made to restore every prewar line of commercial and subsistence agriculture, mineral development, and forest utilization. Some long-range programs finally are being set up for the good of the whole national economy. Trade missions are beginning to make overtures abroad. Limited research programs are in progress for future expansion and growth. Yet, by and large, the current directions of major programs are to reconstitute the prewar patterns of agricultural, forest, and mineral exports. These patterns point chiefly toward the United States as a major market. In good part they are short-range programs, though involving major financial investments aimed at restoring the balance

110

of trade in the easiest way possible in the shortest space of time. They will gain time for a reconsideration of the long-range direction of Philippine economy, but few indications have yet appeared as to what may be those directions at the end of the favorable tariff period in the American market. The burden of readjustment in the event of economic difficulties will fall on the small farmer and laborer who operate somewhat blindly in the midst of shifting patterns of economy.

Chapter 9

LAND OWNERSHIP, TENANCY, AND CREDIT PROBLEMS

ALTHOUGH THERE is enough land for all Filipinos who need it, land ownership and tenancy problems rank high on the list of difficulties facing island society. From a problem of small regional importance in early Spanish times, land problems have steadily increased in number, regional scope, and seriousness. Today they are the pretext for a Communist-organized protest that has assumed military and political form, and is now threatening to disrupt island economy and peaceful society.

The Background of Modern Land Policy

In pre-Spanish times there were many varieties of land ownership among the tribal groups of the Philippines. The simplest culture groups, without agriculture, held tribal resource ranges as public domain under common control. The groups practicing shifting agriculture had a temporary system of land control—all lands not cultivated being public domain, whether recently abandoned or not yet cropped. This practice is one that really pertains to rights of cultivation and harvest rather than to the land itself. Some of the more advanced sedentary agricultural groups had developed the basic features of private land ownership, but had not yet formalized it by any system of deeds, titles, written documents, or tax delinquency forfeits. Moslem arrivals, barely preceding the Spanish, were bringing still other variations of land policy into the southern Philippines.

Social patterns were equally variable throughout the islands, but in general the tribal chiefs were hereditary officeholders and had significant perquisites of housing, crop harvests, land selection, labor contributions, and so on.[51] This gave the chiefs valuable economic advantages over tribal members or families belonging to lower social strata. Freemen, serfs, and slaves were present in the social organization of some tribal groups, depending upon the culture level and the regional strength of the particular group. Social strata were important in the land picture. Freemen were entitled to hold land for themselves, cultivate it, and harvest its crops with the exaction only of limited perquisites by the tribal chief, such as labor on his lands or the execution of tasks considered public services.

The serf, among agricultural groups, was a limited kind of tenant farmer, somewhat similar to the serf in early Europe. He held cultivation rights to land, but had to pay fees amounting approximately to half the annual yield. Serfs owned their own houses, frequently were village residents, and remained with the land rather than belonging to the tribal chief. There were many local variations in arrangements, and beyond the serf, various groups and regions had additional patterns for the rental of crop lands by freemen.

Slaves were chattel property bought and sold, owned by tribal chiefs and by freemen, and one of the trade items of the Philippines. Among the different culture groups of the islands, with Malay, Indian, Chinese, and Arab influences, there were many ways in which people became slaves. There were social distinctions between classes of slaves: hereditary household slaves who seldom were sold in trade, war captives, agricultural labor slaves, debt slaves, and so on. They did much of the menial work for the groups to which they belonged, and never entered the landholding class. Freed slaves sometimes became members of the serf class.

The first Spanish impact on the native land systems came in the form of the *encomiendas* (grants of land and the populations resident thereon) which were allocated in Cebu in 1570.[52] Next came northwest, central, and southeastern Luzon. Panay, Leyte, and western Samar were other locations of grants. In the Spanish theory

113

that all land belonged to the royal domain, these territorial grants were expressions of thanks to loyal civil and military servants. Practice was in conflict with the strict interpretation of the Spanish Laws of the Indies, which prohibited the granting of already claimed lands to Spanish officialdom. Some three hundred grants in all were made before Church protests against excessive exploitation of the natives caused the abolition of the encomienda system. Abolition was ordered before 1600, but it was not fully effective for a half century. In a sense these grants made no sharp break with the past, but merely added another superlayer to the social and economic strata. Certainly they added an alien element that did not understand native economies, agriculture, or social system.

Originally the encomienda grants were to have served as preliminary administrative units of the new Spanish possessions.[53] Abolition meant developing more permanent institutions. The Spanish made the town (*pueblo* in the New World, most commonly *municipio* in the Philippines) the key unit of settlement and administration. The chief officers of the town had the duties of keeping the peace, levying and collecting taxes, and exacting such labor and financial contributions as were needed. Below the town they wisely chose to keep the native tribal district, the *barangay*, which is the modern *barrio* or local district. The tribal chief was kept in power and used by the Spanish as a local administrative officer, the modern *barrio teniente*. Above the *municipio* were the provinces, the first few of which were blocked out before local government patterns were established. Only a few provinces made up the first regional control, and the present provincial patterns developed slowly. Gradually the large towns and cities were put under special charter by the Spanish.

These political institutions helped gradually to turn the mobile Filipinos into sedentary folk, with fixed bases and restricted movement. The town and the village, or barrio, became the fixed points for most settlements. Shifting agriculturists became sedentary farmers to a greater degree than they had previously been. In effect, therefore, the idea of permanent landholdings became the dominant one, whether it referred to crop lands or to village and town residential lands. The Spaniards actually made a late start at issuing deeds and titles in a few parts of the islands, but it never became standard practice with native landholders. Near Manila and among Spanish or wealthy Filipino families with close ties to government or Church, land titles were more common. Land taxes were never a part of the Spanish tax system, so there was no urge by government or by landholders to keep good records.

In the pre-Spanish past, land troubles had been minor, though squabbles over regional and tribal rights certainly had occurred. With shifting cultivation, it undoubtedly was difficult in many areas to determine whether given lands were claimed or not, when permanent land rights came into practice. The acquisitive nature of most Spaniards in the islands and of well-placed Filipino families, the continued power of the tribal chief as barrio teniente, and the interest of the Church and the friars in landed wealth, made conflicts over land inevitable. Duplication of claims was inevitable and increasingly frequent as the Spanish period wore along. The Church accused civil officials of exploitation of the natives and their lands, and counterclaims were made against the Church and the friars. The failure to introduce an effective survey and record system, and to put it to full use, perpetuated the conflicts, or made it possible for unscrupulous individuals to become landholders, at the expense of the powerless and uneducated farmers. Many of the farmers were drawn from slave and serf categories of earlier days. The Spanish gradually outlawed slavery, releasing this element to become part of the agricultural population. Tribal chiefs and some of the more able and aggressive freemen profited most in land acquisition.

Land problems, though sources of conflict and trouble, were not the most important cause for Filipino rebellion against the Spanish. Perhaps this was because vacant land was so readily available and because there were other more pressing burdens upon the native population. The large amount of enforced labor, the relatively heavy head tax, and the required contributions to the Church and to officials were the principal causes of rebellion. But the usurping of natives' lands by officials, the Church, and highly placed individuals during the eighteenth century was a factor in rebellion, particularly in central Luzon.

When the United States assumed control of the islands some of the few land records which did exist were destroyed or lost. It is assumed, however, that those who had possessed documentary titles to land kept them and that their records were processed by the new American government. The wealthy and well-placed families were able to get new claims documented and even to increase their holdings. The poor, uneducated, rural, and migrating groups, on the other hand, were caught in a switch of controls that ended in the institution of new kinds of records and a still more complex system of ownership.

If the system instituted by the Americans had been administered effectively, it could have provided protection to the rural farming element. However, inefficiencies introduced by too small administrative staffs led to much abuse of the new land laws. The small claimant, often ignorant of legal processes but with clear priority of occupation, occasionally was ousted from his hard-won plot of land without the least chance of reprisal.

Sometimes small farmers have been forced into becoming tenants by the false, though technically legal, claiming of a large tract of land by an unscrupulous individual who thus becomes a landlord-owner. Bribery of land-office officials was often part of the procedure. Such unfortunate misapplications of the law still occur, particularly along the settlement frontier, and illustrate a practice that was common during the American period. Seldom has the guilty person been an American, however. Normally it has been the educated and knowledgeable Filipino who has taken advantage of his less fortunate countrymen. In certain parts of the islands also many landholdings have accumulated in the hands of Chinese, usually in some technically legal, but not morally commendable, manner. The intermarriage of Chinese with Filipinos has made the practical application of the law difficult.

Established Land Policy

With the history of Spanish land practice in mind the United States Congress, in 1902, laid down a basic policy that aimed at giving the land to the Filipino in small holdings and at preventing plantation agriculture and corporate landholdings of tremendous size.[54] Although this policy has been circumvented in many individual cases it has never been changed. Congress in 1902 set limits of 16 hectares (about 39.5 acres) on public land released to individual persons, and of 1,024 hectares (about 2,530 acres) released to an association or corporation. Both of these figures were judged large enough to permit development of single family or small company operations, but too small for corporation or plantation agriculture.

There has been much American protest against this policy but in general it has been effective in preserving the reserve lands of the islands for the Filipinos.[55] In fact, the land laws have been drawn steadily tighter as the years have passed, until today land policy has almost completely nationalized the country's lands. The citizens of the United States are now the only non-Philippine nationality permitted to own land, but are subject to the same limits in the issue of public land as are Filipinos. Through dummy owners, other nationalities do control some land. The exact size of the individual release has been changed slightly from time to time, but such changes have not altered the basic principle of small holdings.

The primary method, the free issue of public land to private persons or to corporations, resembles homesteading in the United States.[56] There are two other methods of acquiring government land. They are available only to persons with means, and only small totals of land are issued in these ways. The first of these methods is by direct purchase through the Bureau of Lands. Minimum fees are not high by American standards, ranging upward from $2.00 per acre depending upon the appraisal value. However, even the minimum fees are sufficient to restrict the use of the method by Filipinos. The maximum amount that may be purchased is 144 hectares, about 355 acres. The other method is by lease, at a fee dependent upon the appraisal value. Leases may be renewed in twenty-five year periods providing a reasonable share of the land leased has been cultivated. In all three methods of acquiring public lands the Bureau of Lands has discretion to vary the amounts issuable in different regions of the islands. In practice, issue figures differ according to the roughness and vegetative cover of the land applied for, and according to whether the claimant has animals and equipment to handle a large or a small piece. In subdivisions of different sorts, described in the next chapter, limits are chosen when the region is first surveyed.

The Bureau of Forestry has primary control over the lands of the Philippines. After survey to determine what lands can be used for settlement and what must be preserved in forest, the Bureau of Forestry releases tracts to the Bureau of Lands. The latter then either formally subdivides given units or permits voluntary settlement in the area, and acts upon private claims presented by occupants who have had their chosen tracts privately surveyed. The Bureau of Forestry also releases land to the Bureau of Fisheries for the establishment of fish ponds along the island coasts, and releases land to the Bureau of Mines for administration of mineral operations. The Bureau of Forestry is empowered to prosecute individuals who settle on lands not yet released to the Bureau of Lands, or on lands declared closed to settlement of any sort. In connection with its designated areas of commercial timberland, the Bureau of Forestry also has charge of the inventory of timber cut, forest products harvested, and assessments upon users of the forest lands.[57]

The only difficulty with these administrative provisions is that they have never worked. At no time have the two Bureaus—Forestry and Lands—been given the personnel, the equipment, or the budget to conduct their respective surveys other than in crude reconnaissance form. The Bureau of Forestry refuses, in many areas, to release land to the Bureau of Lands, which, in turn, is being pressed by applicants and by public opinion to make more land available for private settlement. Sometimes this refusal is dictated by sound judgment, after detailed survey, that no more land in a particular region should be removed from protective forestry. But at other times the refusal is prompted by inability to make a survey at all, and a reluctance to release tracts of land without survey to determine the potential limit to private settlement. The Bureau of Forestry has repeatedly brought offenders to court for squatting on forest or closed lands. In most cases the courts have declined to penalize the offenders, on the count that they are poor, need land, and are being deprived of an opportunity to obtain land legally by the failure of the two Bureaus—Lands and Forestry—to carry out their assigned duties. Although this is entirely commendable from the standpoint of individual justice, it does not help check shifting agriculture, soil erosion, or the destruction of forest resources. It is hard on the morale of the Forestry personnel, and it does not mobilize public opinion and support behind enlarged programs of the Bureaus, which could really make effective the land policy of a half century.

Part of American government policy was to do away with the head tax, enforced labor, restrictions upon movement, and the perquisites of Church and officialdom. Revenue-raising procedures of the American type have replaced these methods. A tax on land is now one of the basic taxes of the islands. Taxes are paid on declared acreage, and the former tendency of minimizing holdings has been replaced with a more accurate estimate of farm and cultivated land. There is an assessment procedure whereby lands are classified into three value categories. Land taxes are currently supposed to be assessed on 1 per cent of the assessed value, the rate having increased repeatedly in recent decades.[58] Tax receipts usually are recognized as proof of occupation. Occupation increasingly is being considered as the best legal basis for claims to land, but things do not work smoothly at all times or in all parts of the islands. Tax receipts, as proof of occupation, however, do not constitute titles or proofs of title, and do not prevent claim jumping and unscrupulous legal action to displace uninformed rural occupants.

The tax rate has not been kept standard throughout the islands, but has been increased from time to time until the assessment pattern is quite irregular.[59] Assessment normally takes into account productivity and accessibility of farm land, but different levels of productivity are used as bases in different provinces. The zone of large landholdings in central Luzon has a low assessment rate compared with that of many other provinces. In many cases reassessment has not been made on lands that have undergone marked development and improvement. This factor often operates for the benefit of the influential landholder.

Every recent American mission to the islands has commented upon land problems, and most have recognized their seriousness. There are two ways in which land policy since 1900 has failed to produce the result sought by the United States and by the mass of the Filipino population. First, too many well-placed Filipinos have taken advantage of every opportunity to circumvent the intent of the land laws. Second, the United States neither completed the effective installation of, nor adequately enforced, the land policy set up by American administration in the islands. As a corollary, one must also add that neither Filipino officials before independence, nor the government of the Philippines subsequently, has made a strong effort to put American land policy into practice. A recent recognition of this failure in the Philippines is expressed as: "A land system which creates social discontent is one which obviously has failed to meet the human needs of the citizens who depend upon it."[60]

The Tenancy Picture

In Pampanga Province the area of the land farmed by tenants is three and a half times the area of the land farmed by owners, and tenants are roughly six times as numerous as are owners. The averages for tenant- and owner-operated farms are 8.4 and 15.7 acres, respectively, but the tenant actually cultivates roughly three-fourths as much land as the owner.[61] In Nueva Ecija the land farmed by tenants is perhaps twice that farmed by owners, and the tenants themselves number roughly three times the owners. However, Nueva Ecija has at least one region wherein a single family owns all the farm land in three whole municipalities. Bulacan shows figures indicating that tenants cultivate about three times the land cultivated by owners, and that they outnumber the owners three to one. On the other hand in Palawan there are only a few hundred tenants out of perhaps 12,000 farmers, and in Mountain Province the tenants number less than a thousand, though there must be more than 35,000 owners. Perhaps the five provinces of Nueva

Ecija, Tarlac, Pampanga, Bulacan, and Cavite best illustrate the extreme of high tenancy rates, and Palawan and Mountain provinces the dominance of owner farmers. No single generalization, therefore, will cover the two extremes of the situation.

The other provinces with serious tenancy situations are roughly in order, Negros Occidental, Batangas, Iloilo, Capiz, Cebu, Misamis Occidental, Pangasinan, Leyte, Negros Oriental, Quezon, Bataan, Camarines Norte, and Sorsogon. The tenancy problems of the rest of the provinces are less serious or are confined to local regions within provinces. Tables 8 and 9 give some statistics to indicate the varying proportions of the tenancy situation, and map 10 illustrates the key areas in their regional locations. The colonial frontier regions have few tenancy problems. Misamis Occidental is the only section of Mindanao showing an important number of tenants. Bohol, Antique, Samar, and Marinduque of the Visayan group rank low in tenancy. The first two of these provinces have been contributing to the migration to Mindanao for a long period and, in spite of a surplus of population, have not developed much of a tenancy problem at home. Samar is one of the larger islands still a part of the frontier zone. It is also noticeable that the northwest Luzon provinces show up with a low tenancy figure in spite of their long-continued surplus population.

It is difficult to explain why some of the surplus population regions of the Philippines have developed a high tenancy rate whereas others have not. Thrift, willingness to pioneer, and limited regional resources can be marked down for western Panay, Bohol, and northwest Luzon. These are old, surplus areas with a low tenancy rate. But these characteristics also pertain to Cebu and Leyte, which also are old areas of surplus population but which now have increasingly serious tenancy problems. For central Luzon one notes a tendency toward a luxurious living pattern, extensive regional resources, and an unwillingness to pioneer in farming. And this is the worst zone of tenancy problems in the Philippines today.

Luxurious living patterns and good land also hold true for southeastern Panay, another old, surplus region with a serious tenancy

Table 8

DISTRIBUTION OF TENANCY, 1939

	Provinces from north to south	Number of farms	Alienable land in acres[a]	Tenure of cultivated lands in percentages					
				Owners	Part owners	Share tenants	Mixed tenancy	Managers	
1	Batanes	1,724	0	91	8	1	b	0	1
2	Abra	13,329	0	51	38	10	b	0.7	2
3	Cagayan	36,561	525,000	53	30	16	b	c	3
4	Ilocos Norte	31,234	70,000	38	43	19	b	c	4
5	Ilocos Sur	27,163	0	34	42	23	b	c	5
6	Isabela	32,719	408,000	58	18	22	1	c	6
7	La Union	25,739	0	51	32	16	b	c	7
8	Mountain	36,127	99,000	94	3	2	b	c	8
9	Nueva Viscaya	10,114	521,000	56	18	25	b	c	9
10	Bataan	6,305	112,000	31	19	35	12	3	10
11	Batangas	50,316	0	24	28	47	1	c	11
12	Bulacan	36,014	26,000	15	18	62	4	c	12
13	Cavite	22,463	7,000	22	18	53	5	1.5	13
14	Laguna	25,720	0	29	25	43	1	1	14
15	Nueva Ecija	78,319	0	20	11	66	1	1.4	15
16	Pampanga	23,628	0	14	17	65	1	1.5	16
17	Pangasinan	86,615	0	33	33	30	2	c	17
18	Quezon	52,874	496,000	50	14	35	3	0.6	18
19	Rizal	14,149	102,000	29	29	29	b	2.3	19
20	Tarlac	28,651	0	20	20	50	10	7	20
21	Zambales	12,165	84,000	24	46	19	2	c	21
22	Albay	31,913	0	59	13	25	b	2.5	22
23	Camarines Nor	10,011	165,000	46	6	47	b	c	23
24	Camarines Sur	35,822	110,000	56	15	24	1	3.4	24
25	Catanduanes	12,348	0	d	d	d	d	d	25
26	Sorsogon	31,688	25,000	52	12	30	b	4.7	26
27	Antique	23,662	70,000	62	25	12	b	c	27
28	Bohol	63,388	0	57	28	15	b	c	28
29	Capiz	43,527	0	45	16	31	4	3.8	29
30	Cebu	121,548	33,000	46	20	32	b	1.2	30

No.	Province	Number of farms	Area	%	%	%	%	%	No.
31				58	10	40		2.4	31
32	Leyte	100,794	419,000	52	14	33	b	°	32
33	Marinduque	9,931	0	53	35	12	b	°	33
34	Masbate	17,723	0	69	5	24	b	1.4	34
35	Mindoro	16,271	185,000	64	9	22	b	4.5	35
36	Negros Occ.	35,896	382,000	32	3	28	6	31	36
37	Negros Or.	47,440	133,000	49	13	30	b	7.4	37
38	Palawan	11,304	1,666,000	85	1	4	b	9.3	38
39	Romblon	14,521	84,000	55	1	32	2	b	39
40	Samar	63,388	1,427,000	78	7	14	b	b	40
41	Agusan	12,072	1,099,000	80	4	14	b	1.3	41
42	Bukidnon	6,561	481,000	55	2	19	9	14.5	42
43	Cotabato	25,018	1,980,000	76	1	13	1	7.7	43
44	Davao	26,251	2,471,000	65	2	22	2	8.4	44
45	Lanao	24,529	681,000	76	3	18	b	1.2	45
46	Misamis Occ.	25,650	80,000	51	14	34	b	°	46
47	Misamis Or.	22,521	237,000	72	8	16	b	3	47
48	Surigao	28,982	870,000	72	16	12	b	°	48
49	Zamboanga	32,877	1,489,000	74	3	19	b	3.6	49
50	Sulu	20,384	151,000	77	b	12	11	°	50
	Totals	1,634,726	15,916,000	49.0	15.0	30.7	1.7	3.5	

a Data from Mamisao, applicable to 1948.
b Less than 1 per cent of farms are in this category.
c Less than 0.5 per cent of farms are in this category.
d Data for 1939 were included in Albay Province.
SOURCES: *Philippine Census*, 1939, J. P. Mamisao, R. G. Hainsworth, and R. T. Moyer.

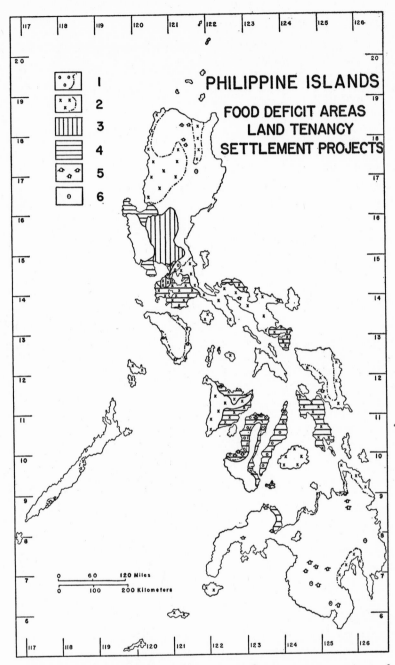

Map 10. Food deficit areas, land tenancy, settlement projects. 1 = Areas of serious food deficiency. 2 = Areas of mild food deficiency. 3 = Regions of serious tenancy problems. 4 = Regions of mild tenancy problems. 5 = Bureau of Lands subdivisions. 6 = National Land Settlement Administration projects.

problem. But the Ilongo has been a willing pioneer. Iloilo Province has contributed much to the present population of western Negros Island, which resembles southeastern Panay, whereas Cebu has populated much of eastern Negros and is similar to it. Both parts of the island have tenancy problems with basically different economies. Other such contradictions could be noted, and it is evident that there is no easy answer to the origin and persistence of the regional phase of the tenancy problem.

Certain features of the tenancy problem come from far back in the pre-Spanish past, some developed with the Spanish, and others belong to the American period. In the pre-Spanish era the average fee paid by the serf class for cultivation rights was half the crop. There must have been many local variations throughout the islands in provision for seed and labor. Many of these local practices carried over into the Spanish period, but became complex as populations enlarged, draft animals came into use, the total of agricultural land increased, and trade developed a demand for agricultural products. The gradual Spanish freeing of the slaves added a class of landless individuals who now had to provide their own livelihood. Most of them became part of the serf class in its evolution into the tenant class.

The main currents of Spanish time—the granting of encomiendas, the continuation of power in the hands of the tribal chiefs now become barrio tenientes and town heads, and the failure of the Spanish to develop a new and effective land system that protected the former serf—all operated to maintain the position of the former upper class, to solidify it as a landed aristocracy, and to increase its wealth and power. Many a migrant moving onto the frontier was able, of course, to better himself and perhaps to join the landed aristocracy. Intermarriage with Spaniards was another way of gaining a position of wealth and power and the special privileges attached. Though tenancy problems had not yet become crucial by the end of the Spanish era, their seeds had sprouted and were growing all the time.

There are several kinds of tenancy arrangements in different parts of the islands. The most frequent is sharecropping; another is cash tenancy. Certain parts of the islands use a combination of both types, and a number of local regions have their own particular patterns. No effective data on degree and distribution of tenancy are available for the Spanish period. Data gathered by the first American census of 1903 are not very reliable on this subject because of the newness of American control, the inability of census takers to cover the islands completely, and the lack of definitions of what constituted an owner, a tenant, and a squatter. The summary figures for 1903 indicate that 80.8 per cent of the farmers were termed owners, 16.2 per cent were classified as sharecroppers, 1.8 per cent were labeled cash tenants, 0.1 per cent were listed as labor tenants, and 1.1 per cent were designated as squatters.[62] Other data indicate a total of some 400,000 squatters for the year 1900, a figure roughly half the number of farms listed in the 1903 census.[63] Figures from the more reliable census of 1939 list 49.2 per cent of the farmers as owners, 15.6 per cent as part owners, 33.5 per cent as share tenants, 0.5 per cent as share-cash tenants, 1.0 per cent as cash tenants, and 0.1 per cent as farmers using managers who hired paid laborers to do the work. This would leave a balance of 0.1 per cent who supposedly could be termed squatters if the figures were accurate. Government officers today assert their inability to determine how many squatters there actually are but privately put the figure at "many thousands" who are occupying lands illegally. The 1939 total of owner-operated farms, 804,786, was almost equivalent to the total farms listed in the 1903 census, 815,453.

One is not sure from these figures whether tenancy has really increased or not. Certainly the 1903 census figures cannot be taken too literally. There can be no doubt, however, that in some of the regions settled and cultivated chiefly during the American period there has been too great a proportionate increase in tenancy. Nor can it be questioned that a great many tenants are unfairly treated and advantage taken of them by their landlords. Still widely practiced in the Central Plain of Luzon, and in Nueva Ecija Province in particular, is the "inquilino" system of tenancy, by which a middleman leases a large acreage from an owner and in turn subleases to a number of "kasama" farming tenants. This parasitic pattern requires an extra division of the fruits of the land, and can only lessen the economic opportunity of the tenant farmers.

In other words, American control of the islands should have been accompanied by a thoroughgoing overhaul of the whole land system, with all of its related customs, laws, and procedures. This would have started a new series of patterns by which further population increases in the islands could have been accommodated. American action did make certain breaks with the past, and piecemeal set up government machinery, which was never effectively put into action. Landlord-tenant relations in a few rural areas have changed little since 1565, and in many areas not in the lifetime of the generations now living. Island population has increased more than two and a half times in the American period, thereby similarly increasing the magnitude of the tenancy problem.

Early American action seemed to help the islands toward the better life that had been the goal of American intervention in Spanish affairs. Peace, a growing trade, mobility, and the freedom to expand their culture patterns unquestionably came to the islands. But no provision was properly made for lifting the standard of living for all Filipinos. The purchase of the Friar Lands alleviated only a small segment of the tenancy problem that affected some sixty thousand tenants.[64] No real steps were taken in other areas where the problem of tenancy also was growing serious. When bad planning caused the failure of the few small, early resettlement ventures they were not followed with effective programs. No adequate steps were taken to alter the traditional rules that had governed the old relations between tribal chief and serf. In the early American period these were the relations between landlords, barrio heads, municipal officials, and their tenants. No steps were taken to assure legal protection to the tenants of crowded areas moving to new localities to acquire their own lands.

Those Luzon and Visayan people who did go to Mindanao of their own volition, or to other areas, sometimes were victimized and sometimes fared well. Some became landlords, following the traditional patterns. The old and settled part of the Central Plain of Luzon was inhabited by people who did not like going to distant places. During the American period they simply spread out over the remainder of the plain. Nueva Ecija largely has been settled within the American period, but its settlement duplicated the older patterns with traditional landlord relations. What today is one of the worst tenancy regions has therefore developed during the American period.

An element in the tenancy picture, new during the American period, is the corporation operating a large landholding. Some corporations, such as the Mindanao pineapple concern, use a paid labor force which is housed, supplied with food at favorable rates, and given space for private gardens. Others, notably some of the sugar companies, use tenant labor which sometimes is well treated but often is not. Incorporation is a method by which individuals or families can secure more than the normal small holdings, and this form of land acquisition has been steadily increasing in recent years, both in frontier areas and in the old, settled areas. It is a system obviously beneficial to the upper classes with some capital at their disposal.

Tenancy is most serious among sugar-cane and corn farmers, least so among producers of vegetables, fruits, coconut, and abacá. Tobacco, rice, and poultry are in a middle category, taking the country as a whole. However, some of the most serious regional tenancy situations, with the greatest oppression by landlords, now exist among rice and coconut producers. Farm managers are relatively most common on livestock, poultry, and sugar-cane farms, but also are found on the larger coconut, tobacco, and abacá plantations. On managed farms paid labor is employed. Wages, as well as living and working conditions, generally are somewhat better on managed farms than on tenant-operated farms. Some managed farms are corporation-owned, but some are under individual ownership.

An attempt was made in 1933 to ameliorate the lot of the rice-tenant farmers by the passage of a Rice Share Tenancy Act, but it was rendered ineffective by subsequent legislation that made the act difficult to apply. Particularly in the Central Plain of Luzon there has been trouble since the passage of this act—tenants trying to secure relief and landlords moving to thwart every such attempt. One of the consequences has been the rise of tenant organizations whose objective is to secure redress. Their effectiveness has not been very great, and the main consequence has been what the landlords would term the fomenting of trouble, disobedience, and strife. Government projects such as the Rural Progress Administration, described in the next chapter, have resulted from the failure of amelioration measures, but this approach to the basic problem of too many tenants in too small an area can never solve the difficulties adequately. The infiltration of tenant organizations by communists is a development of recent years, with the inevitable result of discredit upon the organizations.

Today tenant fees are in a state of flux throughout the country. Further postwar legislation has served to make the matter more, rather than less, involved. Legally, a share tenant retains 70 per cent of the crop, with 30 per cent going to the landlord. In practice, this does not always work out. In areas where agitation has been extensive but not violent, where tenant organizations have been helpful rather than troublesome, where landlords are amenable, or where government action has interceded for the tenant, some tenants actually have secured such arrangements.

Ignorance is one great bar to the rural tenant's progress. Many tenants have abstained from use of legal methods, fearing costly involvements in which they may ultimately be the losers. There are many ways by which individual landlords have prevented action. Landlord intimidation of tenants is a frequent deterrent in crowded areas, and often a tenant is so deeply in debt to his landlord that he has no hope of taking steps that could lead to redress. In many parts of the islands, however, officials report that the traditional half-and-half share arrangements continue in force without protest. And in many local areas there is real amity between landlord and tenant.

Tenant ignorance of economic, legal, and social trends in island life may be responsible for the slow advancement of Philippine rural society. It would be unfair to place all the responsibility and blame upon every landlord. However, the generalization must be permitted that unless the educated upper classes, or the government, or the landlords themselves take the lead in carrying out an effective program of land reform, the agrarian situation will become so aggravated that it will explode into militant, bloody rebellion.

Communist programs thrive on just such untended situations as exist in the Philippines today. The islands possess the makings of a first-class exhibit of "vested capitalistic interests" versus the "downtrodden lower classes," in spite of the fact that oppressed tenants do not form the majority of the population.

There are no good public opinion summaries of reaction to recent or current efforts to solve the tenant problem. However, many people gradually are becoming aware of the nature of the problem. It is clear from the continued support of the dissident groups that many feel that current land reform programs are ineffective. During 1948–1950 covert help to the "Huks" was extensive; in no other way could they have succeeded in eluding government punitive forces. Undoubtedly some of that help was unwillingly given, motivated by fear of Huk reprisals, but not all of it can be ascribed to fear. Early in 1950 the official name of the leading dissident group was altered to Hukbong Mapagpalaya Sa Bayan, translated as "People's Liberation Army."[65] This indicated an attempt to rally support from all possible sources, and also pointed to a long-range program of opposition to the present government. The tenancy issue remains a key point in this whole program of opposition.[66]

During 1950 some organized expression of public opinion against the Hukbalahap began to appear. Anticommunist leagues, rural workshop programs, and similar activities began to mobilize democratic strength against the communist-led Hukbalahap.[67] These programs linked the agrarian problem to the communist problem in recognition of the danger to the Philippines. However, most effort of this sort seems to be urban in origin, to be concerned chiefly with preventing the spread of communism, and does not yet focus directly upon the problem of tenancy.

Available Land and Labor

Unfortunately the tenant often is his own worst enemy. In a crowded region of scarce farm land, landlords know that tenants will underbid each other to get a parcel of ground on which to eke out a bare existence. To be landless in a crowded rural area is to invite starvation. Throughout much of the Central Plain of Luzon, therefore, the landlord often has but to threaten to eject the tenant to gain his submission to agreements that will place him more firmly in the landlord's power.

Government purchases of large estates in such areas will do no ultimate good, because locally there is not enough land to provide an increasing standard of living for the present agricultural population. Individual ownership of even small holdings admittedly is better than tenant occupation. Dependence upon plots of land too small to support single families is a modern predicament common to other parts of the Orient in which there is hardly any reserve land left. This is a situation to be avoided in an agricultural country, for the problem of providing supplementary income for the individual farm family has not been solved.

Costly bureaucratic projects of moving a few farmers out of such a concentration will be useless without correlated programs of social change. Before it is too late these rural elements must be taught that there is available land elsewhere. They must be induced to move. And then land must be provided them promptly. Some help, too, must be given them in the moving process, but not through the involved methods of the past. The basic features of transport, education, and health must be organized and developed as these migrants arrive in new areas; not years afterward. This is a large order for the present Philippine government, but its alternatives are ominous!

Underbidding by tenants is only one part of the situation. In areas less crowded, where some margin of land still exists, the landlords bid for tenants by making their offers seem real inducements when they really are not. The advantage lies always with the landlord. Along the north coast of Mindanao the tenant is in demand because people were able to stake out earlier claims much larger than they could cultivate. Here farm jumping is continual among tenants who think a new landlord's terms better than those of their old. Although the individual tenant has the illusion of betterment, there is no real program of agrarian improvement. With a continued influx of population such an area will reach its saturation point and conditions soon will resemble those in older centers, the tenants being more and more caught in debt and competition for too little farm land.

In other regions well into the frontier, the very scarcity of labor plays a role too. Here a tenant may himself drive a hard bargain with a settler who already has cleared some land. The cost of clearing land and harvesting a first crop is high, and in a tenant-tolerant culture some migrants will always look for tenant openings. Even the tenant, on the frontier, suffers from a labor shortage because he has few neighbors with whom to exchange labor coöperatively in time of need. So much work capacity is consumed on the undeveloped frontier in transport, marketing, and other basic activities that real productivity remains low in many areas.

Inherent in Philippine agricultural economy is a strong seasonal contrast in labor demands. A nonmechanized rice culture makes heavy demands upon labor for short intervals each year. This is true of sugar cane, of corn, and of tobacco. The unproductiveness of that labor, largely working with the simplest tools and equipment, increases the demand for numbers. The slack periods offer neither alternative outlets for labor nor source of income. This is the crux of the chronic underemployment of the islands.

The Problem of Rural Credit

Related to tenancy are the problems of rural indebtedness and rural credit. In pre-Spanish times cultivators had been tied to the land, and rates of annual produce-payment, debts, fines, and penalties were fairly well established, though there were certain regional and tribal differences. Tribal chiefs and nobles had responsibilities as well as perquisites, both of which, in a nonmoney economy, produced a certain stability. The lack of a money economy, the small population, and the great abundance of usable land meant that the problems of land and debts at no time threatened the operation of society.

Boeke suggests, in writing of Indonesian economy, from which much of Philippine economy derives its patterns, that interest exacted on credit extended indicates occidental influence.[63] This may be accurate where money transactions alone are concerned, but it seems doubtful if this was completely true in the Philippines for transactions in kind, since the Filipinos did not operate a collection of self-contained and isolated village economies. The economy, at its upper levels, included interregional and international exchange of goods and services, though it undoubtedly is true that most of the exchanges were in kind, with a rough-and-ready system of barter, and that money transactions and accounting never became widespread or important in pre-Spanish times. The introduction of money economy came slowly during the Spanish period, and was largely accomplished after the relaxation of tight Spanish controls in the latter half of the nineteenth century. American political control and the many new economic practices rapidly completed the transition to an economy dominated by money transactions or transactions in kind computed on a money basis.

Modern problems of rural tenancy, debt, and credit are the result of a growth in population and the shift to a money economy. They are the result of grafting occidental ideas and practices onto an Indonesian culture, and evolved during Spanish and American times. Features essentially sound in the original native economy were retained and have become harmful when translated into the patterns of money economy.

Population pressure within local regions made its appearance only in middle to late Spanish times. One of the most damaging factors has been the failure of the supervisors of the changing economy to provide all those facilities that are mandatory in a money economy. Although the use of money and money accounting has spread to almost all parts of the islands, traditional methods of arranging loans and credit have remained in force, with interest rates on traditional levels also. However, collections, taxes, and penalties for failure to pay have all been arranged on new bases. The well-to-do have facilities to meet changed conditions, but the mass of the rural population has not been provided for.

In a simple agricultural society the small farmer seldom has a source of cheap credit. His very pattern of living normally involves simple barter and payment in kind, for the production of which his own labor and the good earth usually are adequate sources. Landowners, regional headmen, village traders, and town merchants normally are the sources of credit open to him. These sources set the terms of credit, establish the interest rates, control the collections, and administer the penalties for failure to pay. An interregional or international trader maintaining contact with such a society often becomes a source of credit to local merchants but not to farmers. It normally happens in an agricultural society that interest rates are high, that loans and payments are in kind, and that profitable surpluses are large but are subject to rodents, spoilage, weather, and thievery.

In the Philippines tribal chiefs, nobles, village merchants, and a variety of Filipino, Chinese, and other traders were the original active sources operative in the credit picture. During Spanish times Spanish officials, landlords, merchants, and the Catholic Church were added to the list of credit sources, concentrating their operations upon a number of urban communities and their rural hinterlands. The role of the Chinese as a credit source also increased slowly around Manila. Spanish restriction of the population was accompanied by the accumulation of land and resources in the hands of native officialdom, an increasing number of big families, village traders, and urban merchants. The gradual growth of international trade continued this process of selective accumulation of wealth. The evolution of new institutions such as banking and industry among the urban elements to meet these new conditions was not accompanied by the development of equivalent economic institutions among rural farmers or fishermen.

The first modern bank was established in Manila in 1851, to be followed during several decades by a number of others. The emphasis of these banks was almost completely urban and international. An agricultural bank was established by the government in 1908, but its location in Manila and its small capital prevented it from circulating money in the most needy rural environment. In 1916 this bank was reorganized into the Philippine National Bank, and its agricultural small-loan activities were reduced to insignificance. An Agricultural and Industrial Bank was formed in 1939, to be transformed in 1947 into the Rehabilitation Finance Corporation, which became the main government agency for financing postwar reconstruction.[69] In the interval from January, 1947, to June 20, 1950, about 40 per cent of the Rehabilitation Finance Corporation loans were for agriculture or land. This was about 18 per cent of the total funds dispersed.[70] A few small farmers were loaned money, but the largest sums went to large landholders, and this agency cannot possibly directly serve the small farmer.

In 1950 there were thirteen separate commercial banks operating in Manila, excluding government reconstruction agencies and the government Central Bank. All these place only slight emphasis upon agricultural loans and none are in a position to deal with the small credit problems of the rural countryside. Only the Philippine National Bank has a real system of branches outside of Manila, with thirty provincial and city branches and more than fifty agencies.[71] Although the Philippine National Bank holds about half the total credit facilities available, it almost never has engaged in a real program of agricultural loans to small farmers.

The commercial banks have reduced interest rates to less than 8 per cent per annum, and have nearly $500,000,000 in assets. Practically all of the loan fund is available to the big families and the big landowners with clear land titles for trade, industry, or transportation. In contrast: "The small farmers with few exceptions are expected to secure their mortgage funds, as they have always done, from private individuals."[72] And one may add, at rates of interest that are many times the rates available to borrowers from banks, and with conversion factors and penalty clauses that put the small farmer at the mercy of the individuals making the loans.

With the Bureau of Lands so far behind on its surveys, very few new colonists can get title to their new lands, since they often cannot afford private surveys and court costs. Without title an owner occupant cannot hope for a loan from private or government banks. His only recourse is the private lender, with all the risks consequent upon a private loan.

135

Far too many tenant farmers never can hope to be anything else under the present pattern of land and credit controls. There is no effective protection from the unscrupulous landlord for the illiterate tenant, or even for the literate tenant already deep in debt to his landlord. There are too many ways to manipulate cost accounting when making advances, using payment in kind computed in money terms, when the tenant cannot read the agreements he is forced to sign, or when the tenant is forced to purchase his supplies from a store operated by the landlord.[73] The various government bureaus assigned the duty of purchasing landed estates in which tenant problems are severe, have floundered along for several years liquidating fewer problems than are arising in other localities. This failure is in part owing to overlapping directives, fundamental government misdirection, and inadequate funds, but also it is provoked by the lack of aggressive policies and by the lack of concern over the problem by the highest levels of the Philippine government.

Both the small owner and the tenant farmer need several kinds of aids to improve their situations. Enlargement of the land-survey program would benefit both groups by making new lands more available. Legislation with real teeth in it, effectively enforced, could relieve the private borrower from usurious persecution by the unscrupulous landlord. Rural coöperatives could solve some credit problems. The establishment of rural land banks or loan agencies commissioned to cater only to the small borrower, offering reasonable interest rates, and providing an efficiently managed and aggressive program of lending could lighten the load of debt for the small farmer and provide him with credit which would permit him to increase his agricultural output and lift his standard of living.[74] This type of program would do more to remove the accumulated agrarian unrest and the threats of communism than any number of punitive military expeditions.

The Role of the Coöperative

One of the solutions for credit problems suggested by occidental reformers is the coöperative organization. In theory the coöperative draws together the small capital resources of many private individuals and welds the total into an effective working fund for the collective use of the group. Coöperatives are held to be ideal for decentralized and rural activity. There are several different plans of organization and several types of coöperatives. However, nowhere in the Orient has the coöperative been as successful as its protagonists assert that it can be, though the reasons therefor are difficult to assess properly. Interference by vested interests has sometimes prevented the success of the coöperative, as in China in 1939–1942. Individualism and the refusal of local populations to coöperate have frequently been causes of failure. Mistakes in organizing the wrong kind of coöperative have produced a share of the failures. Probably the most serious bar to success has been the low degree of literacy of the peoples among whom coöperatives have been organized. Rapid setting up and lack of educative supervision have been all too frequent. A few simple lectures and some lessons in bookkeeping do not make for permanent success of the coöperative movement.

The coöperative was first introduced to the Philippines in 1915 to deal with the small farmer's credit problems.[75] Growing slowly during the years before World War II the coöperative movement was faced with mismanagement, a lack of interest by the small-farmer element, and the wrong types of organization. A government agency had been created, the National Coöperatives Corporation, to supervise and foster the movement. This was replaced in 1941 by the National Coöperatives and Small Business Corporation, which in 1951 was turned into an office of the Department of Commerce and Industry.[76]

As of December, 1941, there were several hundred coöperatives active in the Philippines, with more than a hundred thousand members, most of the organizations being consumer coöperatives.[77] During the war most of the coöperatives became inactive, if they had not already run out of funds. At the end of 1948 there again had been a marked increase in coöperative organization, with a corresponding increase in membership.[78] Most organizations still are consumer coöperatives, not well organized or administered, and not extremely effective in function. The tendency toward specialized organizations and the lack of adequate educative supervision have contributed to the scant success of the coöperative as a rural credit instrument. The generalized coöperative which can cater to all the purchasing, producing, marketing, and credit needs of a local region would give more of the help that is needed by the rural population. It would make unnecessary complete village or rural farm dependence upon the Chinese commercial trader who now gives all these services at a high cost to the Filipino and at a good profit to himself.[79]

Castillo's data for 1948 suggest that coöperative activities touch about one million people, most of whom are inhabitants of the rural countryside. This is a fairly significant share of the total population, and tremendous good could come from the generalized coöperative if its organization were effective and management really efficient. However, my own opinion is that the greatest success lies among groups in which the level of education is fairly high and among people with the greatest degree of "know-how" in dealing with the complex money economy of the islands. It is my opinion that the segment of the population that most needs credit, relief from the middleman, and general economic assistance does not really profit from the coöperative movement at present.

Successful operation of coöperatives, except on the very simplest levels, requires real understanding of money economy and some management skill—an ability not yet widespread among rural Filipinos. Castillo mentions a lack of interest as a cause for failure.[80] It is unlikely that educational propaganda about the value and the management of coöperatives has been a long-run part of rural school curricula. The groups that most need relief are either not aware of the possibilities or have been disillusioned by stories of mismanagement. The coöperative is a powerful long-range tool with which to improve the lot of the rural populace, but education, skilled supervision, and good management are needed to make it work effectively. Its role among rural Filipinos should be increased, but it cannot be thought of as a cure-all for rural difficulties.

Chapter 10

INTERNAL COLONIZATION

THE PHILIPPINES are no exception to the rule that dividing available lands among a population creates problems that almost no regional society has solved equitably. The islands, however, illustrate an interesting aspect of land settlement. The surplus people of most overpopulated countries must look elsewhere for living space. In other situations, a society may modify its economy to make room for the excess at home. The Philippines fortunately has adequate space for this generation's surplus population. This land adequacy always has been taken for granted in the past, and little thought has been given to it.

Under American supervision a brief start on a program was made but, by and large, the regionally surplus people of the islands have solved their own problems in the past. Some of these solutions were inefficient, creating other problems for contemporary Philippine society. This whole matter will eventually become more serious, and new solutions will be called for. However, if there is space for all at present, then settlement becomes a question of how to make local surpluses willing to move to available open spaces and how to put them on a self-supporting basis in their new locations. A review of past and current colonial settlement procedures should be helpful for orientation.

Past Settlement Procedures

A part of Filipino history is the coming of Malay tribal chiefs from Borneo with groups of followers to purchase settlement sites on Panay and southern Luzon from the Negrito or Indonesian owners.[81] Rules of settlement were simple but operative parts of tribal law. Different culture levels were then found over the islands, but gradually the agricultural peoples, with evolving theories of land ownership, had taken over the greater share of the islands. New land could be had for the taking, with but simple restrictions. Settlement of new sites, by tribes practicing shifting agriculture, might be likened to the gradual drift of a flock of sheep across a grazing range—individuals moving in company as an organized band. Other tribal groups which were sedentary, remained on fixed sites for long periods of time, slowly expanding their settlements and the density of occupation of each.

Among coastal fishing populations fixed bases with periodic moves were usual. By all tribal peoples of southeastern Asia complete removal of residence sites was not uncommon. Normally such moves were decided by divination, omen, or the will of a tribal chief. With more advanced groups, wholesale abandonment of dwelling sites was uncommon, and more formal government patterns were operative, with greater control over lands. All in all, many patterns of settlement were followed by different culture groups. Individual action probably was less common in this early period than today. Something of these early patterns has remained among the pagan interior tribes even today and must be taken into account when formulating new settlement policies for regional surpluses. Both village concentration and dispersed dwelling upon farmlands have long been standard in the islands. And even among Christian Filipinos, some earlier land and settlement practices remain today, though markedly altered by Spanish and American controls.

As soon as the Spaniards secured control over any part of the islands they replaced native tribal government with their own administration.[82] Hand in hand with civil government went the

1A. *In southeastern Luzon a village sits astride a paved highway. Grassy shoulders are used for drying laundry or copra.*

1B. *The nipa palm thatch and plaited bamboo house of the rural Filipino often is set in a banana clump. Southern Luzon.*

2A. *Rice fields patchwork lands at the lowest levels, with coconut, bananas, homes and gardens on the higher spots. Northern Panay.*

2B. *Upland rice, a scattering of corn, and a few coconuts are the standard crops of this upland farmer of southeastern Luzon.*

3A. This is a typical view of the rugged mountain landscape of northern Luzon which has not been touched by terrace builders.

3B. A neighboring valley has been turned into a mosaic of stone-walled terraces unlike the average Philippine farm landscape.

4A. Sugar cane carpets rolling terrain above the wet rice lands of parts of Negros, Panay, and Luzon Islands. Eastern Negros.

4B. A small "sugar central" or refining plant in central northern Panay is ready for the milling season which runs from December through February.

5A. Corn, coconut, and bananas are the common crops of several Visayan Islands. Southern Cebu.

5B. Formal plantation plantings of coconut are widely spaced and cleanly cultivated, unlike older native plantings. Southeastern Negros.

6A. *A first year catch crop of upland rice was harvested from small patches while good timber rots and the balance is cut by a pioneer. Central Mindanao.*

6B. *In interior Mindanao wood for housing is cheap but nipa palm thatch is scarce and is replaced by split bamboo shingles.*

7A. *A plantation operator fells tropical forest in wholesale manner when expanding manila hemp plantings in southeastern Mindanao.*

7B. *Young manila hemp planting in foreground about a year old is surrounded by mature plantings in southeastern Mindanao.*

8A. Fishing boats dot the bay at Camohaguin in southeastern Luzon, backed by a thick fringe of coconut palms.

8B. The typical small Filipino fishing boat is a slim-bodied double outrigger.

9A. In interior Mindanao many a dugout canoe still is hacked out of a whole tree trunk with the simplest of tools.

9B. Facilities are simple and few at most island ports and are similar to those at Larena, Siquijor Island.

10A. *Both the products and the clothing are distinctive in a Moslem market scene at Dansalan, Lanao Province, Mindanao.*

10B. *Quite different is the Christian market scene of a southern Luzon town.*

11A. *The traditional market in the foreground contrasts with the modern general store of a California-trained Filipino in Bogo, northern Cebu.*

11B. *Bridge problems plague transport on Panay. A bus trying to ford is stuck in the center of this scene, as the raft-ferry approaches from the right. Western Panay.*

12A. *The lack of vehicles packed twenty-five students onto one jeep for a homeward journey on Siquijor Island.*

12B. *A Panay Autobus Company bus makes a stop for breakfast at seven o'clock along the east coast of Panay.*

13A. *An ox and cart await a planting crew in a southern Luzon low-land rice area.*

13B. *These two central Luzon farmers are cultivating for the last time before transplanting lowland rice.*

14A. *Lowland rice normally is transplanted by large crews of men and women working together. Southern Luzon.*

14B. *Typical oriental rice culture requires a large amount of disagreeable hand labor, particularly at the planting season. Southern Luzon.*

15A. *Rice harvesting is tedious when wind beats down many plants, and normal cutting practice is impossible. Southern Luzon.*

15B. *In northern Luzon water buffalo tread out grain which is then hand winnowed, in one of the oldest Asiatic agricultural techniques.*

16A. *On plantations coconut is scientifically processed into copra at central warehouses. Southeastern Negros.*

16B. *The traditional method of smoking copra over a coconut husk fire produces a low-grade product. Southern Zamboanga.*

Roman Catholic religion. Following these two basic features came modification of older settlement patterns. Undoubtedly new settlements were founded by the Spanish, but often they took over existing native towns.

The most distinctive items in the whole settlement procedure were the organized and formal patterns that evolved. The plaza, the church, and the government buildings were key units, with shops and the homes of leading families near the central area. Other families lived farther from the plaza and even at some distance. Garden and farm lands lay scattered around the outskirts of the town. At variable distances from the chief settlement, village and smaller settlement clusters formed the nuclei of the barrios or local districts. As long as, and wherever, the Spaniards were able to control the Philippines this was the standard formula by which new territories were organized.

In this organizing procedure the Spaniards devoted more attention to regularizing existing conditions than to providing new settlements. The Church did establish mission stations in advance of political organization and the formal laying out of municipalities, but colonization seems to have been left entirely to the native population. The earliest increases in regional population, and the first marked expansions of the Spanish period, developed just before 1800. Panay, Cebu, the Manila hinterland, and the Ilocos coast of northwest Luzon were the first regions to show marked increases in population, with Bohol and Leyte not far behind. Laguna suffered early decreases, and Cagayan was similarly affected; if data were available undoubtedly other local regions would be identified in which the early Spanish impact was severe.

Most of the Central Plain of Luzon, much of eastern and southeastern Luzon, Catanduanes, Samar, Negros, Mindoro, Palawan, and of course Mindanao were but thinly populated before 1800. Many of the smaller marginal islands must have had few, if any, permanent inhabitants at this time. From the Manila region population spread northward through the main part of the Central Plain; the Ilocos folk spread into the Cagayan Valley in small numbers, into the western hilly reaches of Mountain Province, and southward into the upper end of the Central Plain. Panay and Cebu settlers first migrated to the coast of Negros Island nearest each, and then both joined the Boholanos and people from Leyte in establishing a thin line of Christian settlements along the north and northeastern coasts of Mindanao. In Mindanao the Spanish regularizing of settlements is less evident. The plaza is absent or often irregular; the church may be located other than at the center of town; the buildings are less massive and sturdy; and even today one recognizes certain signs of immaturity in the settlements.

Projects of the American Period

The pressure of men upon the land in certain parts of the islands was one of the first features recognized by the Americans when they took over the administration of the Philippines from the Spanish in 1899. The open and empty regions of the islands impressed them also. The need to prevent further bad feeling between Christians and Moslems was recognized because, even then, it was obvious to some that one of the chief potential regions of the islands was Mindanao. American colonial policy makers thought in terms of improved transport, efficient government, and the stimulation of agriculture, but they also were concerned with restricting the control of lands to Filipinos. This policy was largely indirect at the outset, but gradually it became fixed administrative policy in the islands, and gained strength with the passage of time and the greater participation by Filipinos in their own government.

Filipinos feared that the islands would turn into a land of American absentee-owned plantations, and that the Filipinos would be reduced to the status of colonial plantation workers. Although American policy favored relatively small holdings by individual Filipinos no colonization schemes were developed in the early years of American control. Provisions were made for land survey and formal claiming of land at an early date, but these provisions were inadequate to the needs.

The first formal attempts at colonization came only after it was evident that Filipinos from the overcrowded provinces were not rushing of their own accord to take up new lands in the open frontier regions. Plans were made to stimulate private settlements, mixing Moslems and Christians together in Mindanao, but comparatively few settlers took advantage of the opportunities.[83] These projects were initiated between 1913 and 1917. Supervision of colonization matters was transferred to the Bureau of Labor in 1919, where it remained until 1939. The Bureau of Labor aided only families who were themselves able to provide for most of their own needs. A few provincial projects furnished additional opportunities to acquire new lands but these were uniformly of little help to the surplus populations from crowded areas of the islands.

In 1939 a new organization, the National Land Settlement Administration, was set up to operate on a large scale, chiefly in Mindanao and northeastern Luzon.[84] The NLSA was planned to handle marketing of agricultural produce, purchase of consumers' goods, and education and religious matters until the colonies should become well established. In Mindanao the program was preceded by road building. But bad publicity and World War II both interfered with the settlement plans at a critical juncture, and by the end of the war much of the good had been undone. To date all these projects moved not more than 50,000 people to Mindanao. Location of the projects is shown in map 10.

The Bureau of Lands, itself, has operated a long-range program to open public lands. Crews have prepared detailed surveys of alienable tracts, divided into residential and agricultural plots, for disposal to the public. These subdivisions are scattered all over the islands, and are shown in map 10. A variable number of survey crews have been in the field, normally about thirty, currently thirty-six. Each crew is permanently stationed at a subdivision to handle allocation of lands. Success has attended most of these operations, and the Bureau currently has some surveys in progress.

Another government project in settlement operations pertained to the great estates of the Catholic Church, accumulated during the Spanish period. The first steps in this program were taken at an early date, 1904–1905, at the beginning of American control. The accepted official record for Church land, undoubtedly much too low, was a little more than 400,000 acres in 1904 and of this, the first purchase amounted to some 375,000 acres including a large number of properties in twenty-three major locations. These lands were in Cebu, Mindoro, and, chiefly, central Luzon.[85] Some small purchases have been made recently, but nothing to compare with the early purchase. This entire program was not designed to move resident populations to new areas, but to alleviate agrarian problems in local trouble spots. Lands were resold to tenants in terms of the plots they operated under previous ownership. Relative success attended the operations, but ignorance of the tenant population made difficulties, and often the plots sold were too small for families to attain the desired standard of living.

Another organization, the Rural Progress Administration, was set up in 1939 to promote small-land ownership in critical tenancy areas. It chiefly purchased large private properties in rural areas, though some urban properties also were acquired. Before its abolition in 1950 it had acquired twenty-seven pieces of land totaling approximately 106,000 acres.[86] The Philippine government never appropriated sufficient funds to permit the organization to carry out a really successful program.

Still another government agency, the Peoples Homesite and Housing Corporation, has been operating on the margins of this field. Its operations, for the most part, have been confined to the Manila metropolitan region, and it hardly enters into rural land settlement.

During 1949–1950, fluctuating government action juggled these and other agencies interested in settlement, land, and agricultural production. Plans announced near the end of 1950, following suggestions of the Bell Economic Survey Mission, call for centralizing under the Bureau of Lands all programs having to do simply with opening new lands to settlement.[87] All agencies concerned in the past with specific settlement projects are to be combined into the Land Settlement and Development Corporation. This simplification could facilitate settlement progress, if operations are efficiently carried out by the two agencies.

The Future Prospect

With more than 17,000,000 acres currently in farms in all parts of the islands and a rural population of more than 10,000,000 interested in land ownership as a primary means to a livelihood, there is no question but that the Philippines is predominantly a country of small holdings. Census data from 1939 indicate that just about half the total farms then contained less than five acres each. Laws have periodically changed the maximum acreage that can be obtained by homestead, in subdivisions, or through the various settlement agencies. The figure, in actual practice today, varies between ten and thirty acres. Corporations may obtain up to 2,500 acres. A recent law restricts land ownership in the islands to Filipinos and Americans.[88]

Private purchase of land is possible in any amount, of course, if the purchaser has capital and is willing to chance securing title. Indications are that the Catholic Church has retained control of large blocks of urban and rural land, and currently may even be increasing its holdings though, for technical reasons, no total estimate may be given. Moslem residents of Mindanao, through alleged historic occupancy, often claim title to large tracts which they control. Similarly, other groups and individuals, in all parts of the islands, if knowledgeable, can maintain claims to large holdings. This large-holding situation will continue in spite of any contemplated program. Basically, of course, it does not invalidate the generalization that the Philippines is a region of small landholdings.

Unquestionably, at present, there is land enough for all. Without question, also, is the fact that present government programs of subdivision, settlement, estate purchase, and the like are ineffective.[89] The demand for land is much greater than all present organizations, put together, can care for. At the beginning of the American period a long-standing fear of the southern Moslem zone was delaying migration from overcrowded regions of the north. Psychologically this fear remains in the minds of many peoples in Luzon. One has only to mention going to Mindanao in many parts of Luzon to evoke the refrain-like reply: "Oh!—Mindanao—Moros—Trouble!"

Bad publicity from the colonial regions has an inhibiting effect upon peoples who are not educated about the geography of their own country. Stories of poor transport, of health problems, of the lack of educational facilities, of the lack of consumers' goods, of the ruinous effect of plant, bird, and animal pests, and of the inability to harvest and market crops more than counteract current government information on the potentialities of the colonial regions. Bad planning of past projects, the failures of government to survey and make known what lands are to remain forest lands and what lands are alienable, and the continued inability to make possible the securing of clear land titles all rebound unfavorably. In Pampanga, Pangasinan, and Laguna, where pressures are heavy, the population does not even now willingly consider moving to colonial areas. Ilocanos from northwest Luzon have a sound knowledge about their country's colonial zones and are thrifty and willing to rough it in spite of hardships. Not so with most of the peoples of central Luzon.

One is tempted to say that never has government more than fractionally performed its duty to the colonial zone. Certainly it did not under the Spaniards. American government, with long experience of the American frontier, first made only token gestures toward a solution, and then almost entirely retreated when the populace seemed not interested. The Filipino had never been accustomed to fixed titles to lands, having a background that included shifting agriculture with its periodic selection and abandonment of a piece of the public range. His culture background did not include meeting problems of overcrowding. But American government kept the sedentary patterns of the Spaniards, added some specific features of its own, and made fixed land titles an integral part of the machinery of society. With the need for more land, the American government set up survey machinery that was not able to keep up with the voluntary movement out of older centers into frontier zones.[90]

The Philippine government obviously is faced with many difficulties that relate to this whole subject. Experience to date would suggest that large sums of money spent on formal settlement projects will never achieve the basic need, and the government cannot afford the outlay that formal settlement will require. I suggest that money spent, in addition to regularly budgeted funds, on transport, communications, education, rural health, and basic land survey, combined with an intelligent program of educating the public of the overcrowded regions, could accomplish much more. Once the basic facilities are available, and the population is awakened to the possibilities, people will do much more themselves than can be done by costly government settlement projects.

In all the formal colonization schemes in Mindanao since 1913, exempting the regular Bureau of Lands subdivisions, not more than 50,000 people have been settled, and a few of these were Mindanao natives. Population increase of the whole Philippines today is more than 300,000 per year, chiefly in the densely crowded regions. In 1900 the population of Mindanao Island amounted to a bare 500,000, whereas by 1948 it had reached 2,450,000 on the main island alone. Some of this increase, of course, occurred among families permanently resident in Mindanao, so that not all the increase was immigration. But the increase from voluntary immigration greatly exceeds that from formal settlement projects, and voluntary increase took place in spite of government. The Spanish destroyed much of the mobility of the island population. This mobility must again be developed, so that the people of the islands' dense spots will be able to help themselves.

Where are these frontier empty regions of the islands? One cannot be too precise since basic surveys have never been made to delimit what should remain as permanent forest land, what is too severely damaged for any kind of cultivation, and what lands can be released to the public for private ownership. Results of preliminary surveys are available, however, and those for 1948 are shown in table 8. Among the dozen or so important provinces, from the point of view of reserve land, are seven of the nine Mindanao provinces.[91] These figures, of course, include some of the smaller islands lying off coast, which are politically attached to Mindanao provinces. Southern Mindanao—Davao and Cotabato—forms the chief reserve zone. The central north coast—the two Misamis prov-

147

inces—is the only part of the island not now wide open to further settlement; this coast was the chief area of earlier migration from the Visayas.

Palawan and Samar also are major reserve areas, though each has a variety of special use problems which settlers must meet. Mindoro and Negros still possess reserves, but they are neither very extensive nor are they easily used at present. The four east coast provinces of northern Luzon possess a number of reserve areas of lower quality land. Their whole reserve total, however, is less than that of the Mindanao province of Cotabato alone. There are many smaller islands and some large islands off coast that offer additional reserve territory. These smaller islands present special problems of settlement and development and must be more selectively used than the larger areas.

A case in point is Jomalig Island, the easternmost member of the Polillo group, off the central east coast of Luzon.[92] It totals somewhat less than 13,000 acres in area, a rolling island with no height more than 300 feet. It is a reef-ringed island, with two breaks suitable for small ship entry, but currently there are no port facilities of any kind. There are no roads on the island, no facilities for public health, and no sources of agricultural assistance. There have been no land surveys of any kind. Three primary schools serve a small school population. The 1948 census recorded a total population of 900, a figure which had risen to about 1,300 in late 1950. The whole island apparently has been caingined at one time, and the present population lives by a mixed subsistence agriculture and fishing economy. A few coconuts and fish are marketed under difficulties. There is a small amount of reserve land available for any settler willing to face the problems presented by the relative isolation of the island. New settlers must eke out a living on subsistence agriculture of a very simple sort until they develop a permanent cropping system with coconut, abacá, rice, and other crops. Even then the problems of marketing are formidable, and the handicaps to a reasonably high standard of life are numerous.

There are also small untouched areas in a number of the main islands, relatively close to densely populated trouble spots, which have been passed by or pose special problems to settlers. In many of these, regional isolation and what might be called regional oversight are responsible.

There is no quality reference made concerning available land shown in table 8. Here one must refer back to earlier chapters. Many of the currently unoccupied areas can be used only in ways other than agricultural. In some sections there are only rough country or small, scattered patches of land. In some parts of the islands available lands are dry lands much of the year and must have water to be productive. The northeastern half of Luzon is damaged by typhoons almost every year. Many uncultivated areas were cropped at one time, but are now covered with heavy grasses, and have poor soils. Much of Mindanao has land with real problems. Some of the island is aquatic lowland without adequate drainage, but most of the reserve is upland subject to erosion. In many areas major deterrents to settlement are malaria and related diseases.

Since all past government settlement projects have been able to accommodate only a small part of a single year's population increase, it is obvious that the usual projects can be only a fraction of the answer to the problem. Most of the government's expenditures, aiming toward a solution, should be concerned with the basic facilities of life: land survey, roads, communications, health facilities, educational facilities, local government machinery. Money spent on formal settlement projects should be carefully allocated to alleviate conditions in those danger spots which evidence past neglect by Filipinos, Spaniards, and Americans alike. The population must be encouraged to solve its own problems of moving, housing, tools, and financing, and not to rely completely upon government.

Chapter 11
IRRIGATION AND ITS PROBLEMS

ONE OF the peculiarities of the Philippines is that, though rice is the most important agricultural crop, the farmers have very few developed systems of water supply. Typical of the Orient is the wet field landscape with controlled water supply that helps to make rice culture one of the world's most productive crop systems. Photographs of the spectacular terraced landscape of northern Luzon, with glistening water-surfaced fields, have been reproduced so frequently in the literature on the Philippines that few non-Filipinos are aware of the serious lack of water for irrigation. Most Filipino rice farmers have grown up with a different tradition of rice farming and few of them are conscious of the problems of providing water artificially for their fields. When farmers have been aware of the need, few of them were in a position to do anything about it. In recent decades government agricultural officials and others have repeatedly voiced the need to do something about the water shortage. We should distinguish between piped domestic and agricultural water systems. The former now exist for every sizable town and city. Small irrigation projects have been carried out in many local areas, and a few large ones have been developed, but the total artificially irrigated land is small in comparison to the total rice land. Irrigation is chiefly a need of the rice farmer, but many other crops would benefit from irrigation, and the productive capacity of several regions could be increased were water available.

Because the Philippines has no cold weather, many fields now cropped but once could be double cropped if water were available to tide over the annual dry period. The magnitude of the problem is serious today, and certainly its solution must be a long-range program.

Rice Culture and Water Control

In the first chapter two agricultural systems were described, each using rice as one of its chief crops.[93] Both systems have spread as the cultivated land of the Philippines has increased in acreage. Rice is the preferred crop today of the upland farmer in most parts of the islands and is the chief crop of the lowland farmer in large areas. It enters into almost half of the cropping combinations listed in the first chapter.

The only region is which water systems and water control are effectively integrated into the agricultural landscape of a whole region, is the northern Luzon area of terraced fields. Elsewhere it is a piecemeal matter of variable effectiveness. In the aquatic swamp fringes where rice is grown today there is water in adequate amounts, but such areas do not bulk large in statistical terms and water is not really controlled there. Harvesting in such areas often is done under severe handicaps.[94]

The well-developed rice landscape of the Orient is the creation of farmers over a long period of time. It cannot be developed in a short span of years, but there are two phases that must be developed simultaneously. First is the laying out of fields in whatever units the natural landforms will permit. In hilly country fields must be contour fields, of odd shapes and sizes, closely fitted to the earth. In a broad floodplain of little slope, they may be larger, rectangular, and regular. Second is the arranging of a continuous flow system for water. Dams, intakes, canals, catchment basins, lakes, ponds, or reservoirs—all are used in one area or another. A closely articulated flow pattern must match the field layout to permit water to move across a landscape giving benefit to all and damage to none. This calls for gates, canals, distributaries, check-points, and avenues for disposal. The flow pattern must be amenable to control at all times, that is, to hold off water until wanted, to spread it properly, and to drain the fields when harvest time approaches. Natural drainage lines cannot be blocked without endangering the entire cultivated region when an unusual flood brings too much water.

In China the elaboration of this kind of integrated rice landscape took centuries of coöperative labor by many generations of farmers. Its use is very old in south China. This is the agricultural system brought to the Philippines by the ancestors of the northern Luzon pagan peoples. Unfortunately these migrants chose an exceptionally rough landscape in which field patterns must be very small. Their descendants have had to cope with the handicaps of this landscape ever since.

Elsewhere in the Philippines, immigrants came who perhaps were not acquainted with this integrated pattern or who may not have thought it necessary. They were individualists without the social concepts of the early northern Luzon immigrants. Gradually their needs caused them to reach out beyond the aquatic fringe, and slowly their descendants spread their fields over the islands. But they did not spread water control systems at the same times that they laid out rice fields, though of course they used water when it was fortuitously at hand. Only very late in their period did the Spaniards repair this lack by installing a few small irrigation systems on lands controlled by the Church or by Spanish landlords. The Americans have done all too little in this direction even though some progress has been made. Today a broad cultivated landscape is spread out, with upland slope fields and lowland flat fields, but with inadequate facilities for irrigation.

Historically, the water control system of the Chinese rice landscape cost tremendous effort and money. It could not possibly be financed today by the Chinese as a new installation. But its cost has long since been amortized and spread over generations of farmers. A Philippine water system might likewise have been installed piecemeal and its cost borne by generations. To install it now is a formidable enterprise, with financial aspects even more ominous than its engineering problems. And to overlay an extensive water control system upon an already cultivated landscape is both a nuisance and an operation that would deprive many farmers of parts of their fields.

It is doubtful, of course, whether the Philippines should now seek to install as intricate a field pattern and water control system as that in parts of China. Such a landscape requires tremendous manpower, since it is not highly amenable to mechanized agriculture. It is a landscape pattern that, once set up, is neither adaptable nor easy to operate on a productive basis. Its very operation requires a considerable population but, alone, it cannot support that population on a very high level of life.

Whereas Philippine land policy aims at keeping the islands a region of small landholders, to carry it all the way along the path taken by some other regions of Asia is to invite permanently the problems of overpopulation and low standards of living. The happy objective would be the development of water systems in areas where fields can be large enough to allow some laborsaving mechanization, and in regions where a dry season now limits productivity of the land. Even this much of a country-wide water control system would be slow and costly to install.

Development of Irrigation Systems

The total cultivated land today, with facilities for irrigation, is about 1,300,000 acres.[95] By double cropping, the total land in irrigated crops each year equals 1,500,000 acres. Of this area more than one-third is located in the Central Plain of Luzon. Northwest Luzon has about 100,000 acres under irrigation, about one-third of its cultivated land total. Elsewhere the totals and the relative shares are much lower. All Mindanao has barely 80,000 acres under irrigation out of its 1,800,000 cultivated acres. Panay has less than 80,000 acres irrigated out of some 750,000 acres cultivated. Cavite Province, a center of Spanish irrigation works, has somewhat less than 40,000 acres irrigated in a total of approximately 135,000 acres in cultivation. But Samar, with almost 400,000 acres in cultivation, has less than 2,500 acres properly irrigated. Catanduanes, an overcultivated island with about 135,000 acres in cultivation, has but 3,000 acres under irrigation.

153

Admittedly irrigation facilities are more needed in the crowded parts of Luzon than in some of the frontier areas of the islands. The need for irrigation facilities is partly a question of annual rainfall total and of seasonal distribution. Samar has less need for irrigation than northwest Luzon, and Mindanao as a whole has less need than does all Luzon. Comparison of the maps of rainfall regimes and population at this point will be interesting.

Of the total irrigated land at present, some 300,000 acres are supplied from systems controlled by government agencies. No irrigation systems were built by the government during the Spanish period, though the Church was responsible for a number. Most irrigation works of Spanish time were built in the provinces around Manila or in the Central Plain of Luzon. Construction of irrigation projects during the American period began in 1908, with the period 1922–1930 witnessing the completion of a number of large systems. Roughly 425,000 acres of land are irrigated from old, private systems built by individuals or local groups before the government was interested in water rights and their distribution. Approximately 550,000 more acres are provided for by private systems installed more recently, with water rights allocated. These were established principally during the late Spanish and early American periods.

Just before World War II began, another series of irrigation projects was in process of construction or planning. The largest of these was the Pampanga River system, designed to irrigate approximately 50,000 acres. A current program of survey, planning, and construction is under way to add another 250,000 acres to the total irrigated land within the next decade, if all goes well. This will be a big step forward, but it will not bring under regular irrigation more than half the lands necessary if rice is to continue to be the most important crop. Looking to the time when perhaps 30,000,000 acres will be in farms, in line with a general program for better land use, the irrigated share must be greatly increased beyond that now planned. Today's long-range planning program must not only catch up with its services for presently cultivated lands in Luzon and the western Visayan Islands, but also must devise a schedule for the whole Philippines to take care of lands that will come into cultivation within the next two generations.

Developers of irrigation systems have devoted most of their attention to diversional-distributional systems operated by gravity flow. There are local situations in which power pumps would lift and move water short distances from easily tapped surface sources. A few of these have been installed by private owners for their own use. Also experiments with electric-powered pumps are being carried on in the region around Manila, to irrigate small areas of a few hundred acres each. This program undoubtedly should be enlarged, both by government agencies and by private individuals.

Hardly any attempt has been made to tap artesian water sources. Little study has been made of ground water in the islands, but in many places supplies adequate to irrigate large areas certainly can be obtained. Water levels probably are not very deep in most lowland regions in the islands and, whether artesian wells are brought in or not, pumping costs for well irrigation should not be excessive compared to costs for large gravity systems using surface waters.

Problems and Benefits

Water supply is assuredly one of the critical elements in productive rice culture, but it is neither a cure-all nor an absolute guarantee of high-crop yields. Rice grown as an upland crop, whether by caingin cultivator or permanent upland farmer, gives a return that ranges from about 250 to 1,000 pounds per acre per year, with an average of 600 pounds.[96] Lowland rice gives a return that varies between about 700 and 3,800 pounds per acre per year, with an average that may be close to 1,200 pounds. The average rice yield, calculated from total acreage and production, is nearly 925 pounds per acre per year, which is low compared to yields from some other countries in the Orient. It is low because of the small yield from upland rice acreage and because not all lowland rice is irrigated.

Indications are that rice that is effectively supplied with irrigation water will normally harvest almost twice as much as nonirrigated rice. The colonial frontier, of course, repeatedly gives higher returns for rice, as well as for other crops grown on new lands, but these figures drop off sharply after a few years.

Irrigation alone is no guarantee of continued high-crop production. The evidence indicates that falling rice yields are to be found both in nonirrigated and in irrigated sections of the islands. There probably are not sufficent data with regard to irrigation and other crops than rice to broaden the generalization. Irrigation does seem to slow down the relative decline of yields on new lands, however.

There is evidence that rice grown on artificially flooded fields has a lower nutritive value than rice grown under conditions in which rain water is the only moisture supply.[97] In part at least this seems to be because some of the chemicals and vitamins entering into formation of rice grains are water soluble, but there may be other factors also. However, this loss of nutritive value is more than outweighed by the variable treatment given rice after the harvest, that is, the pounding, polishing, the excessive washing, steaming, or boiling. Improved dietary habits should be encouraged to compensate for lower values of irrigation-grown rice because the greater yield with irrigation is too important to disregard.

Irrigation installation today will be a relatively costly matter for the islands. Many million dollars every year for the next several decades must go into the irrigation program, if the islands are to keep up with their own need for food supplies and other agricultural products. One estimate has put the total necessary expenditure in the vicinity of $250,000,000 for the next two decades alone.[98] The long-range program will possibly need to double that. Per-acre costs for construction and maintenance of government installations completed during the 1920's ran from an annual charge of just less than two dollars to almost five dollars per acre, funded on a long-term basis of twenty years or more. The average Filipino holding is about ten acres, but there are many smaller and a few larger. There were many delinquencies during the 1930's, and charges were reduced. After the recent war, however, charges again were increased, and it remains to be seen whether the local economy can satisfactorily carry the heavier costs.

Added to the actual cost of installation will be the impact upon the field systems. If island agriculture is to make headway, more than irrigation will be needed. Mechanization, to be discussed later, will add to the problem. If both irrigation and some kind of mechanization are applied to the same landscapes throughout the islands, changes in field layouts will be required. Perhaps changes in ownership will permit better concentration of individual holdings. Decreasing field areas in certain localities, added road-building costs, water drainage problems, and other features—all will follow upon the development of more irrigation facilities.

Currently the islands are trying to become self-sufficient in basic foods at least. On a short-run basis this can be accomplished in a number of ways. Replacing some rice by sweet potatoes, cassava, and green market vegetables would be one approach, since they have heavier yields per acre. Increased land cultivation would be another. Fertilization could do it, at the cost of imported fertilizers. Improvements in the use of wild products not now gathered, and reduction in general food consumption are others. Two long-range methods are improvements in crop plants coupled with pest controls, and the enlargement of irrigation facilities.

In all these efforts there is one long-range factor that must be offset. That is the sharp decline, over a period of three to ten years, of yields from lands newly put into crop. Yields on older lands also are declining, owing to soil erosion and depletion. Therefore, a successful program of increased production must offset this decline. Irrigation is one of the best possibilities, but it must be recognized as a long-range solution. A way must also be found to keep government programs sufficiently economical so that the rural farmer can afford this type of agricultural improvement.

Chapter 12
Rural Mechanization

The Filipinos are very interested in the mechanization of their agriculture, and American manufacturing firms are doing their best to make equipment available in the islands. At present most farms are too small to adopt mechanization on a large scale effectively. The size of the average farm is nearly ten acres, but about half are less than five acres, and these account for a fourth the total farm land. Table 9 gives details about the size of farms. The farm of the Philippines is larger than in most other parts of the Orient, and perhaps the islands permit the use of mechanization better than any other Oriental country. The development of a program of mechanization has many challenges and will not be easy to carry through to effective long-run operation. Besides the size of farm holdings, the seasonal wetness of the flat-land rice fields, the hilly nature of much of the farm land, the high cost of imported equipment, the very small working capital of the average farmer, and the scarcity of mechanically educated farmers are all problems that confront mechanization.

Small-Farm Economy

There are more than 1,700,000 individual farms in the Philippines, with the average size, as said before, of ten acres.[90] Of these a good 400,000 are less than 2.5 acres each. More than 500,000 range between 2.5 and 5.0 acres each. At least 575,000 farms fall into the group of 5.0 to 12.3 acres. About 200,000 farms measure from 12.3 to 50.0 acres and there are nearly 22,000 farms more than 50.0 acres in area. Of the total number of farmers, roughly half own their farms outright. Owner-operated and manager-operated farms account for about two-thirds of the land in farms. Owner farms tend to be a little larger than tenant farms, whereas manager-operated farms are the very large ones. Partly owned farms in areas of frontier settlement average larger than owned farms, but this is not true in older settled regions. In such cases they normally are composed of an owned piece too small to provide full support, and a separate piece that may include some pasture or forest land.

Since not all the average farm is cultivated, the above figures are not too valuable. The cultivated part of the owner-operated farms is 5.95 acres, for the partly owned farm 5.75 acres, for the tenant farm 5.50 acres, and that for the manager-operated farm 218.1 acres. It is fairly obvious that if these averages were exact figures, only the managed farms would be potential places for mechanization of any important sort, and that mechanization applicable to five-acre farms would have to be both simple and cheap. But manager-operated farms number not more than 2,000 and would not present much of a potential for a mechanization program or a market for farm equipment firms.

From these figures, the potential of mechanization for existing farms can be estimated roughly. Under usual circumstances it perhaps is the farm of 12.3 acres and more that offers opportunity for the use of some kind of machinery. Including the last two size categories, there are approximately 225,000 farms more than 12.3 acres in area. Not all of them, of course, will have their full surface in cultivation, so the mechanized potential at first must be a smaller total. Just what this figure might be is hard to say without access to the detailed census data. One might estimate that perhaps 175,000 farms now have the first requirement of mechanization—a cultivated area of several acres to which modern machinery could be applied to some extent. It has been a frequent rule of thumb in the Philippines to encourage purchase of a tractor only if an area of some 250 acres were in cultivation, but smaller machinery can

Table 9

DISTRIBUTION OF FARMS BY SIZE, 1939

	Province	Number of farms	Farms less than 2.5 acres	Farms between 2.5–5.0 acres	Farms between 5.0–12.3 acres	Farms between 12.3–50.0 acres	Farms more than 50 acres
1	Batanes	1,724	742	541	385	56	0
2	Abra	13,329	6,063	4,290	2,543	415	18
3	Cagayan	36,561	5,835	12,515	14,586	3,419	206
4	Ilocos Norte	31,234	14,805	12,025	4,072	304	28
5	Ilocos Sur	27,163	11,914	9,790	5,055	397	7
6	Isabela	32,719	3,052	10,070	13,076	5,727	894
7	La Union	25,739	10,568	9,003	5,521	641	6
8	Mountain	36,127	21,554	8,473	4,910	1,095	95
9	Nueva Viscaya	10,114	1,408	4,310	3,876	601	19
10	Bataan	6,305	1,426	1,858	2,178	783	60
11	Batangas	50,316	10,065	16,178	20,301	4,097	426
12	Bulacan	36,014	5,120	13,480	15,480	1,909	25
13	Cavite	22,463	2,310	6,926	10,278	1,858	91
14	Laguna	25,720	3,820	6,113	10,494	4,949	344
15	Nueva Ecija	78,319	4,921	15,116	48,668	9,156	458
16	Pampanga	23,628	2,468	3,469	12,029	5,461	201
17	Pangasinan	86,615	23,454	30,969	28,065	4,016	111
18	Quezon	52,874	5,156	12,695	20,699	13,404	920
19	Rizal	14,149	3,808	4,962	4,468	838	73
20	Tarlac	28,651	2,607	6,891	15,149	3,897	107
21	Zambales	12,165	3,275	4,594	3,649	582	65
22	Albay	31,913	5,725	9,681	10,817	4,995	695
23	Camarines Nor	10,011	792	2,357	3,912	2,718	233
24	Camarines Sur	35,822	5,610	9,998	12,345	7,668	1,202
25	Catanduanes	12,348	2,556	3,674	4,492	1,497	129
26	Sorsogon	31,688	3,993	9,258	11,923	5,862	652
27	Antique	23,662	6,153	8,101	7,380	1,920	108
28			21,??5	20,449	16,501	4,097	426

No.	Province						
31	Iloilo	66,915	9,137	20,815	29,982	5,627	515
32	Leyte	100,794	23,574	35,789	33,182	7,713	546
33	Marinduque	9,931	1,196	2,342	3,825	2,390	178
34	Masbate	17,723	1,488	4,035	7,172	4,454	638
35	Mindoro	16,271	1,030	3,373	6,617	4,537	714
36	Negros Occ.	35,896	7,529	11,676	10,969	4,818	1,904
37	Negros Or.	47,440	20,971	15,823	8,316	1,988	342
38	Palawan	11,304	6,085	2,513	1,501	949	256
39	Romblon	14,521	1,482	3,469	6,275	1,944	114
40	Samar	63,388	10,572	18,001	24,481	9,593	547
41	Agusan	12,072	526	2,519	5,591	2,349	227
42	Bukidnon	6,561	307	1,198	2,666	1,718	672
43	Cotabato	25,018	1,818	6,037	9,096	6,898	1,269
44	Davao	26,251	1,145	4,193	9,463	9,953	1,497
45	Lanao	24,529	1,569	6,673	11,179	4,630	478
46	Misamis Occ.	25,650	4,775	9,482	9,057	2,155	181
47	Misamis Or.	22,521	2,857	6,412	8,640	4,083	529
48	Surigao	28,982	2,771	7,931	13,084	5,031	165
49	Zamboanga	32,877	3,051	7,874	10,979	9,185	1,789
50	Sulu	20,384	4,079	6,665	7,081	2,306	253
	Totals	1,634,726	368,903	489,053	565,060	190,954	20,756

SOURCE: *Philippine Census*, 1939.

well be used on smaller farms. If such an area were to be the lower limit for mechanization it would apply only to a few really large farms, many of which already have some machinery.

The motor truck seldom enters directly into agriculture, for rarely do Filipino farmers own trucks as do American farmers. There probably are about 2,500 tractors in the islands today, but not all of them are in good operating condition. Most of these are postwar acquisitions, many being surplus army equipment. That means that only a small percentage of the large farms have mechanical power available. Many of the tractors are in Mindanao. Compared with the draft carabao population of perhaps a million, the number of tractors is not yet very impressive. And that volume is in the hands of upper class or well-to-do farmers who can afford it. The real shortage in power lies among the small farmers who cannot afford animals.

There are several additional questions to be asked, however, before one can be assured of the basic number of farms to which mechanization may be applied. What are the fields like and are there little patches on different levels? Is some of the land, if not in terraces, too steep for normal farm equipment? Does a farm consist of several separated holdings, as is usual in other parts of the Orient? Does the farm consist of wet rice land, all dry farm land, or two different types of land, each of which could call for different basic equipment?

No easy answer can be given to any of these questions, but some indications are possible. Terracing of rice fields exists in very few areas of the islands to an extent that would prevent the use of mechanical equipment. In the scattered spots in which terracing does occur it is in small patches and on farms of a size that in any case would preclude the use of mechanical equipment. The one real terraced area, northern Luzon, is not adaptable to mechanization in the ordinary sense, but it represents only a small part of the island farm landscape. Many larger farms do include some hill land, and much of this is too steep for mechanical equipment. For the most part, these steep surfaces should not be cleared, plowed, or cropped anyway. Quite a few of the larger farms, on the other hand, have a sizable area of arable ground well suited to mechanized agriculture.

Many middle-size farms and many of the partly owned farms consist of two or more separated pieces of land. Probably a few larger farms are divided also, but private land ownership in the islands has too short a history for the full complexities of divided holdings to have developed, as in some parts of the mainland Orient. Most of the larger farms were acquired in one piece and, except for the few great estates that have been broken up, have remained in one piece.

The last question is more difficult. In the Central Plain of Luzon most large farms have uniform land-use patterns, some for rice, some for sugar. On the island of Negros both sugar and a food crop such as rice or corn are found, but often in large acreage. In the Davao area of Mindanao, many of the abacá farms are of a size permitting mechanization, though the type of equipment needed is different than on other farms. Throughout the whole southern half of the islands there are some large coconut farms, again calling for particular equipment. In some areas the combinations of rice with coconut, corn, abacá, tobacco, or other crop patterns will be troublesome in mechanizing.

Where the rice crop is of the upland variety, however, it resembles any other dry-land crop and presents no problems of a special nature to the farmer interested in machinery. Wet rice land, particularly when it can be well irrigated, poses special problems. The farmer needs a different equipment to operate a wet rice farm than is required on other farms. And he needs equipment different than that so far available. There are many large rice farms scattered over the islands; most are lowland farms. Many of the farmers do not formally irrigate, but take advantage of any water coming naturally onto the fields. This creates the problem of the muddy field for the mechanizer. As irrigation systems grow, the special equipment problem will grow also.

Certainly at present, island agricultural economy is chiefly small-farm economy. Clearly, there are many farms that physically will not permit the use of complex power machinery in agriculture.

However, something has already been done on some of these farms and results will continue to appear and to add to the productive volume. The few farmers who now are mechanized will be demonstrators. Present island rural economy sets one group of limits for the currently cultivated landscape, but that agricultural economy is dynamic and expanding. In the direction of detailed oriental garden culture there is little chance for significant mechanical applications, whereas in a moderate-size, unified farm landscape the chances of expanding mechanization with the expansion of agriculture are substantial.

At present one cannot be sure in which direction Philippine agricultural economy is moving. In 1903 there were approximately 90,000 farms, or 11.1 per cent, more than 12.3 acres in area. In 1939 the census return indicated some 211,000 farms more than 12.3 acres in area, or 12.3 per cent. In 1903 farms less than 5.0 acres numbered about 573,000 or 70.4 per cent, and in 1939 they numbered but 858,000 or 52.5 per cent. This would indicate a move away from the very small farms, but only if the 1903 census data are fully trustworthy. The averages of farm and cultivated area have both gone up slightly, if the 1903 figures are accurate.

Other Aspects of the Problem

Plows, harrows, and tractors are not the whole measure of mechanization, and physical factors of fields are not the entire problem confronting those sponsoring the mechanization program. There is a wide variety of issues to be considered. The whole subject of mechanization still is rather new in most parts of the islands, though individual pieces of equipment, as regional curiosities, have been at work for a good many years.

A primary problem confronting the Filipino farmer is cost. The carabao, whether native or imported, is his chief item of cost and averages between $100 and $150 for an adult animal in good condition. Many a small farmer cannot today afford to buy or keep a carabao, but he cannot properly operate his farm without some draft power. Data on the distribution of carabao are presented in map 8. Most of the farmer's present equipment and tools are relatively cheap. Some can be homemade, with the purchase of a few iron parts to combine with wood. Too simple equipment hinders production. However, the small farmer with a low annual income, who often is either in debt or just making ends meet, cannot afford even simple equipment. The owners of farms of a size to justify the use of machinery cannot afford to buy much costly imported equipment but have almost no other recourse if they are to mechanize at all.

The cost factor affects all farmers. The owner, in theory, should be able to borrow money on his land with which to finance the purchase of machinery, his increased yields later paying for his investment. But the land title difficulty, described above, prevents the majority of farm owners using land as security for loans. No creditable financial institution will lend money on property without clear title. This blocks constructive expansion or forces owners into the dangerous hands of private moneylenders. Little mechanization will come through that type of financing. The government Agricultural Machinery and Equipment Corporation was set up in the immediate postwar period and assigned the task of spreading further mechanization through an installment-purchase program. Some success has attended its operations, but the main job still remains. Among tenant farmers, possibly excepting some renters of large acreage units, there is very little prospect of mechanization, since a goodly number of tenant farmers are regularly in debt to their landlords. Nonencouragement of mechanization among tenant farmers seems to be a part of government policy at present.

A second problem that is acute and serious, affecting the whole trend toward mechanization, is the lack of "know-how." This shows up in improper selection and use of equipment, and also in the failure of maintenance. Equipment that works well on an American farm is not necessarily effective in Mindanao or southern Luzon. Without assistance, manufacturers have not been able, for the limited island market, to develop special equipment suited to the Philippines. Early efforts in mechanization, between 1910 and 1920, employed powerful but heavy equipment in field preparation. These were in a measure successful on sugar-cane lands but failed for other uses. Too heavy and massive equipment probably never will succeed in the islands. The best chances lie with light, adaptable machinery with simple operating and maintenance requirements.

In a region of small farms and possibly mixed and separated holdings, one might expect that coöperative use of implements would be effective. On paper it is. But the Filipino is an individualist who so far has not taken well to various aspects of the coöperative movement. Poor management, the reason often given, may or may not be wholly responsible for the failure of coöperative marketing, purchasing, or equipment pools. But if these have not worked well in old and stable rural areas, they do even less well on the frontier. As one agricultural officer in Mindanao said to me: "I might have a fighting chance in getting four or five neighbors to pull together if they were old friends from the same home region. But around here it normally would mean asking men from northern Luzon, Panay, Bohol, and Leyte to get together, and on such an issue as a piece of farm equipment that would be impossible."

In the face of failure among private groups, there now is under trial a program of government equipment pools. Tractors, plows, harrows, levelers, and seeders are the items first selected for the pools. This program has been on paper for several years but has not yet had a real trial. The first efforts necessarily will be small, and the best methods of handling such pools must be learned. Much will depend upon the choice of equipment, its availability, and the briefing given the operators when the machinery goes out on the job. Once established, mowers, winnowing machines, rice hullers and threshers, trucks, and portable engines could well be added to provincial pools. Present government policy looks toward increasing mechanization in new settlement areas where government aid in land clearing as well as in later cultivation will be part of the settlement program.

It may be that wet rice growing will be the last segment of island agriculture to be farmed effectively by mechanization, beyond the present small development on some of the very large estates. No equipment now made is successful in wet rice culture as it is prac-

166

ticed in the Far East. Dry-land farming of rice, corn, coconut, abacá, tobacco, sweet potatoes, fruit, and other minor crops can be furthered by equipment. Field preparation, planting, cultivating, harvesting, transporting, and processing equipment will vary for different crops. For these crops, on the larger farms now in cultivation and on those that will be established, mechanization will increase. For this kind of agriculture, the technical problems of making equipment work are less difficult than in the wet rice fields. In the latter, the increasing development of irrigation at once poses the question of which will win out in the contest for regional control: occidental mechanized agriculture or oriental hoe culture.

Many Filipinos are aware that American rice growers now profitably compete with them, and that their corn and coconut production is relatively low. They know that one factor in American supremacy is equipment, but they do not know what kind of equipment they need on their own farms, nor how to acquire it. Further, they are not sure how mechanical equipment will help them, since as farmers they already suffer from underemployment. They wonder if mechanical equipment will save more than time, of which they already have too much during many months of the year.

It would seem, therefore, that mechanization of rural agriculture must go hand in hand with other rural programs if it is to be at all successful. The rural farmer needs greater productivity from his land; he needs education and other services; he needs equipment that will enable him to accomplish more work in his rural environment; but he also needs sources of occupation and income beyond those now provided by agriculture if his year is to be full and his standard of living really lifted.

Chapter 13

PLANT AND ANIMAL BREEDING

IN SOME parts of the islands the destructive results of wild animal and bird pests outweigh the constructive contribution of domestic animals and fowls. And in large areas weed pests, grasses, and shrub growth plus plant diseases barely permit the farmer a subsistence return for his efforts at crop growing. This should not be true in a productive and highly progressive agricultural economy. Admittedly controls over many agricultural pests and diseases are not yet known, but in these matters the islands are not keeping pace with many other parts of the world, and the island struggle for advancement and a higher standard of living is handicapped. Plant breeding has been more productive in other regions than in the Philippines. Some progress is being made in the islands, but greater efficiency and development are needed.

Island Plant and Animal History

There are only a few important domestic plants native to the islands, out of an extremely numerous wild flora. There are more than 8,000 species of flowering plants native to the islands, of which more than 1,000 are orchids. There are some 3,000 species of trees that grow to merchantable timber size, of which perhaps three-fourths belong to the Dipterocarp group. Also there are many shrubs, vines, and plants which contribute useful products. Of the small number of native domesticated plants, abacá is perhaps the most important. The lumbang is a minor, though important, nut-bearing tree, a producer of paint and varnish material with a long history of use.

Of the food products, some of the bananas, the jack-fruit, the lanzones, the pili nut, the sago palm, the durian, the calamondin, and the mangosteen are well-liked edible fruits that are widely used. Some of these are native to the Philippine Islands and were domesticated there. Others were native to a large part of south-eastern Asia, including the Philippines, and may have been domes-ticated almost anywhere in the region. The group of roots usually termed yams (which includes a number of odd-colored ones not used in the Occident), and the root and leaf plants generally labeled taro but called gabi in the islands are also probably native to some parts of the Philippines, as well as to much of southeastern Asia. Beyond these, of course, are lesser native plants used for food, for medicine, for housing materials, or as sources of fibers and rattans. Some are domesticated plants and some remain wild plants from which products are gathered as needed.

The more important of the agricultural crops of the islands have been introduced during long centuries. Rice and coconut were brought in at an early date from more than a single source. Many varieties of rice came from outside, and others have been hybrid-ized in the islands. The mango and sugar cane came later, but well before the arrival of the Spaniards. The pomelo and some of the oranges were brought from the Asiatic mainland. Additional vari-eties of bananas were probably brought in on a number of occasions from one or another part of southeastern Asia. Perhaps early settlers also brought new varieties of plants that already were native to some part of the Philippines. Other than strictly food plants were introduced at various early dates. Probably the kapok tree is not native to the islands, but came from the mainland of southeastern Asia. Some bamboos are native but those today most important in housing and general use came in during a moderately early period, before the arrival of the Spaniards.

The Spaniards introduced a number of new crops during the late sixteenth and seventeenth centuries. Corn, sweet potato, cassava, and tobacco were the major items; others were the papaya, sapote (called chico in the islands), pineapple, guava, tamarind, sugar apple, cashew nut, peanut, arrowroot, coffee, cacao, maguey, indigo, and a few minor crops. As these gradually spread over the islands, they made significant additions to the basic and auxiliary food patterns and general economy. Other crops were introduced unsuccessfully, several being the more common mid-latitude crops, such as wheat, barley, apples, and grapes.

The American period has not added many crops to island agriculture. Rubber was introduced with the hope that it might spread over the vacant lands of the southern islands as it did in Malaya and the Indies at about the same period. But land policy, the scarcity of labor, and the Filipino fear of plantation exploitation have prevented rubber from becoming more than a minor agricultural product. The avocado may have been a Spanish importation but most of its spread has been during the American period, and it sometimes has been termed an American introduction. New and improved varieties of older crops have been brought in frequently to add to the vegetable category. Onions, cabbage, eggplant, strawberries, and assorted green vegetable and truck crops have been newly introduced to such areas of the islands as are suitable to their growth. Plant breeding and variety improvement have been carried on with fairly effective results by the various stations of the Bureau of Plant Industry.

The pig was the earliest useful domesticated animal brought to the islands, perhaps a number of times by immigrants from different sources. The water buffalo came in at an early date, again possibly several times, and the island name for native stock now is carabao. The chicken is native to southeastern Asia. Perhaps wild fowl were numerous in the islands when agricultural immigrants first arrived, but certainly they were brought in repeatedly by many different groups. Pre-Spanish Chinese references mention horses and elephants in the islands, but at the time of the Spanish arrival there were no elephants and few if any horses. The Chinese had brought in the duck and perhaps the goose and had taught the Filipinos the culture of both. The only other domestic animal in the islands when the Spaniards came was the goat, scattered over the islands in small numbers.

The Spaniards made numerous efforts at animal introduction. They repeatedly brought horses, donkeys, cattle, sheep, and new stocks of goats, water buffalo, chickens, ducks, and geese. Some of these were brought from the New World and some from China. The donkeys and sheep never succeeded in the islands and their number has remained very small. Horses down-breed and become smaller in the islands, and new stocks must be introduced frequently. Consequently their number also has never become very large, nor have they been particularly popular. American action has been confined to introducing improved breeds of older animal and fowl stocks. Brahman cattle from India, American horse and chicken stocks, water buffalo from several Asiatic sources have been imported from time to time. The distribution of carabao is shown on map 8 and the statistics on the animal population in table 6.

Reviewing the pattern of introductions, one finds that over the centuries a large group of domestic plants and a number of animals have been imported into the islands to round out the agricultural economy. It is a restricted economy because of the near-tropical climate, too warm and too wet for successful acclimation for many of the mid-latitude crops and animals, but hospitable to most of those from other moist tropical and subtropical regions. The list has grown steadily larger. But a difficulty exists in that many of the introductions were not scientifically selected. Hence island stocks, whether plants or animals, were not always the most productive. Some have acclimated themselves to the extent of hybridizing within local island regions, developing local varieties. Nevertheless, they are less productive than they should be in the advancing agricultural world of today. Since they cannot be wiped out and new and improved varieties substituted, extensive breeding campaigns must be carried out which will eventually replace the older, poorer varieties with new and better ones. In a country like the United States private farmer initiative, with some help from government agents and the active encouragement by seed companies or animal breeders, is enough to advance this matter. The process does not operate so well in the Philippines, and has barely begun to affect the over-all picture. In only a few sections of the economy, as sugar cane and pineapple, are real strides being made.

Enemies and Diseases

An inventory of the diseases of plants and animals in the Philippines would produce a long list. Serious damage comes from a small number of diseases, however, and one can pick out a few causes that account for the largest share of the total damage. There are few accurate data on crop and animal losses in any part of the Orient, though a frequent generalization has been made that crop losses rather commonly range from 15 to 30 per cent of the total potential production. Comparable losses in the United States are normally less than 7 per cent of the total crop.

In the Philippines, estimate of losses from all types of destructive causes among plant crops might be about 15 to 20 per cent, though there are no accurate data with which to back up this figure. Certainly it is too high for some areas where crops are under excellent control. But against these regions must be balanced other areas in which losses may run almost to the whole crop in a given season. There are recognizable regional distinctions in losses that sometimes accord with the type of crop and sometimes only with the patterns of occupation and the reach of government services.

Rice, the major crop, suffers from a number of diseases and pests, of which one of the most serious is the rice-stem borer, but even more destructive are birds and rats.[100] The rice-stem borer is found almost all over the islands, and Mindanao shows a concentration of damage from birds and rats that sometimes, on the frontier, causes complete crop losses. Both bird and rat populations are large on the frontiers and, as the harvest period approaches—often delayed by labor shortages—the birds and rats simply take over the fields and harvest the crop themselves. Wild pigs in some areas cause serious damage, in Negros Island particularly.

The other chief food crop, corn, suffers commonly from a borer that penetrates the stalks and kills the plants. Some years the first crop may almost escape, but the second and third crops often will fail to produce their seed equivalent. When it is possible to stagger planting seasons to miss the annual peak periods of borer activity, serious losses may be avoided, but such shifts may in themselves reduce the total yield. Throughout the Visayan Islands where corn is a common crop, annual losses from the corn borer are extremely heavy. Wild pigs and rats often make heavy inroads upon corn crops around the fringes of solidly settled areas.

Fungus disease, known as mosaic disease, spread by infected planting stock immediately after the last war, is one of the factors responsible for the currently decreased production of abacá in southeastern Mindanao. In earlier years the same disease had wiped out the plantings of whole producing regions, as in Cavite Province early in the present century. Since cures previously were very uncertain, control lay only in destruction of infected stock and supervision of the planting of new stock. Recent work has improved control and cure possibilities. Closely related diseases also affect bananas in much the same way that mosaic disease damages abacá.

Sugar cane is attacked by stalk borers and by virus diseases, with regional centers of crop damage. Similarly, tobacco is affected by serious virus diseases which show up regionally. Coconut trees are less affected by major diseases or pests, but suffer a variety of ailments nevertheless. Other major and minor crops have both pests and diseases to which they are subject. New stocks of seeds, plants, roots, or tubers brought from other parts of the world are sometimes very susceptible to island diseases that were not common in their home regions. The locust is a pest not restricted to consumption of any one plant and has been one of the chief causes of crop losses.

Among the animals the most serious disease in the past has been rinderpest, but anthrax and hoof-and-mouth disease have also taken their tolls. These three diseases primarily affect cattle, are less serious among carabao, and rather mild among other animals. Hog cholera often has killed the swine population of entire regions. All kinds of animals newly introduced to improve stocks are normally highly susceptible to these and to other local animal diseases.

The worst enemy of the animal population, however, is man.

There never have been enough animals in the islands to provide the requisite volume of draft power, transport energy, leather products, and meat supply. The unsettled conditions of the Spanish-American transition period reduced the numbers of cattle and horses. In part this was the result of rinderpest and other diseases, but in part man was responsible. Again during the Japanese occupation of the Philippines, every component in the animal and fowl population decreased markedly. Cattle and chickens suffered the greatest relative losses, the former decreasing by two-thirds of their previous total and the latter by five-eighths. Most other animals and fowls were reduced roughly by one-half. It will be several years before the animal population can be restored to its prewar size.

Another major enemy is the typhoon. This tropical storm, sweeping the whole northern half of the islands several times every year and occasionally sweeping off course over some part of the southern islands, accounts for large losses in rice, corn, abacá, coconut, fruit, and root crops as well as damaging minor crops and causing losses other than in agriculture. The most severe storms normally come during the late autumn, often catching rice and corn harvests still in the field. Damage to other crops largely consists in breaking down trees and plants and in knocking off green fruits, so that succeeding harvests are lessened or delayed.

Cogon grass (*Imperata cylindrica*) and talahib grass (*Saccharum spontaneum*) are among the worst enemies of crop plants, forage animals, and the farmer. Particularly cogon grass has followed in the footsteps of the shifting cultivator, quickly covering many of his garden patches with a thick rank growth that defies further cultivation and the early encroachment of the forest. Today the same process of spreading cogon, talahib, red top (*Tricholaena rosa*), kulape (*Paspalum conjugatum*), bagokbok (*Andropogon spp.*), and similar weedy grasses is going on in the wake of the caingin cultivator. The permanent settler has had to clear grass-covered lands and struggle against later inroads of these grasses upon his land. Today about a fifth of the total surface of the Philippines is in grass that serves little real use. The new growth that appears after the grass is freshly burned off is eaten by cattle and other domestic animals only for a few weeks every year, but, by and large, these rank tropical grasses are poor animal browse.

There are many other plants and shrubs that must be termed weeds, from the point of view of the farmer. One that infests the rice fields of many parts of the islands is called tayoc-tayoc (*Eleocharis spp.*) in the Visayas, a sedge-like plant growing just a little taller than rice. It has a minor use in basketry, but the volume needed for this purpose could easily be produced elsewhere than in the rice fields. In parts of the Visayas the lantana (*Lantana camara*) is now a real problem, and its import into the islands is forbidden. In southern Negros, Cebu, Bohol, and Siquijor at least, various of the lantanas cover much of the arable land and the open spaces, quickly encroaching upon cultivated fields. The mimosa has become an unwanted weed, and there are many others that are nuisances in field areas, gardens, or merely along the roads.

The Breeding Program

The Spaniards had accomplished some improvements in agriculture and had started a few experimental farms. They had repeatedly introduced new stocks of animals, had made simple efforts in pest control, and had begun to bring in new stocks of established plants. This program developed late in the nineteenth century because a number of plant epidemics had killed off some of their introductions, such as coffee. No more than a bare start could be attributed to the efforts of the Spaniards, however.

A Bureau of Agriculture was one of the early establishments of the new American government, soon after 1900. The Bureau gradually expanded its operations and organization, separating the activities for plants and for animals. Each unit now has become a Bureau of the Department of Agriculture and Natural Resources. Both the Bureau of Plant Industry and the Bureau of Animal Husbandry have long-range programs for the improvement of rural economy, and since the early years of the century have introduced extensive new stocks of both plants and animals into the islands.

In the earlier period inadequate personnel and token budgets prevented the various programs achieving their ends. It is amazing how much has been accomplished, but this still has never been enough. Gradually experiment stations for field crop, garden, and orchard plantings were established in every province. Each station has a nursery, and the provincial staff is engaged in a program of education of the public, technical farmer assistance, experimental work, and the handling of literature, seed, and planting materials. Both curative and preventive disease, pest, and enemy control work should be a major part of each provincial program.

The Bureau of Animal Industry has somewhat the same type of program, with fewer animal breeding stations and centers, but it places more emphasis upon disease control among animals. The latter aspect has been a highlight of the good work done throughout the islands by the Bureau. Both bureaus have engaged in the import of new stocks from selected parts of the world, and in the hybridizing of new varieties and breeds suited to the Philippines. Locations of breeding stations are shown in map 11.

In general the breeding programs of both bureaus have been excellent. The major criticism is that the program of neither bureau has been large enough. Work along these lines has been better than in some parts of the world, but less productive than programs of countries with which the islands must compete for future export markets. At the inception of American control, general agricultural conditions in the islands were behind those of a number of tropical regions which were becoming important producers of agricultural exports. The islands should have been catching up with those more advanced areas, whereas in fact they have made little relative headway.

American administration set up a skeleton framework for an enlightened program of aid, but never gave the program the budget and personnel support it should have had. Although the individual programs have expanded over the years, they have hardly kept up with, let alone led, rural development. In the future, if island economy is to develop properly, increases will have to be made. There remains much to accomplish in increasing agricultural production. Since range of the several programs seems fairly adequate, one may suggest that what is actually needed is an increased volume of new planting stocks and of animal breeding stock, with a more rapid and effective distribution of those stocks.

The two bureaus mentioned are not, of course, the only agencies at work in this field. A certain amount of experimental work goes on among the large private and corporation farmers. The College of Agriculture, University of the Philippines, has worked valiantly in training personnel, developing new techniques, and breeding new plant and animal strains. In the United States, however, there are literally hundreds of groups working in these same directions, including many universities, state, federal, and county agencies, seed and livestock companies, and private operators. The total effort expended in this direction in the Philippines is less than demanded by the rural economy at present and in the near future.

Agricultural agents are only advisory. They must cajole, coax, propagandize, or suggest. They have little authority and no power to force public action. There are problems that never will be adequately solved in that way alone. The agricultural agents need to be backed by administrative authority and law, if they are to execute programs that can produce results in a reasonably short time.

There has been some attempt to acclimate certain plants, to broaden the range of commodity production, and to produce at home some items now imported. An example is the experimental work to make jute a home product to serve the sacking need of the islands. This work so far has achieved no real success. It is my belief that not enough experimental work has been done with the large number of wild and semiwild plants native to the islands, in the search for a good fiber. Such a plant as the anabó (*Abroma augusta* and *Abroma fastuosa*)—native, well adapted to island conditions, an old and long used fiber plant—would seem a better prospect for a local sacking source than would jute. In other lines there are many plants of traditional uses and values not properly exploited today other than by small local groups. A recanvass of these should produce some commercially practical ones to satisfy domestic and possibly commercial export needs.

Chapter 14

THE PROBLEM OF RURAL HEALTH

DOMESTIC water supplies and epidemic diseases are under better control in the Philippines than elsewhere in the Orient, with the possible exception of Japan.[101] There really is a marked contrast between the islands and some mainland areas in the matter of epidemics and in public psychology about exposure to disease. Cholera, typhoid, typhus, and plague are not the public scourges that they are in parts of mainland southeastern Asia. Comparatively speaking, the Philippines shows some fairly impressive figures on medical facilities, equipment, and personnel (table 10). It has some good medical training programs and a public interest in the medical profession. If one were able to separate figures by regions, however, it would be clear that not all parts of the islands are so fortunate in their medical services or in their general health. And certainly the islands have not yet achieved the maximum health standards possible for their environment or their economy.

The Environment of Disease

The climate of the Philippines is tropical and near-tropical, with amelioration of conditions in the upland parts of the islands. This means that temperatures exist that are favorable for the development of many of the agents and vectors of disease. High temperatures stimulate the growth of bacteria and insects, increasing the likelihood of infection of skin and surface wounds. High nighttime temperatures tend to make people careless of exposure during sleeping hours, and this, too, increases susceptibility to various diseases.

Notwithstanding these facts of temperature, many conditions making for disease that normally are attributed to climate are not actually the product of weather and climate. Some of these conditions really pertain to living habits and customs that are part and parcel of a culture and are quite independent of climate. Others are the results of living standards produced by poverty and ignorance in an economy out of adjustment, factors also quite independent of climate. Still others should be attributed to vegetation and surface water. Regional differences in rainfall and in temperature are, of course, partly responsible for these differences in plant cover and surface water supply, and to this extent climate is indirectly responsible.

Some combinations of features conducive to disease are chiefly rural, whereas others are primarily urban. The disease-incidence data for the city of Manila give quite another picture than would those for frontier settlements. More than this, the recoveries from particular diseases, as against the deaths from the same illnesses would show up in very different ratios in the two extremes of the country. The wet, heavily forested region is host to certain types of disease agents and vectors. The upland grass plateau has others, but perhaps the total is less. The jungle lowland is the home of a large and still different group of contributors. The swamps and marshlands will annoy man with diseases of one sort; the well-drained upland farms with those of another. The continuously moist landscape of northeastern Mindanao presents conditions for disease that are somewhat different than those of the landscape of northwestern Luzon which is seasonally wet and dry. In other words, the Philippine environment of disease is a broad one with many local and regional variations. This is inevitable in a multiple island world of varied physical, cultural, social, and economic conditions, though this theory can be pushed too far in small areas.

I have not been able to obtain sufficiently detailed regional data to carry this analysis through to proved conclusion. Effective studies in medical geography have not yet been undertaken in any part of southeastern Asia that enable one properly to examine the relation of disease to physical environment or to distinguish the factors of cultural environment that are important. More than simple country-wide hospital data or civil registrar's cause-of-death data are needed for the type of study suggested here. Certainly such a study could yield useful data as to ways and means by which the health problem of the islands could be approached.

The disease list of the islands includes a wide variety that belong both to the Orient and to the tropics in general. The standard procedure of dealing with these is much the same in the Philippines as elsewhere. There are, undoubtedly, a few minor illnesses that are peculiar to the islands and do not occur elsewhere as important problems. The Filipinos can be thankful that certain of the more serious oriental diseases are not deeply embedded in the local environment. In the past, many epidemics have spread repeatedly to the islands, but few are endemic there.[102] Reference here is to cholera, plague, typhus, relapsing fever, and similar major diseases.

The absence of endemic homes for certain of the serious epidemic diseases means that the organized medical program of the country can be oriented toward standard procedures of prevention, with only an occasional minor emergency to deal with in terms of curative medicine and the arresting of epidemics. The lack of endemic homes for certain of the oriental diseases largely accounts for the healthful situation of the islands as compared to other parts of the Orient.

An important factor in the public health situation of the Philippines is the relatively advanced development of sanitation, both in technical achievement and in cultural practice. The use of the easily cleaned split-bamboo floor, the washing veranda, and the high standards of personal cleanliness—all are cultural practices of importance in health. The Filipino market gardener does not use night soil and urban wastes as fertilizer as a general practice. The fairly adequate sanitary disposal of night soil and sewage, except in certain Chinese quarters, is regular practice today.

Excellent domestic water systems are important elements in the health picture. Use of medical facilities is a psychological and practical factor of significance. In rural areas water systems, organized sewage disposal, medical facilities, and other less important aspects of preventive health control are not highly developed, but still are improvements over conditions in many parts of the Orient.

The Distribution of Diseases

Malaria is the most serious disease of the Philippines, a disease shared with the Orient and the tropics at large. It no longer is the leading killer of the islands, but its over-all effect on life and economy keeps it in the leading position. Today it is chiefly a disease of the rural countryside and the villages. The cities and towns have a relatively low incidence of malaria and few deaths compared to the rural frontiers. In the prewar period the total reached almost two million cases per year, with roughly 10,000 deaths. Immediately after the war the figures indicate an increase in malaria, the annual death total running about 20,000 in recent years.[103] Added to the death total is the resulting incapacity of people of all ages for varying periods each year.

The chief vector of malaria in the islands is the mosquito *Anopheles minimus,* though there are three other species that share some of the blame.[104] The preferred breeding grounds of *A. minimus* are shaded but clean running streams, though stagnant water sometimes is chosen and will serve if clean streams are not available. Rice fields are not important in the malarial mosquito-breeding picture. The old and long-settled lowland plains do not suffer seriously at present from malaria, though the disease is found everywhere in the island lowlands. The upland territories also do not suffer from malaria, the level of freedom varying in different parts of the islands and depending upon local conditions. Between 1,700 and 2,200 feet is about the level at which malaria dies out.

The regional distribution of malaria shows that newly cleared farmlands, caingin clearings, and forest-cutting zones along the edges of the forests, the jungles and the settlement frontier are the acute places of distress. The most serious areas are the foothill fringes, the deeper inland valleys, and the lower hill country below the ceiling level suggested above. And it is the first several years, under the poorest living conditions, which are the worst. As Pelzer has put it: "In such regions as the interior of Mindoro, Mindanao, or the foothills on both sides of the Cagayan Valley, the home-steaders are exposed on arrival to this disease at a time when they must work hard and live under pioneer conditions and their resist-ance is lowered, . . . Malaria is without doubt the greatest scourge of the homesteader who moves from the coastal plain into the hilly interior anywhere in the Philippines."[105]

The present government medical budget allows about $75,000 per year for this number one health problem of the islands. This is insufficient to make headway against the disease.[106] Some United States Army help was available in the years directly after the war, but not enough to allay the disease permanently. Malaria is one of the chief deterrents to the spread of the colonial settler over the remaining lands of the islands, where the malaria hazard must be faced during the first years.

The disease that currently seems to be the most serious in the islands, in number of deaths, is tuberculosis. It has been steadily increasing during several decades, now taking nearly 35,000 lives per year.[107] This is a serious disease in the cities, towns, and larger villages where overcrowding is found and where many are subject to malnutrition and lower standards of living, but it is doubtful if the effects of tuberculosis today are confined to the urban zones and their fringes. The political area of Manila, only two-thirds of the Manila metropolitan region but with almost half the urban popu-lation of the islands, accounts for more than 10 per cent of the annual tuberculosis death total.[108] Many of the smaller towns and large villages, where crowding and poorer living conditions are found among the more impoverished population, also will show a high frequency of the disease.

On the basis of data available it is impossible to delineate ac-curately the true distribution of tuberculosis or to determine what types of rural communities or regions are particularly hard hit by it. There are suggestions that it is relatively new to this part of the Orient, a disease which began to spread seriously only with population growth, overcrowding, and lowered economic levels where group resistance to any disease is relatively low.

Beriberi probably claims the second largest number of lives annually. This is a deficiency disease, a severe form of malnutrition that is particularly hard on young children. One of the primary causes for the widespread incidence and relatively high death rate of beriberi is the persistent practice of eating polished rice, without other vitamin-supplying foods. A large share of the total rice consumed in the islands is polished, including all that is imported to balance the island shortage. Eating polished rice is a wide-spread custom throughout the Orient, particularly in cities, towns, villages, and rural areas near cities and ports. And urban centers and fringes are the areas that today show the highest frequency of beriberi.

In the rural areas far from transport, in the hill country and on the settlement frontier, rice is normally home pounded. Pounding is a method of dehulling the rice which does not remove the germ or the vitamin and chemical-containing outer layer. In earlier periods all rice was pounded; milling and polishing are modern features accompanying the growth of industry. There is no question about the whiter, softer appearance and better taste of polished rice, and one can understand the preference for it. Other variable practices in washing and cooking rice may also lessen its food values.[109] Currently vitamin extracts, made from rice polishings, can be had to replace the milled-out values, but only the well-to-do can afford them. The total annual loss of lives through beriberi is about 25,000. During the war years its frequency increased markedly, to be followed by a slight decline within the last two or three years.

Pneumonia is a surprisingly widespread and common illness throughout the islands. Though the climate is near-tropical it displays a wide seasonal range of temperature, with marked diurnal ranges also. During the winter months bursts of mildly cool air, corresponding to the cold waves of United States weather, penetrate the islands and reach somewhat south of Manila. These are called cold waves in island terminology and, for a native or long-time resident, produce brisk weather and chilling nighttime tem-

Table 10

SELECTED PROVINCES, MEDICAL SERVICES, AND FACILITIES[a]

Province	Hospitals	Beds	Dispensaries	Puericulture centers	Drugstores	Physicians	Dentists	Pharmacists	Opticians	Registered nurses	Midwives	Population[b]
Abra	1	20	38	2	2	18	3	7	1	15	26	86,600
Agusan	2	36	58	5		17	3	8	1	12	41	126,400
Batanes			6			3				8	29	10,700
Bulacan	4	108	25	18	89	186	14	117	9	39	51	411,300
Catanduanes			7		1	1	1	2	1	5	24	112,100
Cebu	2	106	53	52	50	166	67	64	8	114	112	1,123,100
Cotabato	1	40	34	1	14	21	15	15	1	25	47	439,600
Davao	2	112	21	4	20	57	12	15	3	57	14	364,800
Laguna	2	65	29	17	98	107	66	95	3	43	36	321,200
Mindoro	2	34	18	5	17	26	10	17	1	16	24	167,700
Palawan	3	128	15		2	13	3	1	1	21	24	106,200
Rizal	33	2,571	33	26	177	315	126	203	21	171	101	673,000
Samar	1	20	44	3	10	28	22	15	2	21	20	757,200
Manila	23	3,708	6	34	549	589	247	80	26	?	?	983,900
Totals	120	9,922	1,245	533	2,017	3,460	1,520	1,972	161	1,936	3,390	19,234,100

[a] Data from *Facts and Figures about Economic and Social Conditions of the Philippines, 1946-1947*, Bureau of Census and Statistics, Manila, 1948.
[b] Data from 1948 Census, rounded off to hundreds, from *Special Bulletin No.1, Population of the Philippines, Oct. 1, 1948*, Bureau of Census and Statistics, Manila, 1948.

peratures. Contrasts in humidity in varying rainfall regions at different seasons of the year, plus the temperature ranges, cause variations in sensible temperatures and in reaction to exposure particularly during sleeping hours. Scanty data do not indicate any concentration of deaths from pneumonia, and it may be inferred that the illness is widely distributed. Inadequate rural medical and hospital facilities may cause a higher relative death rate in some rural areas than in regions with good facilities. The annual loss through this disease is about 25,000.

Among the other diseases costly of human lives are a number that call for brief comment. The several maladies and deficiency conditions affecting infants at birth and in the first year probably take between 25,000 and 30,000 annually. This is a figure higher than should prevail. Various forms of enteritis probably cost 15,000 lives per year. The dysenteries, on the other hand, are commonly believed to be less important in most parts of the islands, but insufficient diagnosis and inadequate statistical tabulation may well be responsible for this view. The enteritis-dysentery group of illnesses causes perhaps 25,000 deaths, also a figure higher than should occur, but relatively much lower than in most parts of the Orient.

Heart trouble of all types causes perhaps 10,000 deaths each year. Nephritis, measles, influenza, and meningitis are other diseases accounting for annual totals of several thousand. A host of minor illnesses, each one costing fewer lives than those mentioned, account for a large cumulative total. The number of deaths attributable to old age is significant and is growing each decade. It perhaps is 25,000 per year at present, out of an annual death total of 275,000.

Medical Services and Facilities

Selected data for the year 1947 are presented in table 10. They are not complete, and the current figures should be somewhat higher in most categories. They do indicate, however, that the islands have achieved a respectable standing in these matters compared with other parts of the Orient. The figures reveal that the islands have room for expansion of services, facilities, and personnel, particularly in certain parts of the country. The rural situation generally is not as good as it should be, and on the settlement frontier facilities and personnel are woefully lacking.

The islands had one hospital for every 160,000 people, and one bed for every 1,950 people in 1947 (table 10). The United States figures are roughly one hospital to 22,000 people, and one bed to every 85 people. Such islands as Catanduanes and Samar, however, are poorly served, with but one twenty-bed hospital for the two islands having a population of 875,000. Even the island of Cebu, with two hospitals of 106 beds for 1,125,000 people, really is no better off. Manila and Rizal Province together have 32 hospitals with more than 6,000 beds for more than 1,500,000 people, a much better ratio. Not included in these calculations, since they cannot be used for general medical services, are the nine leprosariums with their 2,835 beds.

Dispensaries are far more widely and evenly scattered, with one in almost every municipality center, and a few duplications. In 1947 there were approximately 1,200 municipality districts in the islands, and 1,245 dispensaries or rural health stations. But in almost every case the dispensary is located in the capital town, and in many cases this means that the rural population is out of touch with it. The Puericulture Center is an interesting public health development of the islands, designed to teach, spread, and further sanitation, hygiene, simple first aid knowledge, and such matters. These centers too, 533 in number, are located in the capital towns of the more developed regions where they do not establish contact with many of the areas most needing their services. There were more than 2,000 drugstores in 1947, but far too many of them were to be found within a few miles of Manila.

Today there is a satisfactory number of physicians, dentists, pharmacists, and nurses, the latter including midwives and registered nurses. Opticians are too few in number to service the population adequately. And in matters of distribution, too many people are not yet served at all by any of these trained personnel, but must depend upon folk medicine and home remedies. On the average, there is one medical person to 1,550 inhabitants for the islands as a whole, but admittedly this is deceptive.[110] Catanduanes in 1947 had

34 such personnel for 112,000 people, and Samar had 108 for about 750,000 people. Figures for Cotabato in 1947 were 124 personnel to some 440,000 people; for Davao, 157 to some 365,000; and for Agusan, 82 to about 125,000. Yet in all three of these provinces the larger towns and cities were the homes and offices for an unduly large share of the personnel, leaving the rural back country with its many frontier health problems far understaffed. Laguna province had a staff of 350 to look after 320,000 people, and Rizal had more than 900 personnel for some 675,000 people.

Since one of the problems facing the country as a whole is the spreading of surpluses from crowded areas into the reserve lands of the islands, the lack of health services in those underpopulated and reserve areas is one of the real handicaps to the leveling of population that must go with the realignment of Philippine life and economy.

Chapter 15
USING THE UPLANDS

MOST UPLAND farmers in the Philippines find themselves with a number of serious problems.[111] These cannot be solved simply through mechanization, irrigation development, or by expanding over the reserve lands of the islands. The farmers' predicament is sufficiently serious to tempt one to suggest that all presently cultivated land of the rough and hilly uplands be diverted to some other form of land use than crop growing. This, however, would be an unrealistic way out of a problem. The hilly landscapes that make up so much of the Philippines must be utilized to provide a progressive island economy.

It is perfectly true, of course, that many of the rougher upland tracts now being cultivated every year by sedentary farmers should be in protective forest or watershed. But there must be alternatives between the present laborious systems of cropping upland terrain and the ideal pattern of protective forestry. These alternatives will differ from region to region depending upon such cultural and natural variables as present population pressures, nearness to seaports and to urban settlements, transportation, elevation, climate, soils, and the severity of landforms.

Normal Agriculture

The upland farmer has several possibilities of combining crops and agricultural systems. It was suggested earlier that the northern

Luzon system involving meticulous terracing, hand labor, and rice-sweet potato crops did not seem worth further expansion in the Philippine uplands. However, the extended use of terracing in connection with soil erosion and with easier farming practice on sloping surfaces definitely deserves expanding. There is much territory to which protective terracing should be applied. It should partake of American "contour farming" rather than oriental "mosaic terrace gardening." This is a type of cultivation to be followed only in the uplands rather than in flat lowland plains, where it is less needed.

The caingin system as practiced almost everywhere in the island uplands is not worth maintaining. The first crop of a permanent colonial farmer on a new site, when he starts with but little equipment, may well resemble caingin cultivation, but his later efforts should be progressively better. In a lightly populated region in earlier times caingin cultivation served as a long-range rotation system of land use in which destructive effects were relatively insignificant in their impact on regional economy.

If field rotation on individual upland farms can be preserved, and a well-regulated system of maintenance practices developed, such a rejuvenated caingin culture actually could become both profitable and commendable. An important factor in such a change will be the prevention of simple land abandonment by individual farmers after cropping, without execution of the next step in the rotational sequence. Also important is the development of long-range rotational planting patterns suited to different upland landscapes. Without these several improvements caingin cultivation will remain seriously destructive. Such local programs will naturally take time, their execution will be difficult, and the fruits will be slow to appear, but they are vital steps in the improvement of upland economy.

Early man, by trial and error, devised two systems of land use which he applied to these uplands, caingin cultivation and detailed terracing. Modern man now must develop at least a third system which is better suited to modern economics than either of the earlier two. Certainly no concerted attack has yet been made upon the problems of this realm.

Rice, corn, sweet potatoes, abacá, and coconut are the main crops of the upland farmer. Rice is the preferred crop. The upland farmer persists in growing it in the face of serious obstacles. Rice yields are extremely poor in many parts of the uplands, often returning only fourfold. If a farmer is unlucky with rats, wild hogs, or birds he will harvest nothing. Of course, even on lands with much better yields such as seven- to tenfold, he may lose his crop to wild enemies. In the uplands rice is both a subsistence crop and a local barter crop when a surplus does exist. However, few areas growing upland rice can point to continued surpluses, though there are some lowland-upland margins on the colonial frontier in which surpluses are produced from freshly tilled lands.

Rice and corn, particularly, need study and development by the plant breeder and the pest expert working with the upland farmer specifically in mind. Coconut and abacá have elevation limits that prevent their use by many upland farmers. It seems certain that among the world's crop plants there must be many that would produce better returns than those now being grown. Vegetable gardening in certain highland localities indicates at least one alternative. Old cropping combinations among upland farmers must be replaced by new ones fitted to particular upland landscapes with a wide variety of micro-climatological situations. Some of the more useful lowland plants can be taken farther into the uplands by selective breeding. In some areas totally new crops must be sought. This program will require careful development and cannot be formulated and fully established in a season or two. So far little agricultural experiment work has been carried on primarily for the upland farmer.

There are a number of fiber plants used domestically in earlier periods of island history, and since neglected, whose possibility of revival should be explored by plant expert and farmer together. Beyond the volume of abacá produced for home use and export, the islands need large quantities of several kinds of fibers for domestic use, a need that will expand rather than diminish. There are several plants, such as the anabó mentioned earlier, that can be fitted into present cropping systems for the upland farmer and will produce a higher financial return per acre with less effort than some crops now being grown. Effort expended upon finding plants already adjusted to the island environment will be more rewarding than trying to acclimate some fiber plant, as jute, from another part of the world.

Animal culture in a tropical country faces handicaps not present in higher latitudes. Many of the rough and hilly landscapes of the islands now are grass-turfed, chiefly with cogon and talahib (*Imperata cylindrica* and *Saccharum spontaneum*) but occasionally with near relatives or similar types.[112] These grasses not only are hard for the crop grower to eradicate, but they are good animal fodder only during the first few weeks of growth. One may ask if the problem has been tackled effectively. With scientific killing of unwanted vegetation and replacement with better types, is the problem of cogon and talahib grass impossible for man to solve in this century? Could a concerted program spread widely a variety of better grasses, leafy shrubs, and leafy vines that would be less hard on the soil and more useful to domestic animals? Many rougher uplands could then be more productive as pastoral ranges than they are today, producing both for a draft animal market and for the domestic meat market.

In connection with the pasture use of some of the cooler uplands not now forested, the development of tree crops should be encouraged. Some of these, like coffee and cacao, are highly competitive and not likely candidates for successful export agriculture. However, both of these are in demand in the islands, and domestic production does not meet that demand. A number of domestic fruits cultivated to some extent but also collected wild from the jungle could become important sources of income for hill-country farmers, at least in the lower elevations. Such are the calamondin, the pili nut, the duhat, and the camachile. There is another group of introduced plants amenable to some levels of upland cultivation. The avocado, the mango, the chico, the orange, and the pomelo are members of this group. Certainly some of the domestic trees of the islands can be planted farther into the rougher uplands. Many common varieties will not be successful in the higher uplands, and selective breeding will be required to fit varieties to local land-scapes. Tree culture as such, except for the lowland coconut, has been too little practiced by the Filipino farmer. A regular program is greatly needed to educate the upland farmer to the possibilities and to develop a greater variety of tree crops specifically for higher altitudes.

The Forestry Situation

A large area of uplands now is in forests of mixed commercial and noncommercial quality. The timber content varies from region to region, depending on climate and on elevation. Certain types of woods are present in almost every forest area, but others are restricted to local environments. The very profusion of lumber-producing species in any one locality has been troublesome to the lumber operator. Since the growth rate is rapid, second-growth forest quickly covers an area if fires are kept out. However, without some kind of control over the species pattern, many poor species take more space than they should. This very growth rate constitutes an economic tool toward better use of uplands near populous centers that are not amenable to agricultural use. Commercial, controlled forestry is practical in the Philippines as a long-range land use for all but the tenant farmer, and it should be developed and practiced. It is not really necessary that huge holdings be accumulated to make this profitable in a region like the Philippines.

Heretofore, there have been adequate forest resources almost everywhere, but since many of the more accessible areas have been cut over the cost of transporting lumber to markets is becoming important. Local production of lumber would benefit domestic economy greatly in the long run. At present, because of inadequate mill capacity, the export of lumber must be limited to provide an adequate supply for island consumers, thus restricting one of the more useful export commodities.[113] Commercially grown timber can be fairly well controlled and can be developed into an important export in the near future. The Bureau of Forestry has plans for permanent forest maintenance, but never has been able to further those plans. An enlarged program of sustained-yield forestry on accessible uplands should be highly developed. Probably most cultivable lowlands should in the end be opened to agricultural settlement, entirely possible if a properly coördinated upland forestry program were put into operation. Much remains to be done in this direction.

Forest destruction by the new settler on the colonial frontier was almost inevitable in the past. It still takes place in many areas of current settlement that are isolated from markets. More effective transport would make it possible to harvest at least a share of this initial cut which now is destroyed. Unless transportation and forestry programs can be made effective through increased authority and funds, much unnecessary destruction of timber will continue and land will be cut over that never should be cleared for crops.

Because forest destruction and caingin cultivation will not cease immediately, grass and jungle cover will continue to replace some of the presently forested lands. On this front, too, the forestry problem is serious. Already nearly one-fifth of the total area of the islands is in grass cover of low productivity. In some areas the problem could be eased if annual grass firing were stopped, to permit natural reforestation. Annual firing is an old island practice in many areas, intended for improvement of pasture land and for other local reasons. Although it does rid the ranges of old, coarse, and inedible grass, the new growth is edible for a short period only, and reforestation and soil replenishment are hindered. This kind of range cover is not one of high productivity and prevents ideal development of the economic landscape.

At least on some of the present upland grass areas a coördinated forestation program should be developed. The mass spread of such a shrubby tree as ipil-ipil (*Leucena glauca*), and the cessation of annual firing of grasslands would permit rapid coverage of many upland areas by a heavy growth. The function of the ipil-ipil cover would be to kill out the heavy grasses through shading and thus permit the start of tree growth. Reforestation would then be much easier, and would take care of itself in certain areas, or could be developed as a long-range program without exorbitant expense. Airplane broadcast of ipil-ipil seed in large areas and the required planting of all noncropped or nongrazed uplands by farmers and local authorities would speed up the program greatly. If such a program were integrated with one aimed at improving grassland pasture ranges, a twofold benefit could result. Combined cropping and forest planting in early years, where lumber producing trees are planted, can pay the cost of some of the final reforestation.

An important program that needs shaping concerns the recreational, protective forestry, and protective water supply uses of the higher uplands. Scattered all over the islands are many localities suitable for recreation or important for protective purposes. A few national parks have been set up, but no true program yet exists. It is not too late to formulate one. This should be integrated with the long-range plans of the Bureau of Forestry as to which lands should be returned to natural controlled forest and which opened to private claims for agriculture.

A critical aspect of this program is what may be termed range control. This involves rotational lumbering, reforestation, watershed control, flood prevention, recreational land use, mineral exploitation, soil conservation, and the preservation of reserve farm lands in the best possible manner. Though these matters seem commonplace in America, even if they are not yet fully practiced, they are not commonplace matters in the Philippines. The United States did not press these matters in its Philippine colonial holding as they were pressed at home. Future profitable range control will require not only research, experimentation, and long-term planning, but a development of public consciousness that so far has barely been stimulated. Public training and education will be required, plus a long program in the schools to insure proper indoctrination of the coming generation.

There remains an important topic which is vital to the inhabitants of the uplands but is not a matter of land use in the strict sense. This concerns an auxiliary occupation for the upland dweller. Farming alone is not enough, nor is cattle raising or timber growing. In some local regions mining becomes a full-time occupation rather than an auxiliary one. Timber cutting, gathering or production of forest extracts, firewood cutting, and other minor occupations are useful but not common enough nor sufficiently developed.[114] A progressive Philippine economy needs a variety of local industry or handicraft to round out the working time of the population. The wood carving by some of the northern Luzon terrace cultivators is an example. Processing of agricultural products or the fabrication of domestic consumers' goods could serve. The various land-use programs must incorporate training in auxiliary occupations for the whole program to be successful.

Chapter 16

CORPORATE PARTICIPATION IN RURAL ECONOMY

THE CORPORATION and the labor union are characteristic of modern industry in much the same way that the guild and the family workshop were characteristic of the Middle Ages. Normally the corporation and the labor union are more closely related to urban life and economy than to rural economy.[115] However, in the pattern of modern development, they are reaching further and further into the rural countryside and influencing rural economy. This development is making itself apparent in the Philippine Islands today. Certain aspects of it predate the American period, though the greatest growth of both unionism and corporate enterprise belongs to the American period.

This trend toward large-scale organization stands in contrast to the declared policy of keeping the islands a country of small landholders and of developing progressive initiative by the individual operator. It is not a development of the Philippines alone, but is fundamental to much of the large-scale production and handling of economic goods of the present day world, whether in agriculture, forestry, mining, transport and distribution, or secondary processing and fabricating. Hence, it is questionable whether its further evolution can be prevented in the islands. There is probably no stopping this type of evolutionary economic development, nor is it the purpose of this chapter to urge it.[116]

At the same time, however, it is apparent that some of the difficulties facing the rural Filipino stem from the continued growth of these two newer elements, particularly the inroads of the corporation upon the small operator. The successful economy will probably be one in which some effective balance is maintained between rural and urban elements, between union and individual efforts, between personal and corporate operations. If in the Philippines a healthy economy is to be progressively stimulated and developed, several adjustments must be made in the operation of both the corporation and the labor union. This chapter concerns itself with the current lack of balance in a number of segments of island economy, and with ways in which balance might be regained.

The Background

The declared policy of small landholdings is not very old in the islands even though small holdings were common in earlier periods. Claims to land and to economic perquisites certainly were not equally distributed, and the serf classes had had little chance for economic advancement among the more highly organized social groups of the islands.

Spanish policy cemented the position of the nobility and the freemen, though it added another layer of economic privilege to the native system. Except among a minority of Filipino families, the further development and accumulation of economic privilege lay open only to the Church, Spanish officialdom, and its friends. A small development of the chartered company and of monopoly control over tobacco began the modern large-scale organization of economic affairs in the islands. During the nineteenth century Spanish and Filipino families were able to obtain title to large landholdings, and a few undertakings were initiated that resemble the modern corporation.

Early American policy declared for the freedom of the individual—the small landholder and the individual operator. The early and widespread appearance of the modern corporate plantation was thus prevented, except in a very few cases. In this the Philippines contrast with parts of the Indies, British Malaya, and Ceylon. At no time during the American period, of course, was purchase of land from owners prohibited, and some large landholdings were accumulated by private purchase. Official policy governed only the issue of public and unclaimed lands at nominal cost, though its objectives did prevent wholesale private purchases of large areas.

The legal right of the small corporation was established by laws making possible the acquisition of as much as 2,500 acres of land, which thereby sowed the seed for more recent developments. Certainly incorporation was recognized as advantageous for processing and manufacturing, and for the exporting and importing of both agricultural and manufactured products. The educated Filipino, Chinese, Spaniard, or American who possessed some financial resources was able to take advantage of this situation to set up corporations in the islands during the years of American rule.

The favorable position of the Chinese during Spanish times permitted the accumulation of wealth by many Chinese families, who gradually intermarried with Filipinos. During the American period many of these Chinese family concerns incorporated for business purposes. The general business acumen of the Chinese, as against Filipino inexperience, enabled these Chinese companies and family enterprises to prosper and steadily to enlarge the field of their operations. Most of them continued to operate in urban localities, to engage in trade, processing, and, gradually, in some fabricating activities. Many of these families also acquired large landholdings which they operated in the Filipino manner with tenant farmers.

The Spaniards who remained in the islands during the American period invested in all economic fields. Many formed corporations to process such products as tobacco and sugar; others turned to urban trading concerns; and a few became manufacturers. Some of the largest corporate enterprises in the islands today are controlled by Spanish capital.

With ample opportunity, American investments in agriculture, trade, processing, and manufacturing gradually increased.[117] Many of the early American investments in agriculture resulted in large farms that produced commodities for international sale.[118] Other investments were in corporations which have continued operations on a large scale.

For a good many years the expansion of agricultural production and international trade was not unfavorable to the small farmer because of the protected position of the islands in the American trade sphere. Gradually, however, changes have come, and difficulties have arisen. Normally the Spaniards, Chinese, and Americans did not compete with the Filipinos in production of rice, vegetables, fruit, or commodities destined chiefly for domestic consumers. Competition did take place in coconut, abacá, tobacco, pineapple, and, to some extent, in livestock raising.

The Contemporary Concentration

To what extent, in a young country just beginning its independence, should there be concentration of land, productive capacity, wealth, and political power in the hands of a relatively few families, individuals, or corporations? Does such a concentration prejudice the future of the tenant farmer, the middle-class private citizen, or the small landholder for whom basic laws were set up early in the American period? Does concentration of this sort threaten to dominate the whole economy of the Philippines and to monopolize international trade? These are rhetorical questions, to which no one can give positive answers for the Philippines today.

Without some method of utilizing the liquid wealth of a country the alternatives in large-scale development are slow lift-by-the-bootstrap methods or the importation of foreign capital and management. Wisely administered, a reasonable concentration of economic and political power threatens no one. The Philippines aspires to rapid large-scale development and a markedly higher standard of living. Government economic policy is torn between what it considers the urgent needs of the country and the dangers of concentration of corporate power. This is complicated by bad administration of the dual policy, chronic favoritism toward a few, and a tendency to too great a concentration of government economic power. Today the government is also heckled by a Communist guerilla movement which charges vested corporate imperialism and economic nepotism by those who would exploit the resources of the islands.

Illustrations of these generalizations may be seen in the formation of government corporations, their frequent reorganization, and the recent liquidation of several of them interested in land, agriculture, trade, or rural economy.[119] The poor record of the Rice and Corn Production Administration in 1950 in Mindanao is proof of the danger of overdevelopment of the government corporation.[120] In the face of the small-landholder policy stands the 1950 sanction of an 18,000-acre abacá-growing corporation in Mindanao.[121] The repeated failure of the Philippine Congress to legislate for agrarian reform that would curb the oppression of the central Luzon tenant farmer indicates the influence of the large landholder who is also an industrialist and capitalist.

Not all corporate undertakings in the islands are exploitive in practice, though for agitation purposes all are smeared with the same brush. The trend has been, of course, to pay hourly wages on the large farms or plantations and in processing establishments, lumbering operations, mines, and fishing enterprises. Payment of wages has been accompanied by provision of housing, medical care, garden facilities, and subsidized food supplies in many of the better establishments. The wage scale has been moving upward, and is subject to union negotiations and to government mediation and regulation.[122] In rural areas and on the rural fringes of urban regions these matters have followed the same trends that take place in cities among secondary manufacturing and processing concerns. Such an organization as the large pineapple plantation in northern Mindanao certainly has been in the forefront of progressive change and today is considered a model example of corporate development. But its very size and efficiency prevent any expansion of the pineapple industry except on competitive corporate grounds. Pineapple is less widely grown today than formerly, though the volume production of the islands is greater than at any time in the past.

Many Filipinos were disturbed by the gradual domination of the abacá industry by corporate plantations. Many of these plantations were Japanese controlled, but some were owned by Americans or Filipinos. Small operators formerly produced the entire crop. Gradually the plantation appeared in southern Mindanao, and the total production increased somewhat, but the small farmers of southern Luzon and the Visayan Islands lost ground. In years of low prices and ample world supply the plantations held on but many small farmers gave up, with serious impact upon their living standards. Higher wages and really progressive corporate agriculture among plantation producers were not immediately forthcoming. At the end of World War II the Japanese plantations were broken up into small holdings and distributed among guerilla and military veterans. Abacá production slumped immediately.[123] First a government corporation and then concessions to plantation operators signified a somewhat desperate attempt to regain production volume before newly competitive regions elsewhere in the world expanded to supply the need and destroy the Philippine monopoly.

If these corporate efforts succeed they will help maintain national income, but the effect is again to expand the corporate pattern that caused the loss of income among the original small operators. Far more public funds and resources are being put into this corporate effort than are devoted to the resuscitation of small-farmer abacá production since, in theory, corporate investment will secure a more prompt increase in production. Here is the contradiction in government policy that illustrates the continued risk of corporate agriculture in a country of small farmers.

Tobacco production in the islands has always been a corporate operation, a government monopoly having been set up early in the Spanish period. Although there are today many small farmers scattered over the islands who grow a little tobacco for their immediate home supply, few of them are commercial producers. Corporate and large-scale tobacco production has been one of the less progressive patterns of agriculture in the islands, declining in importance over the years. As such it has contributed steadily less to the national income.

Coconut agriculture is predominantly small-farmer controlled for the islands as a whole, but plantation owners and corporate production account for a large share of the higher grade and more remunerative coconut products. The benefit of government and private research has gone to the plantation and corporate producer rather than to the small farmer or to labor. The role of the government corporation in this field has been distinguished by its bad results. The government corporation was conceived as a price stabilizer and marketing agent to assist the small farmer. Maladministration offset much of its efforts. Corruption padded the pockets of a favored few at the expense of the taxpayer and the small farmer. Unfortunately too many government corporations participating in agricultural enterprise either as producers or as price regulators and marketers have suffered in similar ways.

Corporate agriculture as such has not found its way into rice farming, or into the production of such auxiliary crops as fruits and vegetables. In rice farming large landholders such as the Church and the Spanish and Filipino families descended from tribal nobility have not used the corporation. However, their large holdings have been perpetuated and affect the tenant and the small farmer more drastically than do the corporations. They add to the effect of corporate undertaking because the large farmer now may use many of the techniques and methods of the corporation. The historic use of tenants as actual farm operators has held the small farmer in his place and allowed the large operators to dominate the marketing, pricing, and supply picture. However, this continued use of tenants has not produced the cash-wage, company-village, union patterns that have appeared around most corporate activities. There are a few large farms under the control of managers, with cash wages and accompanying social features.

In some of the newer attempts in agricultural production, such as ramie, one finds the corporation active from the start. Titles to large holdings in Mindanao have been secured through incorporation by many wealthy individuals and families. If international marketing of ramie is successful, the islands will have another export product dominated by the corporation.

Much of the interregional trade in rice, corn, sugar, and abacá is now handled by Chinese commission and merchandising companies. These firms operate far into the hinterlands, buying cheaply at harvest seasons, shipping to export ports or to deficiency areas, and selling at higher market rates. To some extent Filipino companies compete in these same fields, but the great volume of business is handled by the Chinese. What share of profit drain-off has gone to China in past years is extremely difficult to determine. Some competition has been given the Chinese commercial interests for several years by two government corporations. The National Rice and Corn Corporation (NARIC) and the Philippine Relief and Trading Administration (PRATRA) have extended their operations into various sections of the islands, but the administrative record of neither has been very impressive.[124] It would seem that both government corporations have entered business on the side of the large operator or vested interest. Sometimes small farmers have preferred the never tender mercies of the Chinese.

The sugar industry is perhaps an example of corporate participation. Growing cane is an old activity, for cane is one of the crops spread widely in subsistence agriculture in southeastern Asia. It became a commercial crop before the coming of the Spaniards, chiefly because Chinese merchants exported sugar to China. Commercial export in the modern era began before 1800, and by the end of the Spanish period sugar had become one of the chief exports of the islands. However, its production still was a matter of small landholdings, small mills, primitive methods, and fairly widespread participation in the fruits of production and export. Then the cane grower was the dominant figure in the industry. Not until after the free trade developments of 1909 did the sugar industry expand markedly, though the United States already was the chief market.

The period since 1909 has seen the almost complete domination of this important agricultural activity by the industrialist and the corporation. The change began through the building of improved sugar mills, known in the islands as centrals. Various agreements between millers and growers were tried, one after another. The result has been the concentration of cane production, sugar milling, and merchandising in the hands of corporations. Day wages, seasonal employment, temporary residence quarters, and, on some plantations and at some centrals, progressive worker facilities are the rule. The milling corporation has become the dominant element in the industry. The smaller, more primitive mills gradually have ceased operations and have been abandoned, and with them has gone the small commercial grower. Today the isolated small grower can turn only to the local village or town as an outlet for fresh cane. The chewing of fresh cane stalks by Filipinos is a widespread, interesting, and colorful custom, but it does not provide a large or very profitable outlet.

Part and parcel of this whole evolution has been the world supply picture, the International Sugar Conference with its limitations upon export quotas, the competitive drive to develop more productive grades of cane, and the development of cane by-products. Factors beyond the control of the Filipino small farmer are at work in the international sugar picture, and unless corporate development had taken place the islands would not now be one of the chief sources of world supply.

Today there is more than $250,000,000 invested in the Philippine sugar industry, capital representing Spanish, American, British, and Filipino investors. Just what share derives from island sources and what share of the profits accrues to Filipinos is not clear. At present there are about 10,000 commercial planters, a steadily lessening total which is directly related to the number and distribution of milling centrals.[125] Figure 7 indicates the cane-growing regions and also the locations of sugar centrals. The current number of centrals, twenty-eight in operation during the 1949–1950 milling season, is well under the maximum of forty-six that operated before World War II. Currently less than 25,000 employees are needed by the milling centrals for all operations, whereas the total labor force used by the planters is nearly 170,000 per year.[126] It is asserted that as many as 2,000,000 people are directly or indirectly dependent upon the sugar industry for their livelihood, but this includes a large number of people whose relation to the industry is in consumer-merchandising and transportation.

Lumbering has changed from a small individual operation into a corporate enterprise. Formerly the carpenter or builder cut his own logs or bamboos, moved them, made them into boards or mattings, and put up his building. Increasingly as available timber has receded to remote distances and to less populated territories, the large-company operation with its sawmill, its shipping arrangements, and its urban lumber yards or export markets has replaced the small operator. American, British, and Filipino capital has entered the field. Prices have steadily advanced and supply has not been overabundant in many regions. Since the war, of course, lumber has been in short supply all over the islands, owing to the large amount of reconstruction necessitated by war damage. In many local regions of sparse population and on the frontier, the smaller operator still can carry on. But increasing wage standards, stimulated by an advancing economy and the corporation, make it increasingly difficult for him to do so.[127]

Mining on a large scale is a recent development in the islands. Except for the Baguio area it primarily is a rural occupation, but there it is a corporate undertaking. American companies dominate the picture, but there are some with Spanish and Filipino affiliations and, of course, the ownership of mining stocks is widely scattered. It is unlikely that there would be much of a mine-products output in the Philippines without the corporation. Corporate enterprises, with regular work periods, cash wages, company commissaries, and the labor union are playing an increasing role in the changes in rural economy wherever mining is an important industry.[128]

There are other ways in which the corporation affects rural economy. The role of the merchandising companies selling consumers' goods, agricultural machinery, and agricultural chemicals and fertilizers is important. The transportation company, often a large and complex organization, deals in produce and manufactures at the same time that it provides communications services. The light and power companies that serve urban regions often touch rural economy around urban fringes. The range of participation in rural economy by the corporation is broad and diverse, with many ramifications that vary from harmless customs to dollar-and-cents items.[129]

Summary

Although the impact of the corporation upon rural economy has been suggested, the more significant aspect is the concentration of corporate economic activities in the hands of a relatively few companies and families. There are several private groupings in the Philippines—perhaps fifteen in number—that might be called supercorporations. Almost any one of them may deal in land or interisland sea transport, own an abacá plantation, a sugar plantation and a milling central, a cattle ranch, coconut plantations and processing companies; and at the same time participate in importing, exporting, wholesale merchandising, manufacturing and banking. Other but equally diverse patterns are found, and operations often cover almost the entire Philippines.

It is not the simple curse of bigness or variety of operation that is here objectionable. Many of these family corporations have members in local or national government and in the diplomatic services abroad. Some even possess multiple citizenship facilities among the family members. And they have a complex system of interwoven directorships that strengthens each undertaking and all in turn. Too often government policy has deviated in this or that direction favorable to some group. Repeatedly political office has been used to guide economic activities of a group or to shield individuals or activities. This became increasingly true in the later years of American control and in the Commonwealth period from 1935 to 1946, and it has been even more persistent in the few years of Philippine independence.[130]

There are many Filipinos who feel that there is no real danger in this pyramid of economic power, though they do not condone the corruption that has appeared. They hold that centralized economic power is necessary in a young and nonindustrialized country. They assert that since much of the pyramid is Filipino in ownership no severe harm will come from exercise of its strength. These same Filipinos assert that the real danger lies in the further intrusion into the islands of really large American corporate capital, or in the further increase of Chinese economic strength within the islands. They point to Standard Oil, Westinghouse, or American Cyanamid, each of which, respectively, has offered to devote large sums to the search for petroleum, to the development of hydroelectric facilities, or to the building of fertilizer factories. Whatever the terms of discussion, the three offers have so far been declined, and many Filipinos urge that they, and others like them, never be accepted.

Other Filipinos feel that there is danger of too great pyramiding of economic power in the hands of domestic and outside private corporations. They urge that nationalized industries and nationalized development of natural resources show the way to industrial development to offset the dangers of private corporate domination of the economy of the islands. This type of opinion prompted the formation of such government companies as the Cebu Portland Cement Company, the National Footwear Corporation, and the National Food Products Corporation. Government policy has frequently declared for the setting up of such companies to start home industries, after which a plant may be sold to domestic investors and entrepreneurs. Several government concerns have been sold to private parties, though others have continued in government hands, year after year.

The skeptic, however, looks at the recent and current record of government industrial companies and at other government corporations and wonders what the future may hold. The individual with stronger feelings may even be inclined to agree with the Communist-dominated Hukbalahap, with the debt-ridden tenant, with the poor small farmer struggling for himself that the wealthy family economic pyramid already is much too high and that the services of government are stacked in the hands of those who have, against those who have not.

Corporate operation is more than urban in the Philippines. The future of much of rural economy is directly involved with its operations. In both urban and rural areas the corporation tends to solidify the positions of economic leaders and industrialist families, even as new institutions brought by the Spanish at an earlier time perpetuated the power of the tribal chiefs and the nobility. If the Philippines are to advance toward a rounded and progressive economy that serves the whole population and brings a higher standard of living to all its people, a way must be found to broaden the services of the pyramided yet widely diversified pattern of corporate operation. Both government and private concerns must share this responsibility.

In the last decade nearly thirty government corporations have been operating in the islands.[131] Most of these have either neglected their rural obligations or have participated in rural economy in such a way as to hinder long-range development. In the words of the *Bell Report:* "The most portentous development with respect to the relation of the Government to agriculture is the corporations which have been set up to produce and to trade in various agricultural commodities. Almost without exception they have involved very heavy costs for little or no achievement."[132] The final judgment of the *Bell Report* is that government corporations form the greatest single threat to a sound agricultural program. Although this conclusion may reflect a partiality for private enterprise, it certainly is true that mismanagement, corruption, and operations favorable to the large landholders have marked the history of most Philippine government corporations participating in rural economy.

Another aspect of this situation is reflected in these words from the *Bell Report:* "For the fiscal year 1951, there was appropriated to the Department of Agricultural and Natural Resources for investigation in plant industry, animal industry, fisheries and forestry, the sum of Pesos 1.2 million, about one-fourth of one per cent of the budget. Most of this will go into salaries, wages, travel, and miscellaneous expenses, leaving but a minor part for actual experimental work. The fact is that for the basic informational needs of the industries that constitute the backbone of the entire economy, almost a negligible amount is provided in the national budget."[133] The conclusion is inescapable that had less money been put into corporations of special purpose and more into regular government services available to all parts of the rural countryside more fundamental progress could have been achieved.

Chapter 17

GOVERNMENT SERVICES IN THE HINTERLAND

IT HAS BEEN repeatedly suggested, elsewhere in these pages, that the activities and services of the governments of the Philippines have been both unequally distributed over the islands and of minimum accomplishment during much of the last hundred years. In a sense this is an indictment of the Spanish and the Americans, but also it is an indictment of the Filipinos themselves. The early and middle periods of Spanish control certainly were marked by economic, political, and religious exploitation of the population of the islands. The last period of Spanish rule saw a lightening of the heavy hand of colonial administration, but it had not yet placed the good of the islands above Spanish national and personal gain. The United States took over the islands with the purpose of liberation, with a sense of obligation, and with explicit instructions to its administrative representatives to develop the government institutions of the islands to provide ". . . wise, firm and unselfish guidance in the paths of peace and prosperity to all the people of the Philippine Islands."[184]

The success of American plans for the islands, of course, has depended upon the coöperation, effort, honesty, and sincerity of the islanders themselves. It is commonly taken for granted by Americans that the United States, in the long run, creditably discharged its obligation and can be proud of being the first country to liberate a colonial holding in the Orient. Some Filipinos have felt that the United States gave political but not economic independence, whereas others have been critical of several sectors of past government operation. This study is an attempt to find and point out weak spots in the rural economy of the islands.

Skeleton Establishments

Confronting all forms of land use is the fact that government services as provided in the United States are relatively lacking in the Philippines. In her period of administrative control the United States set up many of the necessary agencies and initiated skeleton programs of services. However, such skeleton programs provided far less than similar programs in the United States gave during the same period. The islands themselves could not have paid for a set of services equivalent to those developed in the United States. Nevertheless, the services were lacking in the earlier years of the century and many of them still are lacking today.

American education has not yet made the Filipinos aware of the need for enlargement in certain of their own government services. These are not visionary or utopian, but primary services that long ago became the recognized province of government in many countries of the world. In inheriting a colonial country in which even the fundamental facilities were lacking, the United States shouldered a huge backlog of needs. What we actually set up in the islands neither made up for the earlier lack nor kept up with the development in other progressive areas of the world.

A fundamental public need in a country which recognizes private property is an effective system for surveying lands for issuance of titles and deeds. Akin to this is the need to survey the public domain so that lands useful to the colonial settler may be classified as farming land, grazing land, forest land, mining land, and the like. In the Philippines this classification survey is the duty of the Bureau of Forestry, Department of Agriculture and Natural Resources. However, the Bureau of Forestry is so undermanned and underfinanced that it never has been able to complete its survey of the remaining public domain, let alone perform many other functions allocated to it.

The Bureau of Lands, likewise, never was able to complete a basic survey of the islands, and is hopelessly behind in its work. Currently it is faced with the herculean task of reconstituting all its prewar land records, most of which were destroyed. At no time, seemingly, did the American administration realize the proportions of the problem it was creating by guiding the Filipino toward a small landholder policy without setting up the machinery to implement it.

Somewhat related to land classification and survey are the other functions of the Bureau of Forestry. It levies charges on forest products removed from the public domain. These moneys are supposed to be allocated to reforestation. Extremely little, however, has been done in reforestation in the Philippines and, since much forest remains, not many people are really concerned as yet. But closely tied with the question of upland use are such matters as permanent forest reserves, national parks, and watershed controls for urban water supply, for hydroelectric power reserves, and for flood control purposes. The Bureau of Forestry has not been given the means to work toward any long-range program in upland land use.

The accompanying map (map 11) indicates the location of reforestation projects that total almost 1,200,000 acres. Some of them date from as far back as 1919; many from the 1930's. A large share of the area has not been planted, owing to the lack of authority and funds. Forest charges upon timber cut and other forest products have often gone into operating expenses rather than into reforestation. In spite of the above-mentioned projects, the grass and ruined surface cover of the islands is growing annually. The whole forestry problem must not be permitted to become worse before truly constructive work begins.

The Bureaus of Animal Husbandry and Plant Industry have done exceedingly well on limited resources. Each is pointing the way toward further progress. And yet there are limitations in the programs of both bureaus that inhibit effective rural progress in many regions of the islands. Map 11 indicates the locations of breeding and experiment stations. Beyond these, of course, are the urban

211

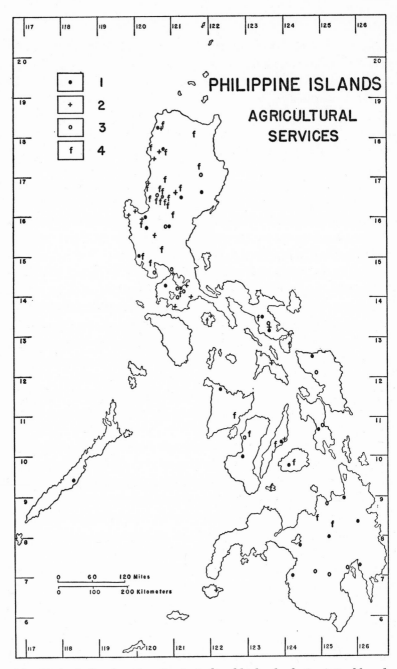

Map 11. Agricultural services. 1 = Agricultural high schools. 2 = Animal breeding stations. 3 = Plant Experiment seed stations. 4 = Forestation projects.

offices of the provincial supervisors of both bureaus, some of which have rural nursery seed stations attached to them. But too many large rural areas are completely out of touch with these facilities. Some private work is being done in both these fields, but the volume is small, compared to the need, and today the islands still have only a skeleton of the services that should be available to the rural population.

Similarly other basic services of government, having to do with soils, mineral resources, water supply, public health, transportation and communications, are still skeleton bureaus. They provide skeleton services that too often are concentrated on central Luzon or other favored regions; that too often assist only the educated wealthy and the knowledgeable; that all too seldom have preceded the settler into such out of the way areas as southern Mindanao, interior Mindoro, Siargao, Polillo or Balabac islands; and that too seldom reach into the poorer rural territories close to Manila.

This is not a plea for increased bureaucracy in the islands, but a comment on the failure to develop effective government programs. In some instances early American administration assigned only a single man to work in a given field. And sometimes he was soon detached from his assignment and nothing more was really done until much later in the American period.[135] Or a bureau was created on paper, a small staff and a small budget were set up at a time when funds admittedly were limited, but when population was less than half its present total.

Now that the population has doubled, some of these problems have grown at a much faster rate than the bureaus themselves. In other cases it has not been personnel that was lacking, but authority to carry out a program. Often the technical ability and understanding of bureau staffs has been far in advance of the scientific and cultural comprehension of the centralized American or Filipino government authority.

Now that the Philippines is independent, it is coming face to face with both historically accumulated and current problems, and an awakening of tremendous proportions has started. Technical personnel, bureau leadership, and public interest—all are beginning to mobilize for individual and group attack upon the problems that face the country. The current food production campaign is illustrative.[136] But politics and vested interests, sectionalisms and regionalisms, articulate lobbies for particular interests and the still inarticulate urges of rural groups are in competition. Methods, procedures, policies, and aims still are in confusion. Government has lagged in its duties, both during the American period and during the Commonwealth period before complete independence. Now one of the chief problems is to educate the population, both the uninformed rural elements and the articulate and wealthy elements, to support the national attack upon the common problems of the country.

Training the Rural Population

The typical reaction of the older Filipino farmer to any urging of new methods and improvement in agriculture is: "I have been farming all my life. Who are you that you think you can tell me anything useful?" Many younger people, however, are becoming aware that something is seriously wrong with their agricultural economy. Many know that their relative production records are low, that their labor expenditure is relatively high, and that American farmers have learned better ways of doing things with crops and soils. But many of these same young people feel that the difference stems chiefly from the mechanical equipment that American farmers use, and that, therefore, the Filipino can do nothing toward improvement because he lacks money for machinery. Others are aware that machinery is not the whole answer, but fail to perceive features which could contribute toward a better solution to the problem.

Some farmers are appreciative of improved seed stock, but expect annual free issues, without effort on their part. Others admire the experimental gardens, orchards, and farm layouts, but do not adapt suggestions for their own use. A few farmers, of course, in all parts of the islands have taken full advantage of chances for improvement and have done very well indeed. In short, the farmers of the Philippines have the same conservative viewpoint that characterizes rural public opinion in many parts of the world. The larger problem of improving land use and particularly upland land use, becomes one of changing the rural mind toward agriculture, forestry, water supply, and the soil.

An important aspect of farmer training involves the cainginero and what to do about shifting agriculture, or caingin cultivation. The caingin problem is specifically a problem of the uplands. Shifting cultivation was useful in pre-Columbian time, but with today's increased population, a great need for commercial timber products, and a highly competitive agriculture, caingin cultivation is both wasteful and inefficient.

Improvements in farming practice will be one of the chief fields of advancement. Included is everything from crop selection and animal breeding through soil management to pest control and marketing techniques. To achieve this the services of the national and local governments must be enlarged, both in scope and in intensity, so far as they pertain to land use. Not only must the program of services be enlarged, but provincial agents must be given authority to require the use of improvements among the farming population. The problem is an urgent one requiring action more rapid than the slow and natural change that results from casual imitation. Many other areas of the world have been speeding up their changes in agriculture, and more will do so in the future; the Philippines cannot expect to improve its relative position without concerted effort.

The Philippines does not have enough universities, colleges, agricultural high schools, experimental farms, and research institutes at work on the problems of land use, agricultural productivity, and the training of the next generation of land users.[137] On the accompanying map (map 11) are shown the agricultural high schools in the islands' education system. The key message of the agricultural educational program must also be carried into the primary schools because too few students go on to high school. In the agricultural high schools particularly this key message must be expanded into practical programs of land use.

Existing agricultural high schools are languishing from lack of support, when they should be the key institutions in the whole educational system of the islands. Small town and city high schools are departing from agricultural-vocational curricula and teaching commercial and industrial courses. Academies, colleges, and universities concentrate much too heavily on the professional goals of law, medicine, business administration, and advanced engineering. It is true that the islands need personnel with this training, but even more they need many times the number of agricultural technicians who are being turned out in the one College of Agriculture in the islands. And a great need is for men and women trained in the modern vocations of mechanics, small industry, transportation, building trades, home economics, food processing, and the like.

There are too few schools of all kinds on the colonial frontiers and in the rural uplands.[138] Too many schools are attuned to urban living patterns only, and too many are concentrated in the easily accessible lowlands around the larger cities. Beyond the formal programs of school education there is needed a general program of public education in the whole field of land use and agricultural production. Means must be devised to carry it effectively into the isolated rural sectors that are not reached by radio or newspapers. This is a two-pronged matter. Better productive methods must be given the farmer, but the population of the islands must be educated to demand better government leadership.[139]

The Chief Need of Today

The Philippines is an agricultural country aspiring toward such industrialism as will give relative independence from foreign manufactured products. They seek also a heightened standard of living for all their people. The problems facing the country are of such proportions as to call for enlightened services of government, since the task is too great for private initiative alone. Some advisory elements urge future development along agricultural lines, hoping for sufficient productivity to accomplish the desired ends.[140] Others urge industrialization of the country to make the islands independent and to lift the standards of living.[141]

No one line of development will achieve the desired ends. Philippine agricultural production is too low in its per-acre yield and per-worker output to allow much real progress in the over-all aim if the future program specializes upon industrialization. But the competitive marketing problems facing agriculture, and the large volume of manufactured imports demanded, prejudice the result if too much effort is concentrated upon agriculture alone. Wartime losses—valued at some $4,000,000,000, with compensation totaling not more than a third—impose a heavy burden upon the population.[142] The misuse of war-damage compensation resulted in a deceptive feeling of progress during 1946–1948. Adequate government services were either not available or not mobilized effectively enough, in the new independence, to guide the reconstruction and progressive expansion of island economy. Government itself has misused funds in trying to produce for the population, and has contributed but little.

Some restraint must be placed on island consumer appetite until real income increases through expanded agricultural production and manufactured consumer goods.[143] It is certain that some control must be exercised over the financial investments being made in the islands. It is equally unquestioned that there must be a marked stimulation of agricultural production in all parts of the islands, in both subsistence and export crops. But they cannot be the only lines along which positive government programs are exercised. The need today is for the services of government expressed in a vital, honest, efficient pattern of administration and fundamental leadership. This calls for programs that will enable the people of the rural countryside themselves to increase their agricultural productivity, develop their local industries, and achieve the training and skills that go with the operation of an independent, balanced economy.

This actually requires an expansion of the services of government in the basic needs of local regions rather than in the direction of complex corporate undertakings. Such things as land survey, roads, port facilities, public health, vocational education, soil survey and technical advice, plant and animal technical aid, rural credit facilities, tenancy reform, and tax reform are among the more pressing. Lip service has been paid too long to many of these needs. The issues have become critical since the granting of independence, and reorientation of government must be accomplished to prevent domestic problems from overwhelming the country.

One of the most effective services of government could well be the decentralized development of power facilities outside the Manila area. Although more power is produced and a few more customers are served today than in the prewar period, the increased service is concentrated around Manila, and fewer towns and rural areas are now served than before the war. In 1948, for example, 72 per cent of the total island electric-power generation was for the metropolitan zone of Manila and its fringes, whereas slightly under 2 per cent was generated in the whole of Mindanao.[144]

Chapter 18
SUMMING UP THE RURAL SCENE

THE PHILIPPINES continues to be a land chiefly of rural, agricultural peoples. Different origins and times of arrival means that these peoples came with different methods of how to utilize the separate landscapes. Some of their practices were simple and have not changed greatly with the centuries. Other land-use patterns have changed markedly as new cultural influences have come in, particularly during the last five hundred years. New peoples have come into the islands—Moslem Malays, Christian Spaniards and Americans, Buddhist and Confucianist Chinese—bringing new political, social, and economic patterns. They brought new crops, new tools, and new cultivation practices. With them came new ways of transport, new arrangements of housing and residential settlement, new patterns of trade, new weapons and tricks of warfare. Also there came new religions, new forms of recreation, new values for old products, new values on human labor, new cultural mores, and new objectives in life.

Many of these new features took root in the cities and towns, leaving the older ways to the rural hinterlands. The rural regions came to support the growing urban localities and gradually to share in limited aspects of the new culture. Certain old and important culture patterns became fixed more firmly than ever, some old values and patterns were discarded, others altered beyond recognition, and a few interesting but unimportant ones merely preserved intact. Except for those refuge groups who withdrew into the back country and the occupants of regions not yet touched by expansion of population, these changes have variably affected every aspect of Philippine life and society, both rural and urban. Many changes have been good, but some of them have been harmful and now are highly resented. Many changes have been planned, whereas others were unexpected, and even unwanted.

The Earlier Trends

The Moslem Malays and the Chinese began coming into the islands before the arrival of the Spaniards. The Malay influences were largely social and religious but were becoming political by the time the Spaniards arrived. They were expressed chiefly in the far south of the islands but worked northward. The influences of the Chinese were primarily economic, and were confined to central Luzon and to a few scattered ports. The Chinese stimulated the first modern international trade in agricultural products, in abacá and in sugar.

Spanish influences were more far reaching than those of the Malays or the Chinese, but they did not penetrate every nook and corner of the islands. They left blocks of upland in many island interiors and the Moslem southern sector of the islands relatively untouched. Certain patterns, harmful in the long run—such as the positions of power and wealth held by the tribal chiefs and the nobility—were only fixed more firmly by the Spaniards. Some long-run problems, for which no remedial steps were taken, made their appearance with the Spaniards. Overpopulation and serious tenancy conditions were the chief of these, though confined to certain provinces. Urbanism appeared under the Spanish rule, to set up a fundamental divergence of forces. A regional division of the islands into the Moslem southern fringe and the Christian center and north was another significant result of Spanish and Malay influences.

The Filipinos did not ask that the Americans intervene with Spain. The United States came to free the Filipinos and pledged an all-round program of reform, development, and help. We made a promise in 1900, of which a phrase was quoted on an earlier page. We took over a situation with many accumulated problems, a situation to which we applied some energy, some thought, and some funds. We stimulated cultural, political, and economic rejuvenation and evolution along new lines. And Americans benefited financially from the islands. In instituting the changes, we laid down certain principles that guided future development. The islands were to remain a country of small landholders and not become subject to corporate plantation agriculture which then was beginning to spread widely in the Oriental tropics. Elective political devices, education, a form of free trade, a market for island products, and many other changes came rapidly under American control. Attacks were made upon basic problems as they were recognized by American administrators.

Many of the American changes effectively solved problems that had arisen. Peace between Moslems and Christians came as the result of the separation of Church and State. Some changes, on the other hand, were completely effective only in particular areas, such as the transport patterns that were set up in the Central Plain of Luzon. Others, like the purchase of Church lands, were isolated attacks upon a problem and not permanent improvements. The increasing urbanism, the advancing role of the Chinese, the economic attachment to the American market, the continuance of destructive land use, and the worsening of the tenancy situation are problems that became more serious during the American period. At the same time other changes were taking place that really constituted improvements in the economy of the islands.

During the 1930's the desire for freedom and independence grew stronger. Instead of suppressing the movement or postponing concessions and really working out many of the fundamental problems, the United States arranged for a ten-year preparatory interval during which the islands were to shoulder more and more of the responsibility for the operation of Philippine society. At that time, on their own initiative, the Filipinos took certain forward steps along lines in which the United States had done nothing since the first few years of American control. World War II interrupted both this Commonwealth period of experimental home rule, and the development of certain lines of growth started during the interval.

We cannot regard the recently given independence as a successful discharge of our responsibility when the islands remain in a condition of cultural and economic dependence, even though a term of years has been allowed during which that dependence legally shall be dissolved. Some of the problems facing the islands today either were of our creation or were not solved by us. The process of cultural, economic, and social change in the islands is still in midstream. The process of political growth has not yet carried the Filipino on to firm ground. The degree of development along these lines varies in different parts of the islands, and varies from the cities to the rural hinterlands. But we have not yet completed the mission in the islands that we took upon ourselves a half century ago. That some of the unhappiness originated in the earlier administrative neglect of the United States will not prevent the government of the Republic of the Philippines from reaping the whole harvest.

The War and Its Immediate Effects

It has been said that, during World War II, Manila was the second most severely damaged large city, only Warsaw suffering more seriously. Many other Philippine cities and towns were almost completely wiped out during the war. These effects were not alone urban, for damage to buildings, real property, and personal possessions throughout the rural landscape also was severe. Wartime losses have been estimated at $4,000,000,000 for the entire Philippines.

Besides losses of personal property there was an intangible loss in agriculture, in that damage to farmlands, orchard trees, planting stock, livestock, and irrigation facilities cannot be measured accurately in dollars. Many farms required much time, labor, and financial expenditure to put them back into shape for cropping. Many village and rural residents in Japanese-occupied parts of the islands had abandoned their homes and fields for a precarious hand-to-mouth existence in the hilly fringes around their home areas. The immediate postwar shortage of good disease-free planting stock for rehabilitation of abacá, pineapple, and sugar plantings will

222

have its effect for some years. The wartime loss of water buffalo, important to agriculture as draft animals and as a source of meat supply, reduced the total to a figure comparable to that of the middle 1920's, with obvious hardship upon the rural farmer, whose number and needs have increased greatly since that date.

Only partly a phenomenon of the rural countryside was the total depletion of commodity inventories during the war. In dollar terms this was greatest among the city and town wholesalers and retailers, but it finally reached out into the farthest corner of the rural hinterland to deplete stocks of food, clothing, drugs, tools and implements, housing materials, and manufactured commodities. The end of the war released consumer needs and desires at a time when prices were exorbitantly high, productive capacity at its lowest, and international trade organization not yet reorganized to satisfy the volume of accumulated demands.

There are no measures of the productive capacity of the islands at the end of the war, but in many respects it must have been lower than at any time since the United States took over control of the islands. Because the area of cultivated land was greater in 1945, the total volume of food produced was higher than in 1899, but in terms relative to the increased population and the altered living standard it is doubtful if the productive index of July, 1945, stood higher than that of July, 1899. The earliest postwar production indices, for the year 1946, show agricultural production at 58.2 per cent of the 1937 base level (table 11).[145] In 1937 food imports were needed to feed a population some 3,000,000, less than that of 1946. Indices of manufacturing and mining, in 1946, stood at 21.0 per cent and 2.0 per cent, and though these are chiefly urban or local occupations they have an indirect impact upon rural economy.

No rural price indices are available, but the Manila wholesale price index for 1946 stood at 672.9 against a 1937 base of 100; the retail price index for Manila rested at 507.2 against a 1941 base of 100; and the cost of living index for a Manila wage earner's family dropped from 676.5 in January to 517.8 in December, for a 1946 average of 584.8 against a 1937 base of 100.[146] Wage rates for Manila skilled and unskilled labor for 1946 averaged only 293.9 and 365.3

against 1941 bases of 100, to indicate a serious lag. Agricultural labor wage rates had risen to an average of 366.1 during 1947, against a 1941 base of 100. Regional variations in agricultural wages during 1947 ranged from 300.0 in Mindanao to 494.2 in southeastern Luzon.[147] 1937 and 1941 base levels of prices and wages are fairly comparable, though in general 1941 levels were slightly higher than those of 1937.

Table 11

INDEX OF PHYSICAL PRODUCTION, 1937–1950

Year	Combined index	Agricultural	Manufacturing	Mining
1937	100.0	100.0	100.0	100.0
1938	98.2	85.3	109.1	129.4
1939	93.4	82.8	98.8	152.3
1940	109.9	98.0	117.1	165.0
1946	38.7	58.2	21.0	2.0
1947	75.6	79.5	77.5	16.8
1948	85.3	86.4	89.4	36.0
1949	91.3	92.2	94.7	49.1
1950[a]	98.2	97.6	103.1	58.6

[a] Calculated through September 30.
   The index numbers are of weighted aggregative type, based upon eight crops, five manufactures, and five minerals.
   SOURCE: *Central Bank Statistical Bulletin*, Vol. 2, No. 4 (1950) 109.

The United States was reasonably generous in its provisions for war-damage compensation to the islands. Of necessity time was required for the survey, processing, and liquidation of claims, and full payment was not completed until the end of 1951. The first private payments were not made until the latter half of 1947, and only a small number were liquidated during 1948. Some of these delays, though inevitable, had a deterrent effect upon the rehabilitation of parts of island economy. War-damage claims were filed by 1,252,000 individuals and by 1,610 public agencies for an approximate total of $1,200,000,000. An initial appropriation by the United States Congress for claims amounted to $520,000,000, to which $100,000,000 in additional funds have been added.[148] Nearly one family out of three filed a damage claim, with much regional variation in the losses claimed.[149] The damage claims alone cannot, of course, represent all the real losses, even though but little over half the value of the claims will be paid. With increased costs of labor and materials, the replacement cost of buildings, equipment, and private personal property will be far greater than the sums received as war-damage payments.

Independence and Reconstruction

The Philippines received its independence before the islands were even well launched upon a program of rebuilding. By July, 1946, a start was just being made on the survey of reconstruction needs, on rehabilitation programs, the reorganizing of local governments in some hinterland areas, and crop planting in the agricultural cycle of the first postwar crop year. To the problems of independent management of the economy were added those of trying to re-constitute it after an extremely destructive interval of Japanese domination.[150] A large amount of Philippine government funds necessarily had to be added to the United States war-damage funds to rebuild the transport systems, the public buildings, port facili-ties, and other public works.[151] An abnormal total of government funds was allocated to measures designed to stimulate the produc-tive industrial, commercial, and agricultural enterprises of the islands.[152] A large investment in education was necessary to place the school systems on a working basis again and to extend the coverage of schools over the islands.[153] The punitive military oper-ations against the Hukbalahap since the summer of 1948 have been costly.[154]

The demands for consumers' goods came before the return of pro-ductive capacity, to add an annual deficit to the balance sheet of island economy and thus pose another problem for government administration.[155] Postwar funds of American origin unfortunately moved too exclusively into the hands of private individuals, to con-stitute an unusually liquid resource that was quite uncontrollable. Inadequate controls were available right at the beginning of inde-pendence, controls that perhaps could have channeled more of these liquid resources into permanent reconstruction and exten-sion of the capital equipment of the islands.[156]

The several accompanying tables on the balance of trade, international receipts and disbursements, national income and expenditures, tax revenues and expenditures, and the gross national product give evidence of the postwar difficulties. Government ex-

Table 12

BALANCE OF FOREIGN TRADE

(In millions of U.S. dollars)
(Quantum indices based on 1937)

Year	Total trade	Per cap.	Imports	Average monthly quantum index	Exports[a]	Average[a] monthly quantum index	Balance[a] of trade
1899	34.1	5.08	19.2		14.8		− 4.4
1905	63.5	8.25	30.0		33.4		+ 3.4
1910	90.3	11.00	49.7		40.6		− 9.1
1915	103.1	11.13	49.3		53.8		+ 4.5
1920	300.5	28.72	149.4		151.1		+ 1.7
1925	268.6	23.02	119.7		148.8		+ 29.1
1930	251.2	19.52	123.1		133.1		+ 10.0
1937	275.9	17.82	109.0		166.9		+ 57.9
1938	279.6	17.63	137.6		147.0	106.4	+ 2.4
1939	280.4	17.32	122.5		152.8	119.2	+ 30.3
1940	290.6	17.53	134.7		155.9	122.5	+ 21.2
1941	296.7	17.28	135.6		161.1	100.6	+ 25.5
1946	360.0	18.62	295.8		64.2	22.6	−231.6
1947	725.9	38.61	511.3		264.5	62.6	−246.8
1948	903.6	47.06	585.8	220.8	317.8	67.9	−268.0
1949	832.4	42.44	568.7	220.7	253.7	80.8	−314.9
1950[b]	690.0	33.50	368.0		321.5		− 46.5

[a] Includes reëxports in all years. Excludes gold exports except for years 1940–1941.
[b] Tentative figures only.
SOURCE: *Yearbook of Philippine Statistics*, 1946; *Central Bank Statistical Bulletin*, Vol. 2, Nos. 3 and 4 (1950); *Manila Times Mid-Week Review*, Jan. 17, 1951.

penditures have been running ahead of nationally derived income ever since liberation from Japanese control and, with the assumption of the obligation for wartime back pay for government employees during 1948–1949, the national debt has been greatly enlarged. Sinking fund accumulations were in arrears as of June 30, 1949. The expenditure rate has risen more rapidly than the taxation rate (table 16) and, if this continues, the public debt will rise rapidly in the near future.

One of the measures recommended by the Joint Philippine-

Table 13

ESTIMATED RECEIPTS AND DISBURSEMENTS FOR 1950[a]
(In millions of dollars)

RECEIPTS	
Merchandise exports	243.7
Freight and insurance	4.0
Gold	2.5
Services	5.7
Tourism	6.1
U. S. government expenses	218.2
Other foreign government expenses	1.2
Investment remittances	9.4
Donations and contributions	28.1
Miscellaneous sources	16.4
Total	535.3
DISBURSEMENTS	
Merchandise imports	426.1
Freight and insurance	42.1
Services	15.6
Travel, educational, maintenance	12.8
Government expenditures abroad	3.2
Withdrawals of investments and earnings	13.6
Donations and contributions	6.1
Miscellaneous expenditures	18.4
Total	537.9
Deficit for the year	2.6

[a] Compare the tentative import–export figures shown in table 12 with corresponding data in this table.
SOURCE: *First Annual Report*, 1949, Central Bank of the Philippines (1950), pp. 7–8.

American Finance Commission in 1947 was the complete revision of the domestic tax system, both assessment and collection.[157] Changes in tax patterns became effective only in 1951, and future years should show increased collections which may be sufficient to offset the increasing expenditures of national and local government and prevent a further rise in the public debt. However, tightened import controls, effective in 1950, with the inevitable restriction of commercial exchange and internal trade—if maintained—would lessen collections from customs and business sources, making a revision of other internal taxes all the more necessary.[158] The ratio of tax collections to national income during 1945–1946 (table 16) was far too low for a country facing serious reconstruction needs to be serviced out of public funds. The low rate of tax collection reflected assessment rates that were much too low, but also it reflected the continuing evasion of tax payments to the Japanese—in wartime an act of patriotism.

The property tax during the first postwar years amounted to less than the tax on cigarettes.[159] Tax rates have been assessed unequally in past years in different provinces and cities, but attempts at current revision sometimes have not been fair.[160] During 1946 less than 60 per cent of the property taxes was collected.[161] By 1949 collections had risen to 71 per cent throughout the provinces and to 81 per cent in the chartered cities, but this still is not an adequate return.[162]

In general, national government taxation has derived about 15 per cent of its funds from income and profit taxes, and the former at least were inefficiently collected.[163] The main sources of national income have been excise and sales taxes, which spread the load fairly evenly, but which do not stress the ability to pay.[164] Effective reorganization of the tax system must take into account a full review of sources, the weighted levying of taxes by economic classes, the realignment of property assessments, and the more honest and efficient collection of all kinds of taxes.[165]

By the autumn of 1949 the financial plight of the Philippine government began to be really serious. Some planned public works projects, to be financed by government funds, were canceled, and school teachers' salary obligations could not all be met, so that payments had to be made out of provincial funds.[166] Continuing extraordinary expenses were encountered in the punitive operations against the Hukbalahap without either success or the end of the struggle in sight. During early 1950 the financial situation of the government grew steadily worse. A wave of coin hoarding was set off by fear of the possible decline in value of paper money. The appearance of a black market in money exchange early in 1951 indicated a lack of faith in government administrative ability and financial policy.[167]

Early in 1950 President Quirino requested that another in the series of American survey commissions be sent to study the economic and administrative situation of the islands.[168] During late 1950 the proposals of this survey, embodied in the *Bell Report,* began to crystallize into changes in government policy and procedure. These will continue over several years, since all needed changes cannot be implemented at one time. A late development of 1950 was the signing of the Quirino-Foster agreement of November 14, 1950, by which the Philippines will receive more economic assistance from the United States through the Economic Coöperation Administration.[169] As a condition for such aid a variety of improvements must be made in the administration of Philippine economy, including marked tax revision.[170] A minimum total of tax revenues was set for the fiscal year 1951–1952 at $282,500,000, a very marked increase over past collections.[171] United States aid for the fiscal year 1951–1952 may approximate $50,000,000; like sums being allocated each year of a five-year period.[172] If the domestic tax goal can be realized it will enable the government to more than meet its regular expenses from tax funds; the American aid then will be available for import of capital equipment and the development of domestic capital resources.

Most of the production of agricultural crops and a share of the yield of fishing, forestry, and mining comes out of the rural countryside. A small amount of tertiary production is similarly derived from the rural parts of the islands. One of the chief economic problems of the islands is the smallness of rural secondary and tertiary production, and the chronic underemployment of the rural population.[173] Tables 6, 7, 11, and 17 indicate that the redevelopment of rural primary production has been proceeding.

As suggested earlier a large share of government money and effort has been devoted to programs aimed at reconstituting rural

Table 14

FOREIGN TRADE RETURNS FOR 1941 AND 1949

Exports

Commodity	1941	1949
Coconut products	$31,661,000	$129,446,000
Sugar	28,615,000	45,230,000
Abacá	17,500,000	28,901,000
Pineapple	2,500,000	6,837,000
Embroideries	3,647,000	5,985,000
Timber and lumber	4,437,000	3,260,000
Chrome ore		2,730,000
Tobacco products	3,604,000	2,043,000
Gold bullion	47,032,000	[a]
Miscellaneous exports	16,715,000	20,842,000
Reëxports	5,421,000	10,518,000
Total exports	$161,134,000[b]	$255,850,000[b]

Imports

Commodity	1941	1949
Cotton and manufactures	$30,306,000	$66,895,000
Rayon and other textiles	[c]	48,071,000
Grains and preparations	8,005,000	44,391,000
Iron and steel mfgrs.	29,275,000	39,769,000
Automobile products	[b]	31,026,000
Petroleum products	14,973,000[d]	27,627,000
Paper and products	6,500,000	23,989,000
Machinery, excl. agric.	[e]	23,970,000
Dairy products	5,581,000	23,417,000
Tobacco products	8,314,000	17,745,000
Miscellaneous imports	32,837,000	220,164,000
Total imports	$135,591,000[b]	$567,072,000[b]

[a] Separate figure not available.
[b] Individual and total figures rounded off to nearest thousand. Figures for 1949 vary slightly from those given in table 12, the several government bureaus being slow to accept finalized and adjusted figures.
[c] Included with figure on cotton textiles.
[d] Includes some other nonmetallic minerals.
[e] Included under iron and steel manufactures.
SOURCES: *Yearbook of Philippine Statistics, 1946; Summaries of Philippine Foreign Trade, 1931 to 1948; The Philippines, 1950.*

primary and secondary production. Reconstruction in agriculture is almost complete, that in fishing and forestry is close to completion, but mining is still lagging. Reconstruction, however, does not feed, provide incomes for, or raise the standard of living of the whole population when the recently increased numbers and primary needs for a higher plane of living are taken into account. Reconstruction of prewar land records is barely completed, but no progress has been made with unsurveyed lands, and there has been too little increase in ability to meet presently accumulating needs in this field. Similarly, other aspects of rural life and economy neither have returned to the prewar normal nor increased in facility to service the increased population.

If reconstruction is defined as repair of material damage or replacement of production lost during the war, the close of the calendar year 1951 should almost see an end to the major phases of reconstruction. If it is construed to include development of production and services for the wartime increase in population, then reconstruction is not complete by a wide margin. Or if reconstruction includes the setting in order of the independent Philippine government, its effective administrative machinery and procedures, its financial policies, the material economy of its people, the social and economic climate of the Philippines, then several more years of truly progressive activity will be needed before reconstruction can be declared complete.

Although data can be presented to indicate the production of agricultural or forest commodities in the rural hinterland, or factory products in the cities, there is no effective index by which to judge the complex of social-economic-psychological-cultural reconstruction in the rural hinterland. Rural families form the mass of the population and, though city dwellers may currently administer island economy and national government, it is the well-being and mass opinion of the rural populace that will ultimately decide the success or failure of reconstruction. At this point in Philippine history, reconstruction must not stop with the simple restoration of conditions to those of a prewar year as indicated by an index figure alone.

Here I can only conclude that reconstruction in the above sense has not yet been completed, for the appreciation of independence is saddened by the inefficiency and misdirection of government. The chances for successful reconstruction and real progress still are good in spite of local festering sores upon the body of rural

Table 15

NATIONAL GOVERNMENT INCOME, EXPENDITURES, AND PUBLIC DEBT[a]
(In hundreds of dollars)

Fiscal year[b]	Income	Expenditures	Public debt
1935	41,419	37,966	76,400
1936	51,751	46,183	76,950
1937	119,072	56,945	75,300
1938	65,707	69,672	75,300
1939–40	79,015	91,808	76,950
1940–41	79,334	83,884	81,200
1945–46	95,527	106,712	73,300
1946–47	216,885	192,256	129,300
1947–48	180,527	187,281	134,550
1948–49	198,760	221,472	310,450[d]
1949–50[c]	212,372	263,718	380,250[e]

[a] General, Special, and Bond Funds accounts. These data supposedly include all income and expenditures.
[b] For the period 1935–1938 the calendar year was the fiscal year.
[c] Tentative figures only.
[d] Involves assumption of obligation for wartime back pay for government employees.
[e] Of this total, on June 30, 1950, $264,178,000 represented domestic bond and loan debts, whereas $116,082,000 represented foreign debts. On June 30, 1949, the sinking fund accumulation showed a deficiency of $11,744,000 for all types of public dept. This public debt approximates $19.00 per person at this point, about 16 per cent of the per capita income.
SOURCE: Adapted from tables in *Central Bank Statistical Bulletin*, Vol. 2, No. 3 (1950).

economy, and perhaps some of the current changes will lead to real achievement toward the proper goal. One can only hope that the leadership of the Philippines can be so motivated as to interpret reconstruction in the broad sense of readjusting all the critical failures of government in the past for the good of all Filipinos.

The Balance in Rural Affairs

The Philippine government has been pitting its constabulary, its army, some of its government corporations, and part of the efforts of some of its regular government departments against the rural problems of the islands. It is hard to evaluate these efforts in terms of dollars, or to judge the constructive application against the wasteful and destructive application of money and effort. Certainly the efforts of the Bureau of Public Works, for example, in repairing and slightly extending the road and irrigation systems are constructive. The great share of the efforts of the Department of Agriculture and Natural Resources have been on the constructive side, some of long-range value and others of more immediate use. Additional entries on the credit side of the ledger could be made.

The case for participation of government corporations in rural economy is more difficult to appraise. Some of their activities undoubtedly have been helpful, but the corruption, the waste of money, and the practices that tend to make it more difficult for private initiative are of doubtful value. The *Bell Report* pointed to the obstructional, if not destructional, nature of the efforts. Although some of the military efforts have repressed lawless destruction, it would seem that much of their weight has been a drag upon the economy.

If one were to tabulate the money and effort spent on ill-planned programs the total would bulk large. By contrast the funds allocated to reform, frontier development, research, and progressive aid to the small farmer—the backbone of island economy—have been very small in total and scattered in application. More could have been accomplished if the large sums spent on the complex corporate enterprises and on punitive operations of the army had been given to the regular government departments for use in such fields as: the survey of land and opening it up for easy settlement; the building of roads into reserve areas; the setting up of facilities for rural vocational education, public health, and agricultural extension; the alleviation of tenancy problems in critical areas; the development of power supplies in decentralized rural areas; the development of rural credit facilities for small borrowers; and the mobilizing of public morale behind a real program of total reconstruction of problem segments in island economy.

It is extremely doubtful if all past funds spent on agrarian reform projects equal a single annual budget which now must be expended fighting the Hukbalahap, who got their start and find their support in agrarian unrest. It seems logical to reason, even now, that the current investment of the equivalent of several years of military budgets in soundly planned, progressive agrarian reform would be very profitable. Such programs would need the wholehearted co-

Table 16

GENERAL FUND, TAX REVENUES, AND EXPENDITURES[a]

(In hundreds of dollars)

Items	1945–1946	1946–1947	1947–1948	1948–1949
National govt. tax revenues	24,802	75,801	112,008	136,385
Local govt. tax revenues[b]	7,875	15,876	24,491	27,832
Total tax revenues	32,677	91,677	136,499	164,217
Gross national product	1,614,000	1,871,000	2,048,500	2,313,000
Per cent of tax revenue to gross national product	2.02	5.00	6.66	7.10
National govt. expenses	106,818	179,906	155,408	201,385
Local government expenses	19,500	26,649	34,293	35,803
Government corporation expenses	c	73,841	98,169	94,163
Total govt. expenses	c	280,397	287,871	331,351
Per cent of expenditure to gross national product	c	14.98	14.05	14.32

[a] These figures apply to the general fund only, and thus do not agree with figures given in table 15.
[b] Real property tax collections, applicable to current and previous years, and municipal license collections for the several years were:

Property	4,476	7,898	10,714	11,897
Munic. License	2,828	5,217	5,586	6,586

[c] Data incomplete, thus no totals available.
SOURCE: Adapted from several tables in *Central Bank Statistical Bulletin*, Vol. 2, No. 3 (1950).

operation of all levels of island society, but stimulating the creative initiative of individual enterprise can accomplish more than the continued use and misuse of the government corporation and the military force. Given a reasonable chance, the small farmers can do much for themselves that the government corporation never can do.

Concerning agriculture, admittedly still the heart of Philippine economy, the *Bell Report* noted: "The problem of inefficient agricultural production is partly a matter of putting to use better methods of cultivation, partly a matter of giving incentive to those who till the soil. . . . The difficulty is not so much in knowing what to do as in getting it done."[174] And on the matter of psychological mobilization an earlier commission stated: "The Commission regards the next few years as a period of national emergency . . . in the sense that emergency measures and an emergency national psychology will be required if the country is to grasp the opportunities for rapid economic development which are presented."[175]

The conclusion is inescapable that, so far, the problem of "getting it done" has not been solved, and neither has there developed the needed "emergency national psychology" requisite to the solution. There is now beginning another five-year trial period of United States aid during which relative success or relative failure may point the way to a happier or a stormier future. If many of the problems in rural economy suggested in earlier chapters are not well on their way to liquidation by the end of another five years, the rural unrest and the agrarian unhappiness feeding the fires of civil strife may grow steadily larger until those fires, under communist leadership, get out of control and the Philippines becomes another of the "hot spots of the Asian fringe."

Whether industrialization is or is not a good thing for Philippine economy today is not, in itself, the chief policy problem facing island leaders. The primary problems of the Philippines today are problems of rural economy, just as the primary problems of China during the 1930's were problems of rural economy. The most pressing policy decision is how to solve the problems of average and numerous small farmers. A group of Chinese leaders during the 1930's gambled on trade and industrialization alone, without agrarian reform, but, beset with increasing corruption and the Sino-Japanese war, they finally lost everything.

The United States already has given the islands their political independence, and today we cannot undertake to carry out the reform programs directly. Perhaps political freedom was given too

Table 17

COMPARISON OF ESTIMATED GROSS NATIONAL PRODUCT[a]

(In millions of dollars)

Production	1938 Values	1948–1949 Values	1948–1949 Per cent
Primary production			
Palay (rough rice)	241	368.7	15.9
Corn	b	53.6	2.3
Fruit and nuts	b	35.7	1.5
Root crops	b	44.8	1.9
Beans and vegetables	b	9.5	c
Coffee and cacao	b	4.2	c
Peanuts	b	3.0	c
All other home-use crops	b	2.5	c
Fish and fish products	30	236.8	10.2
Meat and poultry products	26	132.3	7.9
Milk and dairy products	d	6.5	c
Total for domestic consumption		947.8	41.0
Sugar	b	103.7	4.5
Coconut products	b	129.8	5.6
Abacá	b	31.5	1.4
Tobacco	b	8.7	c
Maguey	b	0.2	c
Rubber	b	0.5	c
Total for export purposes		274.1	11.8
Total	297.0	1,221.9	52.8
Secondary production			
Forestry	30 e	58.0	2.5
Mining and quarrying	36	34.0	1.5
Agricultural processing	f	212.5	9.2
General manufacturing	15	71.0	3.1
Total	81	317.5	16.3
Tertiary production			
Value added to imports	68.5	252.5	10.9
Professional services	135.0	463.0	20.1
Total	203.5	715.5	31.0
Total gross national product	581.5 g	2,313.0 g	100.0

a The total gross national product value for the year 1945–1946 has been put at $1,614,000,000, that for 1946–1947 at $1,871,000,000, and that for 1947–1948 at $2,048,000,000. Lower prewar prices must be considered against postwar totals, but the current trend shows rising production.
b Data for 1938 distinguished no details of agricultural production; all included under rice.
c Less than one-half of 1 per cent.
d Included under meat and poultry products.
e Included some building construction.
f Included in general manufacturing.
g These data give a per-capita income figure of about $32 for 1938 and about $118 for 1948–1949.
Sources: Adapted from *Central Bank Statistical Bulletin*, Vol. 2, No. 3 (1950). Data for 1938 from *Report of the Joint Philippine-American Finance Commission*, 1947.

Table 18

(In millions of dollars)

Agriculture, forestry, and fisheries	
Agriculture crops	
Rice..	58.9
Corn...	29.5
Coconut...	0.7
Sugar cane..	15.0
Abacá...	2.3
Tobacco...	2.9
All other crops...	9.2
Total...	*118.5*
Livestock..	218.5
Agric. implements..	12.5
Direct government projects.....................................	27.5
Total...	*258.5*
Sugar mills..	72
Forestry...	28.5
Fisheries and ponds..	27.5
Total...	*128.0*
TOTAL...	495
Industry, transport, and utilities	
Manufacturing..	237
Mining...	32
Transport..	99
Utilities..	86.5
TOTAL...	454.5
Commerce and trade	
Construction...	145.5
Furniture, fixtures, equipment.................................	45.5
Inventories..	436.5
TOTAL...	627.5
Building construction	
Public works: bldgs., roads, ports, etc.	
Philippine construction..	76
United States construction.....................................	49
Total...	*125*
Residential and other nonbusiness..............................	251.5
TOTAL...	376.5
TOTAL...	1,953.5

SOURCE: *Central Bank Statistical Bulletin*, Vol. 2, No. 3 (1950).

soon, or too casually, but this can no longer be a topic of argument. We must now work with the Filipinos, encouraging and aiding them to the effective development of a cultural, social, and economic independence on a stable political base that may strengthen their political independence. All levels of Filipino society must coöperate in this program in wholehearted manner, but most particularly the upper classes who, in terms of past economic, social, and cultural profit, now hold the reins of island leadership.

Chapter 19

THE ELEMENTS OF A PROGRAM

THE RECOGNITION of causes in a state of crisis is important, but more important is a concerted program of action designed to remove the causes. This study concludes, then, with suggestions and ideas useful in reducing the crisis, though a program of priorities and specific proposals lies beyond the scope of this study. These suggestions are in part the contributions of others, for each commission to visit the islands since the end of World War II has proposed remedial measures, and many Filipinos themselves have made critical proposals. The arrangements and phrasing of these ideas is my own, however, and the consideration is one of long-range solutions rather than of expedients of the moment.

It is difficult to prove which is the most basic element in the crisis that faces the Filipinos. Perhaps a geographer naturally reacts differently here than would an economist or a student of government. It is my feeling, however, that land and its management is the basic key to the problems of the rural Filipinos. It is here that the major elements of a program pointed toward solution of rural problems must focus.[176] First and foremost is land survey, both for classification of reserve lands and for cadastral record. The chief island need is for more farm land open to settlement, with easily secured titles on which farmers may obtain loans and credits to finance their improvements. Already far behind in its land survey program when independence came, the government of the Philippines has made no adequate provisions for speeding it up. What is needed are personnel and funds allocated to the Bureaus of Forestry and of Lands to bring the program not only up to date but to project it into the future in advance of demand, so that further pressures upon land will not build up into problems of agrarian unrest.

Related to the basic matter of provision of more land for settlement is the settlement of the tenancy problem in the crowded Central Plain of Luzon. All previous approaches have been repressive or legalistic only. This now is a large issue and only a large-scale solution will suffice. The solution will be costly, but not more costly than years of rebellion, punitive military action, possible civil war, and the accompanying destruction of property and lives. A share of the present farm population should remain where it is, but a large number of the tenant farmers must move to other reserve areas where they may become landowners; and the landlord equity within the central plain region must be liquidated in some fair and peaceful manner.

This major resettlement program cannot begin, however, until the Bureau of Forestry frees potential farm land by classifying it and releasing it to the Bureau of Lands. And it needs to delimit those areas best suited and most needed for watershed control, those most useful as parks and recreational areas, and those now needing reforestation, before it is too late to permit their proper control and development. The reforestation program should serve several ends. Reforestation by public and private agencies should be carried out for timber-producing purposes on a permanent sustained-yield basis in selected areas near domestic lumber markets and ports for foreign shipping. In other areas, reforestation should include watershed control and water-supply servicing. In still other areas, it should be carried out as a means of reducing the wasteful grass cover that inhibits more profitable forms of land use. When grassy areas are brought under control, final long-range land-use programs should be developed, and some of the former grass land should go into agricultural or other uses.

The land problem is larger than the matter of reclassification and survey alone, however. The Division of Soil Survey and Conservation has just been enlarged into a Bureau, with increased duties. But it badly needs increased powers, funds, and personnel. Both remedial and conservation work is urgently needed in many localities. The present personnel of the Bureau knows what to do, but is unable to accomplish the task on present authority and funds. The survey of soils and the preaching of new farming practices is not enough. Remedial action, backed by legislative authority, should include all farms of project areas in the most critical zones at an early date. It should not wait for a new generation to become convinced reluctantly that some of the new ideas may be of value. Such programs gradually can be extended beyond initial projects to almost all parts of the islands with profit.

The extension of irrigation projects can never cover the whole of the farmland of the islands, but in many areas the gradual development of facilities would be extremely profitable. Huge projects alone are not the whole answer. There are many small projects well worth fostering. Though they need to be shown how, landowners and community groups themselves can do much in the matter of leveling fields, adapting local water supplies, and working out rotational water-use policies. This whole field of endeavor should be a coöperative program fostered by the several bureaus of the Department of Agriculture and Natural Resources.

The legal and practical concepts of land ownership should be carefully reviewed in relation to tenancy problems of the present and the future, and in relation to the modernization of island agriculture. There is too great a gulf between law and practice in this matter. Although policy since the coming of the Americans has been to keep the islands a land of small farmers, people with knowledge, wealth, and influence have too often nullified policy. In many areas physical geography permits mechanized farming, but in practice the Bureau of Lands restricts individual issue of new lands to farms so small that effective mechanization is impossible. Although it is perfectly logical to restrict corporate and family holdings so that they do not become dominant elements in the economy, it should be recognized that this aim has not been achieved. And it must be realized that two branches of government cannot successfully preach mechanized farming on the one hand, and on the other restrict holdings to areas too small to permit mechanization.

The present programs of encouraging mechanization of farming are far too limited. They do not reach a sufficiently large section of the population. Whereas much of mechanization must be an individual matter of application by the farmers themselves, too little is being done to educate the farming population to the possibilities. Companies selling machinery cannot do all the training that is required, and the present efforts of government agencies are too restricted.

Too much effort, over the last two decades, has been devoted to formal government settlement programs and government agricultural production and marketing programs. In a country aspiring to personal freedoms and private initiative, government cannot expect to participate too directly in the matter of moving, settling, and caring for its rural population. Nor can it effectively compete with privately operated agriculture. Rather than enlarge or continue its efforts in these directions, government should restrict its role to setting up and managing those public facilities that will enable a rural population to act for itself, to do its own moving, settling, producing, and marketing.

Although early American action had almost to start from the beginning in building a highway system and in establishing port facilities, both programs have moved too slowly. Rural settlement is far ahead of government services and is greatly handicapped by its isolation. Long settled areas never have acquired the facilities needed. Reserve areas are unavailable to profitable and progressive settlement owing to the total absence of all such facilities. This applies to large islands and to small. There are dozens of small islands that have neither roads nor port facilities and almost none have airfields. Airfields, ports, and the highway system need doubling. Neither airfields nor ports need to be expensive or large, but facilities for small-to-medium planes and for small boats to medium-size interisland ships are badly needed on many islands and isolated peninsular sectors. Frontier highways also should have high priority. The building and maintenance of roads, ports, and airfields should be the responsibility of government. Automobiles, trucks, ships, boats, and airplanes will be privately supplied if government does not restrict opportunity for acquisition.

Telegraph, telephone, and radio communication seem to be both private and governmental in various parts of the world. In the Philippines the telegraph system is government operated and greatly needs extension. Government encouragement for other communication facilities has not been adequate. The mileage of telegraph and telephone lines needs doubling at the very least at the earliest possible date. Much of the new mileage should be allocated to frontier areas now difficult of access.

Related to land and its management are technical matters of productive capacity. I refer here to experiment, research, and development of crops and animals, to work on disease and pest control, on detailed farming practices, and to the need for testing services. Philippine agricultural land use needs to broaden its range and increase its variety of production on improved levels. Enlargement of the Bureaus of Plant Industry and Animal Industry, of the Fiber Inspection Service, and of the Agricultural Extension Service is greatly needed. Not only is enlargement necessary, but authority is needed to enforce practices that are for the good of all. In too many lines Philippine production records now rate near the bottom, compared to world averages. There are too many areas in which a farm family simply has no access to services which could raise its productive capacity. Today this is a recognized function of government, and government has lagged far behind.

Closely related to the above is the whole pattern of agricultural education. Elementary school gardening is fine, but much of it is impractical for the farmer to adopt. The situation calls for a reorienting of the programs of many secondary schools, for many more agricultural and vocational high schools, and for a marked increase in educational facilities on the college level. This enlargement cannot be directed toward one thing alone—as, for example, rice production. It must be comprehensive and deal with crop products, animals, forestry, irrigation and water control, range man-

243

agement, fisheries, mechanics, home economics, business and farm management, marketing, agricultural economics, and other aspects of progressive rural life. The one College of Agriculture now at Los Baños, Luzon, falls far short of filling island needs in these matters.

The nationalizing of fishing waters and the continued research and development of fishery resources are important in creating self-sufficiency of the island food supply. In part this is a matter affecting the rural population along scattered coasts, and in part it touches the commercial fishing activities of urban-based operators and companies. In the last three years some progress has been made in this direction, but its results have not yet reached the rural populace that should also benefit from it. Continued development, specifically to aid the small-scale village and small-town coastal fisherman, is needed.

Public health programs designed to reach beyond the cities and long-settled areas are vital parts of a program of spreading the crowded populations of the islands out into reserve areas. Some of these efforts must precede settlement and colonization and grow in scope with the population rather than waiting until large populations accumulate and cities develop to attract private medical services. Too large a share of the medical services of the islands, both public and private, is concentrated in urban, settled, and relatively healthy areas.

There is no doubt that tax and fiscal reform must be carried out as a vital part of both national and local government administration. In large degree work in this direction already is going on. Higher and more carefully levied taxes will and should result from such change, so that the total tax burden is more evenly spread. But higher taxes will make even more urgent the problems of local financing for the rural population. As changes continue—changes such as the improvement of agriculture, the increase of animal husbandry, the mechanization in agriculture and in local transport, and the greater expansion of developing local resources—the problem of rural credit will become steadily more serious. It will be necessary to lessen the role of the Chinese as a village moneylender and of the big landholder as a tenant creditor if the rural population is to develop financial strength and stability.

The establishment of rural credit facilities that enable all elements and all geographical sectors of the rural countryside to participate is an urgent need. The coöperative can be but one element in this program, though with proper educational encouragement it can be an important one. Private banking is another element in the larger program of regional financing, though it should be more important than it now is. In the coming period in the Philippines, government credit agencies are fundamental necessities. They must be arranged and managed to extend credit to the small farmer, the small merchant, the beginner in rural industry, transport, and trade. In the past such agencies have been highly centralized, have declined small dealings, have benefited the already well-to-do, and have completely failed to provide effective rural credit. The inability to make contact with the rural element and the absence of land titles and other security guarantees have been inhibiting factors in credit development. But also the refusal of private and government banks to deal in small amounts in the rural countryside has been important in past failures. A rural mindedness is necessary if future programs are to succeed. Such credit provision programs, of course, can only go hand in hand with land survey, the issuance of land titles, the freeing of the debt-ridden tenant class, the development of transport, and the growth of communications facilities.

Problems of marketing and management need attention. The inexperience of the rural and small-town Filipino in commercial dealings, in financial management, and in effective marketing procedures is a serious handicap to the development of a stable and prosperous rural populace. In part these difficulties arise from lack of contact of many of the rural element with advanced and complex elements of economic and social culture. In part they arise out of the failure of the educational system to acquaint them with techniques and skills needed on the higher economic and cultural planes to which the Filipinos aspire. The solutions probably lie in no single direction, but in improved transport and communications, in more effective agricultural and vocational education, in the establishment of libraries and the facilities for adult education, and, perhaps, in the simple element of time and maturity of a growing culture.

In the long-range prospect the Philippines seeks a degree of industrialization in order to develop a more stable economy. Legislation, mobilization of government organization, development of power facilities, stimulation of corporate organization, support of financing, and encouragement of production have been under way for some years. Most of these have aimed at medium and large-scale urban industrialization. Advanced technical education is beginning to turn out large numbers of moderately trained personnel. Foreign study applicable to industry is encouraged for various types of personnel. Government stimulation of urban industrialization is more pronounced than for progressive rural and agricultural development. There is no doubt that encouragement of industrialization is important, but the balance currently seems unduly weighted toward urban and large-scale development.

Since one of the chronic problems of the Philippines is underemployment of the rural population, which to date possesses only limited skills, it would follow that a share of stimulation should be given to decentralized, light, and secondary aspects of industrialization that can gradually offer employment alternative to agriculture among the rural population. Eventually these small industries could fill many of the domestic needs for fabricated products and could begin to add to the exports. Basic in this direction is the development of decentralized power systems that would more effectively serve the many small towns and cities and some of the rural hinterlands. Without power the competitive struggle will be between industrial production abroad and handicraft production in the islands, from which only a marginal economic return is possible. With the development of power facilities must go further development of rural resources and industries. Coupled with this should be a greater emphasis upon mechanical and vocational education in the secondary schools and the various colleges similar to that of the many American trade schools. Increase in volume of present lines of export manufactures to other parts of the islands is possible, and there are many forms of expansion possible over a period of time. Almost the whole range of consumer manufactures imported into the islands offers opportunity to rural industry, but until power, some technical training, and some stimulation are given to rural industrialization, developments will be slow and subject to repeated local failures.

Actually the improvements and changes suggested in the above paragraph are the more final and vital part of the whole program of improving Philippine economy. Basically the rural problem is one of insufficient income and the maldistribution of that income. Land reform, mechanization, or improved transport become only means to the end of increased productivity. Widely spread measures designed to drain off excess agricultural labor into other productive enterprise must go hand in hand with improved productivity in agriculture itself. The islands should not remain merely a region of small-scale farmers. Currently ECA activities are moving in directions that should serve both strictly agricultural and small-scale industrial ends. The United States can start the program, but Filipinos themselves must pick it up and carry it forward energetically and efficiently if lasting progress is to be achieved and Communist encroachment upon the islands is to be forestalled.

Many of the above-mentioned needs fall into the domain of the Department of Agriculture and Natural Resources, but several key items pertain to the Department of Public Works and Communications. So far as the nonindustrial development of the islands is concerned, these are the key departments of the Philippine government in future corrective development. These departments, more than any others, must deal with the basic problems of maintaining a livelihood that face the largest number of Filipinos—the rural agricultural element. At no time since the inception of American control of the islands has either been effectively supported in creating or carrying out progressive programs for the development of resources. Time after time proposals from within the two departments have been canceled, postponed, or cut by lack of funds while the very needs have been growing.

This becomes a criticism of American administrative or of Filipino legislative control rather than a criticism of the personnel of the two departments, for both departments have long been technically capable of far more than they have been permitted to do. Recently the Bureau of Mines has received significant support, and the island mining industry has developed rapidly, but too constantly other units of the departments have had to operate on such small scale that only token progress has resulted in many cases. Currently some changes are being made in this matter, but the rate of change is too slow, considering the magnitude of the problems. To recall an earlier comment, "The difficulty is not so much in knowing what to do as in getting it done."[17] The enlargement of duties, authority, personnel, and funds of the two departments is the first step in the long-range solution of the basic problems facing the rural population of the islands. The creation in recent years of special government corporations to tackle particular aspects of different problems has produced little result at great expense. It has often resulted in failure to utilize the resources available in the regular departments, and thus has committed many costly errors.

There is no intention of slighting other departments of government by picking out the two mentioned. Obviously the Department of Education, the Department of Finance, the Department of Public Health, the Department of Commerce and Industry, plus other branches of government, all are integral parts of the machinery needed to elevate the standard of living of the rural population of the islands. In that the rural population of the islands is still largely agricultural, and that so many of their difficulties stem from the land and from problems of basic production and distribution, it has seemed to me that this was a logical order of approach, an order that has not been effectively followed in the whole half century of American dealings with the Philippines.

Notes

Notes

[1] No page-by-page acknowledgment by notes is made in this chapter. The chapter represents the summary of my own years of interest, months of travel and field study, and contributions from every entry in the bibliography.

[2] It has been frequently said that the Philippines could become self-sufficient in rice through short-run improvement in agriculture. My generalization here pertains to recent conditions under which rice continues to be an import in spite of the varied attempts to attain self-sufficiency. Somewhat the same may be said for fish. Very possibly in the near future the import of each will become less important.

[3] Both the high price and the relative scarcity of sugar for home use are a result of the competition between home and export markets. Since the war the urge to restore the export trade has caused the government to set the export volume at a figure which results in the domestic market's being under-supplied.

[4] Reference here is to culture traits rather than to financial and trade dependence. Electric refrigerators, *Life* magazine, the bowling alley, and the latest musical recordings are examples of American items which, rightly or wrongly, typify the kind of higher living standard toward which urban Filipinos are moving.

[5] Outside Manila, wage levels are much lower, of course, but there is some local variation in actual rates. Minimum wage laws and government arbitration of labor disputes now are part of the scene, but the enforcement of minimum or arbitrated wage levels is not yet very efficient in many parts of the islands. The December, 1950, cost-of-living index for Manila stood at 352.2, against a 1941 base of 100. *American Chamber of Commerce Journal*, 27 (1951), 28. The cost of living is much lower in most provincial areas. The Manila industrial wage index for September, 1950, stood at 331.9 and 366.1 for skilled and unskilled labor, against a 1941 base of 100. *Central Bank Statistical Bulletin*, 2:4 (1950), 177.

[6] Admittedly this is not an effective pinpointing of the average rural income, but such data as exist indicate that most income recipients receive less than $500 per year, and rural incomes vary roughly within these limits in different parts of the country. *Ibid.*, 2:3 (1950).

[7] I do not wish to enter, here or in later paragraphs, the discussion of how agriculture began, which were its first crops, or whether aquatic or dry cultivation of rice came first.

[8] Karl J. Pelzer, *Pioneer Settlement in the Asiatic Tropics*, American Geographical Society Special Publication no. 29 (New York, 1945), discusses shifting and sedentary agriculture in their general aspects in various parts of the Orient. R. L. Pendleton, "Land Utilization and Agriculture of Mindanao, Philippine Islands," *Geographical Review*, 32 (1942), 180–210, has some excellent photographs of various aspects of the caingin process.

[9] No reference is made here to contemporary curio and handicraft exports, which are of quite recent origin, but to things made by the people for themselves in their own native ways during recent centuries. In porcelains, copper, iron, silk and other textiles, and in similar materials the Philippines has long been an importer.

[10] There were about 200,000 drivers licensed by 1949. *Central Bank Statistical Bulletin*, 2:3 (1950).

[11] I have used this term in the sense that J. H. Boeke used it in *The Structure of Netherlands Indian Economy* (New York, 1942), pp. 6–13, to indicate a society possessing a degree of communalism and primary production by individual labor, but relatively lacking a dominant money economy. In urban areas and some rural fringes conditions are changing rapidly.

[12] Providing, of course, that arbitrary protectionist policy does not adversely affect island economy by building up too many high-cost industries.

[13] See table xi which presents the comparative indices of production during the period of postwar reconstruction. The data were taken from the *Central Bank Statistical Bulletin*, 2: 4 (1950), 109. On this subject see also repeated comment in *Report to the President of the United States by the Economic Survey Mission to the Philippines* (Washington, Oct., 1950), to be noted hereafter as *Bell Report*.

[14] This assumes that every Filipino uses English. If this were true the country would rank after Great Britain but ahead of Canada. It is not literally true, but the spread of English has been important in social change in the last half century.

[15] *Philippine Social Trends, Basic Documents Pertinent to Long-Range Social Welfare Planning in the Philippines*, (Manila, 1950), p. 17, to be referred to hereafter as *Philippine Social Trends*.

[16] Current calculations estimate the increase of population at 500,000 per year. *Manila Times Mid-Week Review*, Feb. 14, 1951.

[17] I have used modest figures here. Currently all sorts of figures are being set forth, many far higher than these. *Ibid.*

[18] There is no question, however, that a lower segment of the population has suffered a decreasing standard during and since the war.

[19] J. P. Mamisao, "Soil Conservation Problems in the Philippines," *Journal of the Soil Science Society of the Philippines*, 1 (1949), 5–17.

[20] The fertilizer needs of the islands at present are estimated to be four million tons per year, but less than 200,000 tons are imported annually. M. M. Alicante, "The Fertilizer Problem in the Ecafe Region," *Journal of the Soil Science Society of the Philippines*, 1 (1949), 18–30.

[21] See the maps illustrating the progress of soil surveys in *Journal of the Soil Science Society of the Philippines*, 1, supp. (1949), 7, 11.

[22] Tuba is also made by tapping the nipa palm, which is a swamp-growing tree from which thatching materials are secured.

[23] See the import data in my article "The Philippine Rice Problem," *Far Eastern Survey*, 18 (June 1, 1949), 125–128.

[24] For a tabular summary contrasting prewar food balances and imports of 1947–1948, see F. M. Sacay, "The Food Supply and Population of the Philippines," *The Philippine Agriculturist*, 33 (1950), 203–217.

[25] See table 7 for data on fisheries. The most commonly harvested fish is the bañgos, also known as the milkfish (*Chanos chanos*). Literature on the culture of bañgos is easily available, for example, "The Raising of Bañgos," Department of Agriculture and Commerce, Division of Fisheries, Food Production Series, no. 6 (reissued, Aug. 1946). The fishponds of the islands were not destroyed during the war.

[26] In addition to the data in table 5, see also map 10 for illustration of regional food deficiency.

[27] See J. R. Hayden's edition of D. C. Worcester, *The Philippines Past and Present* 1930), pp. 623–629. The road system in 1912 totaled about 4,500 miles, A. V. Castillo, *Philippine Economics* (1949), p. 353.

[28] *The Philippines, 1950, A Handbook of Trade and Economic Facts and Figures* (1950), p. 49, listed hereafter as *The Philippines, 1950*.

[29] *Central Bank Statistical Bulletin*, 2:4 (1950), 118.

[30] *Facts and Figures about Economic and Social Conditions in the Philippines, 1946–1947*, listed hereafter as *Facts and Figures, 1946–1947*.

[31] Import control in 1950 lowered the import of automotive equipment. During 1950 only 2,967 vehicles were brought in, against 6,117 in 1949. *American Chamber of Commerce Journal*, 27 (1951), 60.

[32] From a personal communication of Dec. 7, 1948.

[33] For the earlier period see Hayden's edition of Worcester, *op. cit.*, pp. 622–623. See also *Manila Times Mid-Week Review*, Nov. 24, and Dec. 8, 1948.

[34] In 1949 the Manila Railroad Line on Luzon hauled 863,416 metric tons of freight and express. Ranking cargoes in order were manufactures, wood products, sugar cane, rice, and copra. The total passenger movement for the year was 6,205,076. A little over half the total revenue is derived from the passenger haul. *Central Bank Statistical Bulletin*, 2:3 (1950).

[35] *Manila Bulletin*, Dec. 27, 1948.

[36] The survey work has been completed for the 125-mile distance between the prewar railhead at San Jose, Nueva Ecija, and Echague, in southern Isabela. *Manila Times*, Nov. 1, 1949.

[37] I am thinking here of such items as the possible value of a rail line between the Malangas coal fields on the south coast of northern Zamboanga Province and the potential industrial development at Iligan, on the eastern Lanao coast on the north side of the peninsula, as a secondary consequence of the Maria Christina Falls hydroelectric development.

[38] See the brief comment on the subject in the *Bell Report*, pp. 65–66.

[39] See Hayden's edition of Worcester, *op. cit.*, pp. 615–619.

[40] On June 30, 1949, the interisland commercial fleet totaled 3,771 vessels with a net tonnage of 217,379 as against 3,547 vessels having a net tonnage of 154,613 in 1940. *The Philippines, 1950*, p. 52.

[41] The Philippine Air Lines, the largest domestic operator, is carrying between 240,000 and 300,000 passengers per year, and between 9,000,000 and 12,400,000 pounds of air freight per year in its domestic service, in addition to handling mail. *First Annual Report*, Central Bank of the Philippines, (Manila, 1949), p. 281.

[42] Reference is to the *Yearbook of Philippine Statistics* and to the *Central Bank Statistical Bulletin* particularly.

[43] *Annual Baling Report of the Fiber Inspection Service*, Manila, 1949.

[44] *Facts and Figures . . . 1946–1947.*

[45] *Yearbook of Philippine Statistics*, 1940 and 1946.

[46] Interpolated from data in *Facts and Figures . . . 1946–1947.*

[47] *Summaries of Philippine Foreign Trade*, Bureau of Commerce, Manila, 1948.

[48] In 1949 domestic production of cigarettes was about one-fifth the number imported from the United States. Import controls and restrictions upon American tobacco will help the local industry's home market, but whether the export market will recover is another question. *Central Bank Statistical Bulletin*, 2:3 (1950).

[49] C. Benitez, *History of the Philippines*, (Boston, 1940), p. 426.

[50] Already, in the Philippines, strong suggestions are being made for alteration of details of the Bell Act. See H. Q. Borromeo, "Time to Revise the Bell Act," *Manila Times Mid-Week Review*, Jan. 17, 1951.

[51] See E. M. Alip, *Philippine History, Political, Social, Economic*, chaps. iv and x; Benitez, *op. cit.*, chap. iv; Castillo, *op. cit.*, pp. 84 ff. and 178 ff.; and Hayden's edition of Worcester, *op. cit.*, chap. xxiv.

[52] Although the Philippines is not included in the discussion as such, see Wilhelm Roscher, *The Spanish Colonial System* (New York, 1944), for a general description of Spanish methods and principles.

[53] See E. H. A. Blair and J. A. Robertson, *The Philippine Islands, 1493–1803*, Vol. 1; "Historical Introduction" by E. G. Bourne, particularly pp. 48–61; and J. Foreman, *The Philippine Islands*, 1899, chaps. xii and xiii.

[54] See Hayden's edition of Worcester, *op. cit.*, chaps. xviii and xix.

[55] Protest against the policy came from a wide variety of sources, including some American officials in the islands. It is only proper to record the fact that some of the support of the policy of small holdings came from congressional members supporting the domestic sugar industry of the United States, who feared the results of island sugar industry.

[56] Hayden's edition of Worcester, *op. cit.*, chaps. xxviii and xxix describes the early American period; *Land Resources of the Philippines*, Department of Agriculture and Commerce, Manila, 1939, describes changing patterns; Pelzer, *op. cit.*, reviews the entire matter. Personal interviews with several Bureau of Lands provincial offices supplied recent notes.

[57] Based in part on personal interviews with various Bureau of Forestry officers.

[58] Actually there is great variance in assessment rates, from less than 1 per cent to 1.5 per cent. *Central Bank Statistical Bulletin*, 2:3 (1950).

Notes

[59] D. Z. Rosell, "Land Classification, Valuation and Assessment for Land Taxation in the Philippines," *Journal of the Soil Science Society of the Philippines*, 2 (1950), 238–248.

[60] *Philippine Social Trends*, 1950, p. 13.

[61] Data in this section were taken from R. G. Hainsworth and R. T. Moyer, *Agricultural Geography of the Philippine Islands, A Graphic Summary*, U. S. Dept. of Agriculture, Office of Foreign Agricultural Relations, Washington, D. C., 1945, and from volumes of the *Census of the Philippines*, 1939.

[62] The 1903 *Census of the Philippine Islands*, Vol. 4, p. 190, carries a provincial table of the distribution of tenancy in which two units, Basilan Island and Cotabato show 100.0 per cent of the farmers as owners, and one unit, Benguet (the forerunner of the modern Mountain Province), with 1.3 per cent owners and 98.7 per cent squatters. The only other regional units that show any appreciable number of squatters in the returns are Cavite with 9.7 per cent, Nueva Ecija with 7.0 per cent, and Zamboanga with 7.8 per cent.

[63] *Reports of the Philippine Commission*, 1900–1903, pp. 49–50.

[64] Pelzer, *op. cit.*, has reviewed the tenancy problem in some detail. See the following chapter for details on this and other government action in settlement projects.

[65] *New York Times*, March 30, 1950.

[66] R. H. Fifield, "The Hukbalahap Today," *Far Eastern Survey*, 20 (1951), 13–18.

[67] *New York Times*, Oct. 1, 1950.

[68] Boeke, *op. cit.*, pp. 35–39.

[69] Castillo, *op. cit.*, pp. 484–486 and pp. 731–732.

[70] *The Philippines*, 1950, pp. 61–62.

[71] *First Annual Report*, Central Bank of the Philippines, 1949, p. 92; *Bell Report*, pp. 27–32; *Manila Times Mid-Week Review*, Aug. 2, 1950.

[72] Castillo, *op. cit.*, p. 486.

[73] Pelzer, *op. cit.*, pp. 92–95, provides the details for a number of these procedures.

[74] Owing to the high incidence of default on loan payments in rural areas, government subsidy of interest rates may be needed to lower effectively the rates and stimulate the development of rural credit facilities.

[75] Castillo, *op. cit.*, pp. 250–256.

[76] *Ibid.*, p. 406; *Manila Times Mid-Week Review*, Dec. 13, 1950.

[77] Figures differ on the total. *Ibid.*, pp. 250–256, gives a total of 571 coöperatives scattered over 43 provinces, with a capital of $1,690,000, and some 36,000 borrowers. Another figure for the same date is 718 registered coöperatives, 640 of which were consumer organizations. *Philippine Social Trends*, p. 27.

[78] Figures again differ. Castillo, *op. cit.*, pp. 681–682, reports 1,300 registered coöperatives, with a membership of 254,986 heads of families, whereas *Philippine Social Trends*, p. 27, suggests that 528 coöperatives were organized in the three years 1946–1948, but does not indicate how many prewar groups still were in existence. Both sources agree that most of the present groups are organized as consumer coöperatives. As of September, 1950, there were 1,459 active coöperatives, with $1,309,000 paid-in capital. *Central Bank Statistical Bulletin*, 2:4 (1950), 50–53.

[79] Castillo, *op. cit.*, pp. 682–683.

[80] *Ibid.*, pp. 250–256.

[81] H. O. Beyer and J. C. DeVeyra, *Philippine Saga* (Manila, 1947), pp. 20–23; Alip, *op. cit.*, pp. 32–35.

[82] Beyer and DeVeyra, *op. cit.*, pp. 69–81; Alip, *op. cit.*, chap. xiii; and Benitez, *op. cit.*, chap. vii.

[83] Pelzer, *op. cit.*, pp. 127–135, summarizes these efforts.

[84] *Ibid.*, pp. 137–159 and 243–248, devotes considerable space to the NLSA program in Mindanao and provides some notes on the Cagayan Valley project.

[85] Hayden's edition of Worcester, *op. cit.*, pp. 591–595. Some of this data was acquired directly from the Bureau of Lands. In 1948, some 50,000 acres of the original Friar Lands purchase, chiefly in Mindoro, still lay idle and unsold, largely owing to inadequate transportation facilities in the area.

[86] Personal interview, December, 1948. See also Z. Castrilio, "Government Acquisition of Large Landed Estates," *American Chamber of Commerce Journal*, 27 (1951), 44–45, with follow-up editorial and correspondence comment on pp. 112 and 151.

[87] *Manila Times Mid-Week Review*, Dec. 13, 1950.

[88] *New York Times*, May 4, 1949.

[89] In March, 1951, this statement was valid. Current changes and increases in the program could make this generalization untrue in the near future.

[90] Pelzer, *op. cit.*, p. 110, comments that the 1937 accumulation of work awaiting the survey parties amounted to some 4,000,000 parcels of land, enough to keep thirty cadastral survey teams busy for sixty years. With destruction of records during World War II, the task of reconstituting records alone is enormous, and the Bureau of Lands today has a tremendous task facing it, with quite inadequate help. Although it cannot be termed official policy, provincial Bureau officers in frontier regions often advise settlers to pick out what land they want, cultivate as much of it as possible to establish claim, and pay taxes on it in the hope that something may some day be done about a title. Actually as serious as the lack of survey facilities is the problem of the land registration courts. Reduction of courts and personnel came at a time when cases were piling up. The situation never has been rectified.

[91] Pendleton, *op. cit.*, p. 180, begins his article with a warning that Mindanao can not be a home to every Filipino from a crowded area. These preliminary figures may well prove too optimistic.

[92] I. A. Romero, "Jomalig Island, A Site for Agricultural Development," *Journal of the Soil Science Society of the Philippines*, 2 (1950), 249–254.

[93] There is much confusion in terminology surrounding rice growing. Throughout the Orient the term "upland rice" perhaps is the most common one used to designate rice grown without benefit of irrigation, though a variety of other terms are used. Many terms apply to rice that is variably irrigated in some manner, with no real agreement in usage. Commonly "wet," "irrigated," and "lowland" are taken as nearly or fully synonymous, whereas, "upland," "dry," and "mountain" are similarly considered equivalent. In the Philippines in many valleys and plains regions at both low and medium elevations rice starts out being irrigated rice in the sense of wet-field rice because it is plowed and planted in the rainiest season

of the year and the fields have earth walls around them to impound rain waters falling on the immediate fields. Later many of these same fields dry out at some point before the maturity of the plants or the ripening of the grain, owing to the cessation of the rains and the absence of irrigation systems. This cannot accurately be called "irrigated" rice, but neither is it properly termed "dry" rice. Some of this type of crop land clearly falls into what I have termed upland, whereas some of it certainly is marginal upon the aquatic lowland zone. I propose to use the term "irrigated rice" to refer to rice grown on fields whose natural moisture derived from rainfall is supplemented by water derived from river, lake, canal, or other man-controlled source, whether it occurs in the aquatic margin, the terrace country of north Luzon, or in some other highland locality. The term "upland rice" does not cover everything else, in my application, but pertains to rice grown on slopes, flat surfaces, dry lands, or other sites in which there is no attempt whatsoever to impound even rain water. This, to some degree, is unsatisfactory, but the trouble stems from the lack of understanding of rice agriculture and the inequality of reference to rice-growing practices by those who write of it.

[94] In interior Cotabato, in the Liguasan Marsh, I have seen rice harvested from small boats and have seen men and women wading shoulder deep in their swamp fields plucking the crop head by head. In these circumstances one cannot speak of a controlled water system.

[95] See regional distribution of irrigated lands in 1939 in Hainsworth and Moyer, *op. cit.*, table 5, p. 50. See also G. J. Militante, "Irrigation Problems in the Philippines," FAO *Second Special Report* (Manila, 1948), pp. 1–21.

[96] Crop returns in the Philippines are tabulated in units of cavans per hectare. The cavan is, like the bushel, a measure of volume, and is roughly equivalent to 97 pounds, when used to measure palay, the unmilled grain. Cavan measures vary markedly, however, when used for other commodities. The hectare is equivalent to 2.47 acres.

[97] Food and Agriculture Organization of the United Nations, *Rice and Rice Diets, A Nutritional Survey* (Washington, D.C., 1948), p. 13.

[98] Militante, *op. cit.*, p. 6.

[99] Table 9 is made up from 1939 Census data because the 1948 data have not yet been made available. Numbers must be larger than given in the 1939 tables, and the text here crudely interpolates toward the 1948 totals.

[100] See *A Handbook of Philippine Agriculture* (Los Baños, 1939), chaps. 3, 4, 6; F. G. Galang and F. C. Panganiban, *Agricultural Extension Service Handbook*, Manila, 1949, various sections; *Our National Food Production Campaign*, Manila, 1949, various sections.

[101] See J. S. Simmons, *Global Epidemiology* (Philadelphia, 1944), pp. 406–415, and Hayden's edition of Worcester, *op. cit.*, pp. 329–358, for details of health conditions in the early American period, with comment on the programs of health improvement then being undertaken.

[102] Simmons, *op. cit.*, pp. 413–415.

[103] *Manila Times*, Feb. 12, 1950.

[104] Simmons, *op. cit.*, pp. 408–409.

[105] Pelzer, *op. cit.*, p. 113.

[106] *Manila Times,* Feb. 12, 1950.

[107] Total estimated from data presented in the *Manila Times,* Aug. 8, 1948 and Feb. 12, 1950.

[108] *Yearbook of Philippine Statistics,* 1946.

[109] See detailed examination of this subject in *Rice and Rice Diets, A Nutritional Survey.*

[110] This average was obtained by adding together physicians, dentists, pharmacists, opticians, nurses, and midwives. A few other personnel should have been included but data were not available.

[111] This chapter is adapted from my paper on the same general subject in P. Gourou, J. E. Spencer, and G. T. Trewartha, *The Development of Upland Areas in the Far East,* 1 (1949), 26–58. *Institute of Pacific Relations, 1949.*

[112] In the southern islands silibon (*Themeda triandra*) also is a widespread grass, both on lowland surfaces and in the fairly rough and hilly areas.

[113] During 1950–1951 a surplus of timber resulted from the slackening of domestic building needs. Resumption of timber and lumber exports began on a small scale early in 1951.

[114] Before some of the wide variety of forest products are developed further, a laboratory is badly needed by the Bureau of Forestry to test the possibilities of many of the woods, rattans, and fibers which could come out of the forested uplands and so far find no effective use. See *Bell Report,* p. 58.

[115] In 1948 there were reported 622 labor unions, having a membership of 131,144 (*Philippine Social Trends,* p. 26). Figures for January, 1950, indicate 888 registered unions with 156,403 members (*Manila Times,* Feb. 12, 1950). Labor union members are engaged primarily in manufacturing, mining, and transportation, and are concentrated around and near Manila, Cebu, Iloilo, the Baguio gold-mining region, and a few other smaller centers. Organized labor is not a significant feature in the general rural agricultural scene, though it is beginning to have an effective voice on the large plantations that pay cash wages.

[116] A full discussion of industrialization is beyond the scope of this volume. For a general discussion of the topic in the prewar period see Kate L. Mitchell, *Industrialization of the Western Pacific,* chap. xi. 1942.

[117] Private American investment in the islands had reached a figure of almost $400,000,000 before World War II. The postwar total has not yet returned to that figure. *Manila Times Mid-Week Review,* Nov. 9, 1949.

[118] It is probable that American-owned land totals almost 500,000 acres at the present. *Ibid.*

[119] The *Bell Report,* pp. 53 and 66–68, recommended the liquidation of many of these government corporations, late in 1950. Something is being done in this direction as of mid-1951. *Manila Times Mid-Week Review,* Dec. 13, 1950, describes plans for government reorganization along this line.

[120] *Ibid.,* July 19, 1950 and Aug. 2, 1950.

[121] *Ibid.,* Feb. 6, 1950.

[122] This is a judgment which, of course, is entirely relative. Wage levels have risen less than retail prices in most parts of the islands and, where not accompanied by compensatory services to employees, do not provide recipients with living stand-

ards as high as those of the prewar period. Philippine union labor suffers from some racketeering, but so does United States union labor. The government Bureau of Labor is very badly understaffed and legislatively is poorly backed, so that it cannot perform the role, in the Philippines, that it supposedly performs in some other countries. On the other hand it is making progress and, compared to other parts of the Orient, is doing fairly well. Various commissions to the Philippines consistently have compared island accomplishments with the theoretical maximums sought in the United States rather than with what we actually have achieved. In 1951 minimum wage laws were passed to improve incomes of the lower economic segments of the population, but it will take time to enforce such laws.

[123] See my article "Abacá and the Philippines," *Economic Geography,* 27 (1951), 95–106. Not all large-scale agricultural endeavor is strictly corporate, in the usual sense, but its impact on the farmer is very similar.

[124] Both of these government concerns are scheduled for absorption into other administrative organizations in 1951 as part of the simplification of the government's corporate business structure.

[125] By 1949 only about $15,000,000 had been put into sugar-cane lands and growing facilities, including rehabilitation costs. Investments in the milling centers at the same date totaled some $101,500,000, of which $72,000,000 represented postwar investment. *Central Bank Statistical Bulletin,* 2:3 (1950).

[126] Data derived from the *Philippine Sugar Yearbook, 1950,* published by the Philippine Sugar Yearbook, Manila, 1950.

[127] In June, 1948, there were 342 sawmills in operation, with a capital investment of some $25,000,000, employing about 70,000 workmen (Castillo, *op. cit.,* pp. 278–280). The 1949 forest cut of timber slightly exceeded 1,000,000 board feet, of which some 492,000,000 board feet were turned into sawed lumber *(The Philippines, 1950,* p. 46). It is quite likely that the output of many a rural farmer and woodworker was not included in this tabulation, but there can be little contradiction of the importance of the corporation in the timber and lumber business in the islands today.

[128] See Castillo, *op. cit.,* p. 268, for notes on the development of mining in the islands, and the Bureau of Mines, *Mining Industry of the Philippines,* Information Circular No. 5. Manila, 1947.

[129] By September, 1950, there were approximately 4,379 corporations, 2,355 partnerships, and 1,459 coöperatives, including reconstituted and newly registered concerns, with a total of $410,700,000 net paid-in capital, of which close to $300,-000,000 belonged to corporations. Some 60 per cent of the paid-in capital was Filipino, about 27 per cent belonged to Chinese, and some 9 per cent was American. More than half of the corporations are in and around Manila, whereas not over 6 per cent are in Mindanao and hold no more than 2 per cent of the total capital. This concentration is less marked for partnerships and coöperatives. Not over 8 per cent of the corporations and almost none of the partnerships are registered as directly concerned with agriculture, listing only small capital resources. However, many large families do not incorporate their farms and thus the statistics are misleading at this point. The above data were extracted and interpolated from

several preliminary tables which were not fully equivalent in date or in content. *Central Bank Statistical Bulletin*, 2:3, 4, 1950.

[130] C. A. Buss, "The Philippines," *in* L. A. Mills and Associates, *The New World of Southeast Asia* (Minneapolis, 1949), pp. 18–78; reference to pp. 68–74.

[131] *Bell Report*, pp. 66–68; Castillo, *op. cit.*, p. 406.

[132] *Bell Report*, p. 52.

[133] *Ibid.*, the sum mentioned would amount to about $600,000.

[134] Taken from the last paragraph of "Instructions of the President to the Second Philippine Commission, April 7, 1900," printed in *Reports of the Philippine Commission, 1900–1903* (Washington, D.C., 1904), p. 11. See also Buss, *op. cit.*, pp. 29–30.

[135] See the section on "Soil Conservation—Its History and Development in the Philippines," from *Second Special Report* (1948), pp. 22–28.

[136] This campaign is not a formal three- or five-year plan, but is a concerted national program aimed at rice self-sufficiency first, and secondly at increase of production in export crop products. Involved are such items as opening new settlement areas, financing of farm machinery purchases, expansion of irrigation facilities through local power-pumping systems, and the establishment of a revolving fund for the purchase of fertilizers for small farmers. *Our National Food Production Campaign.*

[137] The *Bell Report*, pp. 55 ff., makes a strong point of the need to enlarge the College of Agriculture, University of the Philippines, which had less than 250 students in 1949–1950, and to triple the enrollment of students in agricultural high schools. The high school shown on the accompanying map at Munoz, Nueva Ecija, is to be turned into an agricultural college shortly. This is one sign of increasing activity in this field. *American Chamber of Commerce Journal*, 27 (1951), 46.

[138] 1948–1949 data indicate more than 21,000 schools of all kinds in the islands, with an enrollment less than 4,400,000. Some 19,000 of these are government elementary schools, with a distribution and a curricular program that are satisfactory only in the long-settled lowland areas. These account for 3,700,000 students. There are more than a thousand high schools, though only about three hundred of these are government schools. Most local high schools are urban in location and in curricula. About 400,000 students in 1948–1949 were attending high schools, more than half of whom were in private schools. There were some four hundred private vocational schools, with about 21,000 students, but few of these schools include agriculture in their programs of study. *Philippine Social Trends*, pp. 35–36.

[139] A postwar program was set up to develop 1,000 public libraries as one of the postwar services. By the close of 1948 only 144 libraries had been brought into existence, and only 8,110 books had been purchased. *Manila Times*, Nov. 27, 1948.

[140] See the recommendations of the *Report of the Philippine–United States Agricultural Mission*, Washington, D.C., 1947.

[141] The *Bell Report* leans in this direction. A more specific statement is contained in S. Araneta, "The Time is Now," *Manila Times Mid-Week Review*, Dec. 20, 1950. Both of these are representative of the plea for industrialization.

[142] Conclusions drawn from *Philippine Social Trends*, p. 14, and from the *Bell Report*, p. 36.

[143] Reference here is to import controls on consumers' goods. These have had a be-

wildering pattern of administration since 1948 when controls first were applied, and a strongly depressing effect upon 1950 imports. See *American Chamber of Commerce Journal*, 27 (Manila, 1951), 6, 9; *International News Financial News Survey*, 2 (1950), 389–390; F. H. Palmer, "Philippines Forced to Introduce Import and Export Controls," *Foreign Trade*, 7 (1950), 328–335.

[144] *Manila Times Mid-Week Review*, Feb. 14, 1951.

[145] Rice production, a major item in the food picture, was sufficient for about 61 per cent of requirements in 1946, whereas the corn supply was sufficient for only 53 per cent of the 1946 requirement. *Bell Report*, Supplementary Data Papers.

[146] *First Annual Report*, Central Bank of the Philippines, 1949, tables 44–46, pp. 282–286.

[147] *Ibid.*, tables 48 and 49, p. 291.

[148] Above data taken from the several *Semi-Annual Reports*, Philippines War Damage Commission, Washington, D.C. See the *New York Times*, April 25, 1950. A cumulative statement of private and public claims by periods of payment is contained in *Central Bank Economic Indicators*, First half of 1950, Central Bank of the Philippines, p. 74.

[149] The Moslem province of Lanao in Mindanao (1948 population, 343,000) put in 79,552 claims, almost one per family, for a total sum of $46,778,000, of which $41,167,000 was for personal property. Negros Occidental (1948 population, 1,038,000) put in 95,542 private claims for $88,608,000, of which the chief claims were $39,945,000 for personal property, $23,014,000 for buildings, $21,098,000 for inventories, and $1,523,000 for motor vehicles. Mountain Province (1948 population, 278,000) put in 31,114 private claims for $29,901,000, of which $6,012,000 was for personal property, $5,942,000 was for buildings, $12,410,000 was for inventories, and $5,578,000 was for land. Manila (population of the political unit in 1948 was 983,000) private claims amounted to only 33,896 in number, but they asked for $242,053,000, about one-fifth of the island total claim, of which most was designated for inventories and for buildings. *Semi-Annual Reports of the U. S. Philippine War Damage Commission*, June 30, 1948.

[150] J. J. Halsema, "Development Plans in the Philippines," *Far Eastern Survey*, 18 (1949), 233–237; and K. Bekker and C. Wolf, Jr., "The Philippine Balance of Payments," *Far Eastern Survey*, 19 (1950), pp. 41–43.

[151] Between July, 1945 and June, 1949, almost $76,000,000 was spent on public works construction, in addition to enlarged maintenance funds provided, out of national government funds. An unaccountable expense total by municipalities also was used on purely local public projects. The over-all use of national government funds for rehabilitation, including corporate advances and revolving funds tied up, perhaps reached a total of about $200,000,000. *Central Bank Statistical Bulletin*, 2:3 (1950); *Manila Times Mid-Week Review*, Aug. 16, 1950. Another large allocation of funds was to the Rehabilitation Finance Corporation, set up in 1947 by taking over two older agencies with new capital added. It is to be the chief agency of government in financing its economic program. With very broad powers it can aid any kind of program, particularly those the banks cannot aid. It will deal in agricultural loans, but is not a source of small-farmer rural credit. Castillo, *op. cit.*, pp. 731–732.

[152] Government corporation expenses, unknown for the year 1945–1946, have exceeded $70,000,000 per year during each later fiscal year. Some of these expenses are chargeable as industrial, some as agricultural, and others as undertakings in transportation. *Central Bank Statistical Bulletin*, 2:3 (1950).

[153] Education is one of the largest single, normal items in the national government budget. In the fiscal year 1948–1949 total allocations, chiefly by the national government, ran to $75,976,000, almost a fourth of the total government expense for the year. *Ibid.*

[154] Although there are few published figures on military expenses as a whole, it is thought that law and order, defense establishments, and military operations since 1948 have taken about $30,000,000 per year. *Ibid.*

[155] Reference here is to the tremendous increase in the import of consumers' goods in the postwar period. See table xii, which gives data on the balance of trade and on the long-run total of imports during the American period.

[156] Import controls were developed only during 1948, first becoming effective early in 1949. Import goods then contracted were exempt from controls. Application of controls was variable during 1949, but grew increasingly tight and restrictive. The calendar year 1950 was the first full year of controls, but additional changes and restrictions were introduced in May, 1950. The effectiveness of the checks upon consumers'-goods imports will not be finally ascertained until the trade returns for the fiscal year 1950–1951, or the calendar year 1951, are available. Lightened controls during 1951 will make it even more difficult. The projected estimate of the balance of trade and funds for the year 1950 is shown in table 13. The preliminary figures on trade returns given for the calendar year, 1950, in table 12 indicate that import controls have been effective in reducing the deficit balance from trade alone, but data are not yet available on the over-all balance of payments and receipts. That import controls caused high price rises is another matter.

[157] *Report and Recommendations of the Joint Philippine-American Finance Commission*, U. S. 80th Cong., 1st sess., H. Doc. 390 (1947).

[158] *Manila Times Mid-Week Review*, Jan. 17, 1951; *Manila Bulletin*, Mar. 27, 1950. Loosened import controls, effective in 1951, because of an improved exchange position, will promote increased collections. Changes in this matter from year to year will affect both trade and tax returns.

[159] *Report and Recommendations of the Joint Philippine-American Finance Commission*, op. cit., pp. 26–29.

[160] *Central Bank Statistical Bulletin*, 2:3 (1950); Rosell, *op. cit.*

[161] *Report and Recommendations of the Joint Philippine-American Finance Commission*, op. cit., pp. 39–40; *Central Bank Statistical Bulletin*, op. cit.

[162] Combined provincial-city figures give these percentages: 1946, 57.6 per cent; 1947, 82.1 per cent; 1948, 72.8 per cent; 1949, 74.5 per cent. *Central Bank Statistical Bulletin*, op. cit.

[163] *Bell Report*, p. 24. In 1947 only 165,949 income tax returns were filed. Of these only 1,129 returns were filed by recipients of incomes exceeding $10,000. Incomes between $1,000 and $10,000 were reported by 102,553. Castillo, *op. cit.*, pp. 605–606. In 1949 filed returns totaled 194,077. Of these, 57,240 were from taxable

individuals and 2,049 were from taxable corporations. *Central Bank Statistical Bulletin,* 2:3 (1950).

[164] *Report and Recommendations of the Joint Philippine-American Finance Commission,* p. 11, states that the 1939 data show that about half of all Filipino families had incomes less than $65 per year, and that at the other end of the scale perhaps 1 per cent of the population received a third of the total income. Using 1948 data, the *Central Bank Statistical Bulletin,* 2:3 (1950), presents a table indicating that 87.5 per cent of the income recipients receive less than $500 per year (which is much too high a figure to throw real light upon the income-level problem) and account for 65.3 per cent of the total income. What might be termed a middle-class group, representing 10.4 per cent of the recipients, received 21.8 per cent of the income, whereas the remaining 2.1 per cent of the recipients shared some 12.8 per cent of the total income. These two tabulations are somewhat contradictory, and there are few reliable data on the whole subject.

[165] Government sources suggest that efficient collections would increase tax collections only by $15,000,000 per year, though one private tax specialist suggests that the increase could amount to some $90,000,000 per year. *American Chamber of Commerce Journal,* 27 (1951), 38.

[166] *Manila Bulletin,* March 27, 1950.

[167] *Los Angeles Times,* March 13, 1951. With the peso-dollar exchange normally at 2:1, pesos were being offered at three and a half to one. This was not yet in large volume, but was an indicator of approaching trouble. During the middle of the year the strength of the peso improved and the black market declined.

[168] The Economic Survey Mission was appointed June 29, 1950, headed by Daniel W. Bell. It spent the summer of 1950 studying conditions in the islands and turned in its report in November, 1950. The report is the one herein called the *Bell Report.*

[169] *Manila Times Mid-Week Review,* Dec. 27, 1950, Jan. 3, 1951.

[170] These, in the main, are contained in the summary recommendations of the *Bell Report.*

[171] Compare the tax revenue of the General Fund and the income totals of the national government given in tables xv and xvi.

[172] This is another feature of the *Bell Report* recommendations. The ECA is the mechanism through which such aid will be given. These annual sums will be in addition to other dollar funds accruing to Filipinos under final war-damage settlement, United States government expenditures in the islands, armed forces pensions, and other similar payments. Some of these will continue for only a year or two more, whereas others are long-run payment patterns. Payments for the calendar year 1951 are expected to total approximately $150,000,000.

[173] In the period 1946–September, 1950, 1,834 of 2,703 newly registered corporations were located in Manila, Rizal City, or Quezon City, the three chief units of the Manila metropolitan area. *Central Bank Statistical Bulletin,* 2:4 (1950).

[174] *Bell Report,* p. 48.

[175] *Report and Recommendations of the Joint Philippine-American Finance Commission,* p. 9.

[176] It may be objected that land problems are not solved by concentration upon land reform measures, which is true enough in a country with a long-established and

mature land system. My own contention here is that if the United States had put into operation a complete and practical land system, and administered it efficiently in the past half century, many of the current land problems would not exist. Further, that complex economic measures carried out without this primary step will not achieve full success.

[177] *Bell Report,* p. 48.

Bibliography

Bibliography

Books and Articles

Alicante, M. M. "The Fertilizer Problem in the Ecafe Region," *Journal of the Soil Science Society of the Philippines,* 1 (1949), 18–30.

Alip, E. M. *Philippine History, Political, Social, Economic.* Manila, 1948.

Araneta, S. "The Time Is Now," *Manila Times Mid-Week Review,* Dec. 20, 1950.

Bekker, K., and C. Wolf, Jr. "The Philippine Balance of Payments," *Far Eastern Survey,* 19 (1950), 41–43.

Bell Report. See U.S. Economic Survey Mission to the Philippines.

Benitez, C. *History of the Philippines.* Boston, 1940.

Beyer, H. O., and J. C. DeVeyra. *Philippine Saga, A Pictorial History of the Archipelago Since Time Began.* Manila, 1947.

Blair, E. H. A., and J. A. Robertson. *The Philippine Islands, 1493–1803.* 55 vols. Cleveland, 1903–1909.

Boeke, J. H. *The Structure of the Netherlands Indian Economy.* New York, 1942.

Borromeo, H. Q. "Time to Revise the Bell Act," *Manila Times Mid-Week Review,* Jan. 17, 1951.

Buss, C. A. "The Philippines," *in* L. A. Mills, *The New World of Southeast Asia.* Minneapolis: University of Minnesota Press, 1949. Pp. 18–78.

Castillo, A. V. *Philippine Economics.* Manila, 1949.

Castrilio, Z. "Government Acquisition of Large Landed Estates," *American Chamber of Commerce Journal,* 27 (1951), 44–45.

Central Bank of the Philippines. *First Annual Report.* Manila, 1949.

Fifield, R. H. "The Hukbalahap Today," *Far Eastern Survey,* 20 (1951), 13–18.

Food and Agricultural Organization. *Rice and Rice Diets, A Nutritional Survey.* Washington, 1948.

——— Philippine Committee. *Special Report.* Manila, 1947.

——— ——— *Second Special Report.* Manila, 1948.

Foreman, J. *The Philippine Islands.* New York, 1899, 1906.

Galang, F. G., and F. C. Panganiban. *Agricultural Extension Service Handbook.* Department of Agriculture and Natural Resources, Tech. Bull. no. 18. Manila, 1949.

Hainsworth, R. G., and R. T. Moyer. *Agricultural Geography of the Philippine Islands, A Graphic Summary.* U.S. Department of Agriculture, Office of Foreign Agricultural Relations. Washington, 1945.

Halsema, J. J. "Development Plans in the Philippines," *Far Eastern Survey,* 18 (1949), 233–237.

Kolb, A. *Die Philippinen.* Leipzig, 1942.

Mamisao, J. P. "Soil Conservation Problems in the Philippines," *Journal of the Soil Science Society of the Philippines,* 1 (1949), 5–17.

Militante, G. J. "Irrigation Problems in the Philippines," *in* FAO *Second Special Report.* Pp. 1–21.

Mitchell, K. L. *Industrialization of the Western Pacific.* New York, 1942.

Palmer, F. H. "Philippines Forced to Introduce Import and Export Controls," *Foreign Trade,* 7 (1950), 328–335.

Pelzer, K. J. *Pioneer Settlement in the Asiatic Tropics.* New York, 1945.

Pendleton, R. L. "Land Utilization and Agriculture of Mindanao, Philippine Islands," *Geographical Review,* 32 (1942), 180–210.

Philippine Census, 1903, 1918, 1939, 1948.

Philippine Sugar Yearbook, 1950. Manila, 1950.

Philippines. Bureau of Census and Statistics. *Facts and Figures about Economic and Social Conditions of the Philippines, 1946–1947.* Manila, 1948.

———— ———— *Yearbook of Philippine Statistics.* Manila, 1940, 1946.

———— ———— *Special Bulletin No. 1, Population of the Philippines, October 1, 1948.* Manila, 1948.

———— Bureau of Commerce. *Summaries of Philippine Foreign Trade, 1931–1948.* Manila, 1948.

———— Bureau of Mines. *Mining Industry in the Philippines.* Information Circular no. 5. Manila, 1947.

———— Department of Agriculture and Commerce. *Land Resources of the Philippines.* Manila, 1939.

———— Department of Agriculture and Natural Resources. *Our National Food Production Campaign.* Manila, 1949.

———— ———— Fiber Inspection Service. *Annual Baling Report.* Manila.

———— Department of Commerce and Industry. *The Philippines, 1950, A Handbook of Trade and Economic Facts and Figures.* Manila, 1950.

———— President's Action Committee on Social Amelioration. *Philippine Social Trends, Basic Documents Pertinent to Long-Range Social Welfare Planning in the Philippines.* Manila, 1950.

———— University. College of Agriculture. *Handbook of Philippine Agriculture.* Los Baños, 1939.

Romero, I. A. "Jomalig Island, A Site for Agricultural Development," *Journal of the Soil Science Society of the Philippines,* 2 (1950), 249–254.

Roscher, W. *The Spanish Colonial System.* New York, 1944.

BIBLIOGRAPHY

Rosell, D. Z. "Land Classification, Valuation and Assessment for Land Taxation in the Philippines," *Journal of the Soil Science Society of the Philippines*, 2 (1950), 238–248.

Sacay, F. M. "The Food Supply and Population of the Philippines," *The Philippine Agriculturist*, 33 (1950), 203–217.

Simmons, J. S. *Global Epidemiology*. Philadelphia, 1944.

Spencer, J. E. "Abacá and the Philippines," *Economic Geography*, 27 (1951), 95–106.

———— "Land Use in the Upland Philippines," in *The Development of Upland Areas in the Far East*, 1 (1949), 28–56. New York: Institute of Pacific Relations, 1949.

———— "The Philippine Rice Problem," *Far Eastern Survey*, 18 (1949), 125–128.

U.S. Bureau of Insular Affairs. *Reports of the Philippine Commission, 1900–1903* Washington, 1904.

U.S. Congress. House. *Report and Recommendations of the Joint Philippine-American Finance Commission*. 80th Cong., 1st sess., H. Doc. 390. Washington, 1947.

U.S. Department of Agriculture. Office of Foreign Agricultural Relations. *Report of the Philippine–United States Agricultural* Mission. I.A.C. Series, no. 3. Washington, 1947.

U.S. Economic Survey Mission to the Philippines. *Report to the President of the United States (Bell Report)*. Washington, 1950.

U.S. Philippine War Damage Commission. *Semi-Annual Reports*. Washington, 1946–1951.

Worcester, D. C. *The Philippines Past and Present*. New York, 1914. (Also 1930. edited by J. R. Hayden.)

Periodicals and Newspapers

(These sources have been used extensively, and no attempt is made to list the particular issues.)

American Chamber of Commerce Journal (monthly). Manila.

Central Bank Economic Indicators (semi-annual). Manila.

Central Bank Statistical Bulletin (quarterly). Manila.

Journal of the Soil Science Society of the Philippines (quarterly). Manila.

Manila Bulletin (daily). Manila.

Manila Times (daily). Manila.

Manila Times Mid-Week Review (published as a weekly section of the daily *Manila Times*). Manila.

New York Times. New York.

Indexes

Index

Abacá: acreage and production, 66; cropping systems, 11–12; diseases and pests, 173; export position 101–102; home consumption, 3, 101; Japanese control, 200–201; map, 63; native in Philippines, 168; northern limit, 29; processing, 94

Agricultural high schools: lack of adequate curricula, 215–216; map, 212

Agricultural processing, 14

Agricultural research needs, 243–244

Agricultural systems: aquatic lowland, 6–7; caingin cultivation, 7–9; government corporative, 200–201; irrigated terrace, 4–6; mechanized, 10, 163–165; oriental garden culture vs. mechanized farming, 163–165; plantation, 10, 117; small farm, 158–159, 163–165

Air fields, map, 76

Air transport, 85; need for expansion, 242–243; traffic volume, 254 n.

American aid, ECA five-year program, 229, 247

American aims in Philippines, 209, 220–221

American cultural impact, 221

American investment, 258 n.

American responsibility, 222

Animal breeding, 168 ff.

Animal pests, 168; destruction of crops, 172–173, 190

Animals: destructive effects of war, 174, 223; diseases, 173–174; failure to acclimatize, 170–171; introduction, 170–171; population, 66; variety, 170–171

Annual incomes of farm families, 4, 251 n.

Banks: failure to serve rural areas, 134–135; growth, 134–135; need for rural, 244

Bell Commission: on agricultural production, 235; on corporations in agriculture, 208; report submitted, 229; request for, 2, 239

Bell Trade Act, 106–107

Beriberi, 183

Beverages, 65; tuba, 34, 65, 253 n.

Bureau of Animal Industry, 175–176, 211; breeding stations, 212

Bureau of Forestry, 118–119, 192, 210–211, 240–241; forestation needs, 240; map of forestation projects, 212, reforestation work, 211

Bureau of Lands, 117–119, 212, 240–241; colonization aid, 143, 147; map of open subdivisions, 124

Bureau of Plant Industry, 170, 211; agricultural services, 175–177, 214–215; map of seed stations, 212

Bureau of Soil Survey and Conservation, 241

Business concerns: American 96; Chinese, 96

Index of Place Names